DREAMERS OF EMPIRE

CECIL JOHN RHODES

DREAMERS *of* EMPIRE

By
ACHMED ABDULLAH
T. COMPTON PAKENHAM

Illustrated by B. K. Morris

Essay Index Reprint Series

BOOKS FOR LIBRARIES PRESS
FREEPORT, NEW YORK

First Published 1929
Reprinted 1968

LIBRARY OF CONGRESS CATALOG CARD NUMBER:
68-57300

PRINTED IN THE UNITED STATES OF AMERICA

To

OUR FRIEND AND BRITHER-SCOT

J. W. THOMSON

CONTENTS

ILLUSTRATIONS

FOREWORD

FED to the verge of nausea on the moraled and
mottoed legends of men who succeed so everlastingly
and so ultra-efficiently that, in the end, their very successes cause a prosy, stodgy anti-climax, there is warm
comfort in the realization that, in the lexicon of youth
and, for that matter, of middle age, we find such a
hearty, honest, fearless word as "failure"; that, side
by side with men weighted down by fat honors and
choked by excessive laurel wreaths, there are those
who failed gloriously and who—perhaps through failing, rather through the lack of selfishness in not always
endeavoring to succeed, at least not always trying to
feather their personal nests of profit or fame—succeeded the more gloriously; that, unlike the traders in
gross, if practical, hebetudes who think only of delivering the goods, there are some who think more
of the goods and less of the delivering; that people
there are who see the Holy Grail shining high and
bright above the god called Moloch—or Mob—or
Money; and that—the which is food for mirth gargantuan or quietly sardonic—in a fair reckoning of
cause and effect most of the sleek, accepted successes
stand on pedestals built for them by the strong, lusty
hands of the failures.

Entering the lists frequently at a disadvantage of
purse or body or social standing, finding themselves
god-knows-where at given moments when, for practical reasons, they should be god-knows-somewhere
else, these non-commissioned officers of the Legion of
the Damned—the "Chinese" Gordons, the Cecil

Rhodes's, the Richard Burtons—had one thing; a thing
non-conforming, therefore anarchic, therefore dangerous; a thing called "ideas." Ideas having nothing to
do with little cogs or wheels or explosives or parliaments or electioneering speeches or mass production.
Ideas not based on any preceding ideas. But independent ideas. Impractical ideas they seemed to the
masses pap-fed on accepted standards. Absurd ideas
they seemed to the safe ones who were climbing the
regular ladders to contemporary success and glory—
and future oblivion. "Ideas ahead of their time"
they were ungraciously acknowledged, later on, by
their early detractors who scrambled for the spoils.

They were not often possessed of single purpose.
They had lean cant or consideration of the ever-ready
market for newspaper-acclaimed paragons. But they
went forward as they listed. They went forward and
carried on, with the few who would follow them,
through, round, or over obstacles man-made or nature-
made—to build the pedestals for the looser, safer
minds—the successes.

Dreamers . . .?

Doubtless.

Dreamers who played the flute before the god Pan
in their souls; who, besides playing the flute, often
played the fool.

But dreamers who enjoyed themselves thoroughly—
dreamers whose dreams became reality after the twi-
light fell upon Arcady.

ACHMED ABDULLAH,
T. COMPTON PAKENHAM.

"Dreamers of Dreams! We take the taunt with gladness,
For God, beyond the years, you see,
Has brought the things which count with you for madness
Into the Glory of the Life to Be."

CECIL JOHN RHODES

[1853–1902]

*who dreamed of an All-Red
Africa and of a railway from
the Cape to Cairo*

CECIL JOHN RHODES

SCHOOL was behind him. Oxford loomed ahead.

Cecil John Rhodes was the type of Englishman meant from birth for Oxford, never for Cambridge; the type of Englishman so excessively English that, illogically, he would have been anathema, and vice versa, to any transatlantic Rhodes scholar.

What to do when he went up?

He leaned toward the law. The family suggested that he should follow his father and take holy orders. He did neither because, at this period of doubt, an ironic twist of fate, through the medium of a bad cold and the doctor's advice, sent him to South Africa. For he was not hardy; and Natal, where a brother was planting cotton, might fill out his chest.

He was sixteen at the time. The thought of Africa stirred his young imagination. For hours he pored over the map until, as he put it later on: "Africa possessed my bones." Already an aggressive imperialist, he would draw a finger across the continent, from the Cape to Cairo, and say: "I want all this red" . . . the arrogant, clamorous red of the Union Jack.

So he took ship; and Britain lost a possible Lord Chancellor or her church a Bishop—to gain instead a multimillionaire, a statesman, an Empire builder; a man who dreamed fantastic dreams and who, amazingly, incredibly, made them come true.

When he arrived in Durban he found out that Herbert, always the reckless adventurer of the Rhodes clan, had gone on a prospecting trip. Cecil had to wait until his brother's return. He chafed at the delay; grew nervous; and, since there was nothing else to do and since Oxford was only put off and not forgotten, he used the time to read the classics—and to think certain thoughts.

Precocious thoughts they were, rather hard. For already ambition, expressed by desire for power and money, was his lode-star. Already he had made up his mind that he travels fastest, and farthest, who travels alone; that he would never marry . . . a decision to which he clung through life.

Then Herbert came back, a few bad stones in his wallet. He took sixteen-year-old Cecil up to his cotton patch and appointed him manager. Cecil objected, saying that he knew nothing about cotton. "You'll learn—you'll have to," replied Herbert, to whom the Umkomaas Valley had lost its charm. Cotton, he considered, was a slow and prosy road to wealth. Better go prospecting again.

The talk of diamonds was in the air. A friend came down from the Vaal with three fair stones and tales of fortunes grubbed out of the blue gravel. Herbert went with him. He pegged a claim on the De-Beers farm close to Colesberg Kopje—presently to grow, noisily, braggingly, into Kimberley—while his younger brother remained behind. It cost Cecil keen pangs to wait till the second crop reached its harvest. But—for that was the way of him—he did his duty; he learned about cotton—and negroes—and Africa.

In due time the cotton was picked, ginned, baled; and Cecil started on a four-hundred-mile trek over the Drakensberg to join Herbert. He found the future site of Kimberley a Babel of all nations and races, of reckless and picaresque adventurers who had drifted there like vultures to the reek of carrion.

By this time Herbert had increased his holdings to

three whole claims. But, always hot-headed and hot-footed, he succumbed once more to wanderlust, leaving the management of his property to Cecil. The latter studied the principles of diamond finding and marketing as efficiently as he had studied cotton. Not long afterwards, he was able to conclude a letter to his mother in England with:

"I average about £100 per week.
"Yrs
"C. J. RHODES."

He was young. He was carelessly dressed. His manners were curt. He was not strong. But his mind was fully formed. Here, in this most brutal of schools, where everybody was on the make and fighting for himself in an undisciplined rush for riches, he held his own—and more than his own.

Success added fuel to his dreams.

Dreams romantic; yet, somehow, essentially practical.

For Cecil Rhodes was that rarest of God's creatures: a man who could dream with lavish restraint; who had the courage to tear his grandest ideas apart so as to find the weak spots—and then to repatch them or to start anew; who never dreamed, or planned, beyond the limits of sane possibility, though this same possibility might have seemed an insane impossibility to lesser minds.

He did not look the part. *"An earnest young mudlark,"* a contemporary described him. But he was a hard claim worker and an astute bargainer.

Popular? No. He had no time to be popular, to be a hail-fellow-well-met. His mind, the day's work done, was busy with problems—problems which, sooner or later, he would translate into action.

Action, from the first, in the larger sense. Drudgery over small details never interested him.

Of course he overworked; and when the wandering Herbert returned, bringing with him another brother, Frank, who was marking time before taking up an Army commission, he decided that Cecil needed a vacation and took him into the north.

Gold prospecting was the excuse. They found no gold. But Cecil found something else: himself.

He looked, listened, imagined. At night—sitting near the ruddy camp fire; talking to people passing on trek, indomitable Boers or doomed natives or drifting, derelict Britons; hearing their gossip that was always of riches to be picked up just around the corner; seeing the Black Continent spreading its magnificent, tawdry vagueness—gradually the dream came to him that this land without a past was the land of the future. He was ever the man to translate his dreams into terms of hard reality, terms of power and money; and from this time dated his conviction that, to use his own expression, Kaffirs—South African investments —were as sound as the Bank of England. During this trek, too, he found the inspiration for the line: *"The wish came to me to render myself useful to my country"* which, four years later, at the age of twenty-four, he wrote in a pamphlet audaciously entitled: *"Some of My Ideas."*

At one of their stops, far in the hinterland, he drew up the first of the three amazing wills made during his life. By this instrument he left all that he might possess at death to the Colonial Secretary in trust, to be used for the extension of the British Empire.

"For," he wrote, *"the more of the world we inhabit, the better it is for the human race. . . . The absorption of the greater portion of the world under our rule means the end of all wars."*

The beginning of the "Cape-to-Cairo" dream? Perhaps.

But there was first another ambition to be realized: Oxford. The time seemed ripe. In 1873, together with Frank who returned to take up his commission, he embarked for home.

He matriculated for Oriel. But the satisfaction which this deferred achievement gave him was of short duration. Late in the year, his mother died. Shortly afterwards, he caught a severe cold after rowing, developed his old lung symptoms, and was hurried back to Colesberg Kopje in the early days of 1874.

He was up again at Oxford before the end of 1875 to commence a strange six years, a double life as undergraduate and prospector, following the summers from England to the Cape where C. J. Rudd was his resident partner, getting the education he craved, and planning a monopoly of the diamond output.

By his own evidence the greatest service Oxford rendered him was in bringing him to the feet of Ruskin. But he had not much use for University life. He was older than the average student; had had tough, first-hand experiences of grappling with the world; and so the cloistered discipline irked him. Nor had he much liking for the recognized undergraduate activities. He considered them tame—and silly. Perhaps silly—because tame.

Still, in the final count, Oxford broadened his outlook and made him more tolerant of others. He never forgot her; always, in later years, welcomed her sons to his bailiwick; and, in the end, provided the one thing which, above all others, will make him immortal: the Rhodes Scholarships.

In 1881 he received his degree and made straight for his claims. He had achieved his first ambition:

education. Now he set out to realize the second, a triple one: money, power, and "to render myself useful to my country."

He discovered that these three aims interlocked; that they were a Trinity.

A holy Trinity? Holy, at least, to him. Quite as holy to him as the other Trinity. England, after all, was his religion; more so than the creed of the Book.

He had ideas. They seemed to him logical and practical.

But how could he make use of them?

A bid at an auction of diamond claims meant nothing unless backed by cold cash. Opinion as to the future development of thousands of square miles to the north—*"I want all this red!"*—were mere castles in the air unless they could be enforced. To build an empire he must have political power, and to have political power he must have gigantic wealth.

The shortest cut to wealth lay in control of the richest available material: diamonds—a monopoly of the precious stones so as to regulate the price and, always, to keep the supply below the demand.

A hard task.

For, by this time, the situation in Kimberley was almost out of hand. The first rush of prospectors had been followed by the usual plague of parasites, Malays, Cockneys, Russian Jews, not to mention more than one Younger Son who had once hunted with the Quorn or the Belvoir and entered the half-mile hunter's stake at Croxton Park . . . but, whatever their social or racial antecedents, *"wallopers"* to-day, who raised the devil at Kimberley, who bought independently on the spot and sold down country in the quickest market. Dangerous business—for diamonds had a point of absorption, and, since they were a luxury, that point was easily reached.

Here then was the opposition which Cecil Rhodes must fight. But this opposition was not yet sufficiently organized for his attack; was still like a hydra with a thousand heads. No use crushing one head, or a dozen, when at once a hundred would jump up. Better, therefore, to wait awhile; to take a look around —for allies—and for enemies.

During these years the cast of the drama to be played out on the veldt was being assembled.

There was Hercules Robinson, a proper product of Sandhurst with Governorships of Hong-Kong, Ceylon, New South Wales and New Zealand behind him, who succeeded Sir Bartle Frere as High Commissioner of the Cape in 1880. A protagonist of responsible colonial government, he believed that the true basis for South African progress lay in friendly coöperation with the Dutch settlers.

Herbert Rhodes, adventuring again, presently dropped out; dropped out for good. Somewhere below Lake Nyassa his grass hut caught a spark from the camp fire, and he was burned to death before his bearers could lend a hand.

A Dr. Leander Starr Jameson was making a name for himself in the Colony as a clever young physician. Between him and Rhodes a stout friendship sprang up which never ended, despite the terrific strain the future was destined to place upon it.

Then there was Neville Pickering, one of the beloved of the gods, beloved, too, of Cecil Rhodes, and fated to die young.

Also there was Paul Kruger, that product of narrow Dutch Calvinism and the stupid blunders of earlier British Colonial administration. Driven with his clan into the self-imposed exile of the Great Trek in 1836 so as to avoid British rule, believing himself

to be the Moses of his people, elected and reëlected
Vice-President of the Transvaal Republic, he was twen-
ty-eight years older than Rhodes. Both men's minds
had, curiously, the same turn: the South African turn.
But one was uncompromisingly and stolidly Dutch, the
other uncompromisingly and aggressively British. So
they hated each other; fought each other until the
end.

Finally there was a man from the East End of London by the name of Barnett Isaacs which he changed
to Barney Barnato; a man who became Rhodes' worst
financial adversary as Kruger was his worst political
adversary; a man, who, a Cockney and a Jew, a reckless
individualist, refused to conform; a man, therefore,
who had to be crushed.

Rhodes' first audience was Pickering. His next,
after the latter's death, was Jameson. The young doctor was an eager listener. It sounded romantic and
patriotic, sounded also plausible and profitable—this
plan of Cecil Rhodes: a Federated South Africa under
British rule.

Not only South Africa. Why stop there?

Also—to use Rhodes' own term—*"the balance of
the map."* That was what he was after. Hold the
balance of the map! It lay to the north and was to
be had for the asking. He only required one thing:
political opportunity to air his views.

Already in 1880—to go back a few years—he had
had this opportunity; had used it.

For in that year Griqualand West, formerly a
Crown Colony, including Colesberg Kopje, re-
christened Kimberley, had been handed over to Cape
Colony. At the first election to the Cape Parliament
the new division of Barkly West, across the Vaal from
Kimberley, had returned as its representative—the

which he remained until death—Cecil John Rhodes, undergraduate of Oriel College in the University of Oxford, then on vacation.

At first the susceptibilities of the self-conscious older members of this offshoot of the Mother of Parliaments were shocked by the youth from the new constituency. His outer man was as careless as ever. He maintained, in fact, that it was possible to legislate equally well in bathrobe or ermine. Besides, he had no silver tongue, no soap-box tricks.

But it did not take his associates long to recognize that there was driving power behind the unconventional exterior. And there was a queer strength in his monotonous way of repeating points: *"The balance of the map . . . the balance of the map . . . to the north . . . to the north . . . the balance of the map . . ."* on and on, over and over again, until the legislators began to suspect that he might be right.

Also he could see the point of view of an opponent. The Dutch colonists were an established fact. Instead of riding roughshod over them, why not work with them hand in hand, satisfying their needs as well as those of the British colonists?

Whitehall did not agree with him. Whitehall just then wanted no further Imperial expansion. The Cape government, weakened by the eternal political bickerings between British and Dutch, had its hands full.

But Rhodes did not despair.

The balance of the map! Federation! The double aim which was his grail!

He decided that the people, British and Dutch, should be taught how expansion to the north was commercially a life and death matter for the Colony. To further the campaign, he obtained control of the *Cape Argus,* with the single proviso that it should print in full all his speeches. They would point the way. He was not interested in the news of the day. Let who wished get divorced or murder or win at cricket.

But—his speeches—they *must* be printed! In full!

The time for this grandiose Imperial venture did not seem propitious. Talk of working hand in hand with the Dutch could hardly be convincing with Colley's defeat at Majuba immediately behind and the House just then discussing a bill to make Dutch the exclusive tongue of the legislators.

But Cecil Rhodes worked on while, across the Vaal, Paul Kruger was preaching to his people:

"Africa for the Afrikanders!"

Kruger, too, dreamed of a Federated South Africa. But a Federated South Africa under Dutch rule. And his slogan was:

"From the Zambesi to Simon's Bay!"

Rhodes' slogan was different. To him the Zambesi was but a step. Up in the north, his countrymen were working down the Nile. Why not meet them half-way? Why not—in other words—Cape-to-Cairo?

He said:

"Give me the center of Africa and let who will have the coast swamps."

But the coast swamps were jumping-off places for treks which might result in definite claims in the hinter-lands. Thus the Transvaal Republic was marching inland, following the Limpopo, while in the west the Germans were exhibiting a threatening activity, were trying to increase their particular place in the African sun—and a place in the sun for the Germans, thought Rhodes, meant a place in the chilly shadows for the British. He could not allow it. The Cape must not be cut off from Central African trade.

So he went to work.

There was first the Basutoland affair.

This territory, bordering on the Orange Free State, had been annexed to the Cape Colony in 1875. Rhodes liked the Basutos. In the diamond diggings he had found them reliable workers. With their lean wages they were wont to purchase firearms which, on their return to their kraals, they used for protection against marauding nomad Boers. Sir Gordon Sprigg, the rather spineless premier of the Cape, became apprehensive when he heard that the tribesmen owned rifles. He reached back into the files and unearthed an obsolete law under which he attempted to disarm them. Trouble resulted. The Basutos resisted strenuously.

Rhodes was angry. Why make enemies of people who were inclined to be friends? His opposition contributed to Sprigg's fall. Sir Thomas Scanlen was the next premier. His first action was the appointment of a Basutoland Compensation Commission—since some kraals had been burned by the British—which was headed by two men: "Chinese" Gordon who was hailed from Mauritius, and Cecil Rhodes who went up from Cape Town.

The former was forty-nine, the latter twenty-nine. Both believed in justice. But Gordon, at a given, a critical moment, with bloody memories of the Taiping Rebellion and the Soudan behind him, would enforce this same justice with the iron fist; while Rhodes —who had always a curious, almost sentimental liking for aboriginal races and, local and quite truth-telling scandal had it, for aboriginal women—preferred the velvet glove at all times.

Naturally they quarreled.

"You must not talk to the Basutos as if you were their lord and master," Rhodes told the other. "Remember, you are only the servant of the Minister for Native Affairs."

"Damn it!" came the heated rejoinder. "You think you are always right."

"I *am* right! I know South Africa!"

Finally Gordon gave in. He handled the Basutos as Rhodes had insisted he should, and, later on, he admitted that the younger man had been right. For the Basutos were satisfied, became friendly to the British—and Rhodes turned his attention to another matter, to Bechuanaland South, where an independent chief complained of Boer raiders who had harried his cattle and squatted on his land.

Rhodes went up country. He came back with exactly what he wanted. First, from the chief, he obtained a cession of all his territory in return for protection; and, second, he produced a petition signed by the majority of the Boer settlers asking to be taken into Cape Colony.

Here was a good start for the *"balance of the map."* Rhodes was jubilant. He introduced the annexation bill into the House. But the legislators voted it down.

Nor had Rhodes better luck with the Imperial authorities back home since, just then, the Whitehall gentry were little Englanders, seeing the world through myopic eyes, building with small-scale minds on small-scale maps.

But Rhodes did not give up. He appealed to Sir Hercules Robinson, the Governor, and found him sympathetic. Robinson pulled wires in London. Whitehall came to heel; offered to take over Bechuanaland if the Cape Colony would stand half the cost of administration. But the South African legislators refused—and, at this moment, outside forces stepped in to give reality to Rhodes' fears in regard to the interior.

For Germany annexed the hinterland of Walfisch

and Lüderitz Bay, thereby laying the foundations of German South West Africa which in time might cut off Cape Colony from the rich Central African markets; while Paul Kruger's schemes of expansion, too, were ripening. He pushed settlers west from the Transvaal. Two parties, under van Pittius and van Niekirk, entered Bechuanaland and declared the Republics of Goshen and Stellaland.

Then, driven by their foes where they had refused to be led by their friends, the Imperial authorities moved. With the situation on the verge of disaster, Whitehall proclaimed a Protectorate over Bechuanaland. Rhodes, by the same token, achieved his end.

But the battle was not yet joined. For MacKenzie, a man steeped in the stifling, narrow prejudices learned by twenty years of missionary work, was sent to take charge of the new Protectorate. He used the questionable methods of his former calling. The Boers belonged to the Dutch Reformed Church. Therefore, to MacKenzie, they were dissenters and, *ipso facto,* scoundrels. He treated them as such. Van Niekirk defied him; and he made matters worse by appealing to the Cape for soldiers to quell the unrest which he himself had fomented.

England, realizing that MacKenzie was a menace, recalled him, whereupon Kruger proclaimed, at once, that Goshen and Stellaland were under the protection of the Transvaal.

Even Sir Hercules Robinson began to lose hope. Rhodes did not. Against the wish of the Cape Town politicians, he went up country to see how he could straighten out the trouble.

By this time, in Stellaland, van Niekirk had gathered a well-armed commando against possible eventualities. Rhodes passed through the Boer lines, alone and unarmed, and demanded a conference. The giant Delarey, deputed by van Niekirk, opened the parley by bellowing loudly that blood had to flow. Rhodes refused to discuss the matter on an empty stomach and asked for breakfast. It was a good breakfast. The liquor, too, was good. For a week Rhodes remained Delarey's guest; and, before leaving, he stood godfather to his uncouth host's grandchild and came to a political settlement. It canceled all MacKenzie's rulings; recognized the land claims of the Stellalanders; and appointed van Niekirk Governor until the end of the year, at which time the British Protectorate was to be acknowledged.

But with the Republic of Goshen he was not successful. He was unable to win over Joubert, the Boer leader. So he pocketed his velvet glove and informed both Whitehall and Sir Hercules Robinson that, unless force was employed, the Boers would join hands with the Germans across the northern boundary of Cape Colony.

Great Britain acted. Troops were sent, commanded by Sir Charles Warren who received the rank of Deputy Commissioner.

Immediately Sir Charles and Rhodes were at odds. The latter believed that force should be most sparingly used and only as a last resort, while the former was a beef-and-brawn-damn-your-eyes-and-mine type of Briton to whom ruthlessness was a dogma. He would not listen to the other's milder counsels; insisted that MacKenzie, whose very name was a stench in the Boer nostrils, should accompany him as adviser; and only allowed Rhodes to join his headquarters on Robinson's insistence.

The Dutch were furious. A spark was needed to cause a conflagration. Then Kruger intervened. He demanded and obtained a conference. This took place on the northern boundary of Rhodes' parliamentary constituency. Here Kruger and Rhodes met for the first time. They took each other's measure. They watched, mistrusted, admired each other; almost liked each other. But one was British to the core, the other Dutch to the core. They were enemies. Still, Kruger admitted that the terms which Rhodes offered to the Boer settlers were more than fair. He was satisfied; but not so the uncompromising Imperialist in Sir Charles Warren who, directly after the meeting, repudiated the terms of the settlement.

He imprisoned van Niekirk. He demanded that Rhodes be withdrawn from his headquarters. It meant a loss of face to the latter. But, rather than have the Boers left to Warren's tender mercies, he agreed to accompany the expedition as a mere subordinate. Even that would not work. The choleric Sir Charles made it impossible for him. So, finally, Rhodes resigned. The Protectorate itself was an established fact. But he protested at the terms. At a Kimberley meeting he declared:

"I wish to say that the breach of solemn pledges and the introduction of race distinctions must result in bringing calamity on the country."

He had succeeded in one way and failed in another. He had been forced to take a back seat. He knew the reason. His name did not yet carry enough weight. He needed wealth and political power; made up his mind to get both.

The diamond monopoly—here was the answer.

He had thought of it during his undergraduate period. Thirteen years had elapsed since then—thirteen years of varied preoccupations during which he kept his eye on the formation of the company to which he ever after referred to as his *"bread and butter."* Buying quietly here and there, he and Rudd managed to form the DeBeers Mining Company, with a capital of £200,000, in 1880. Its principal antagonist was the Kimberley Central Mining Company headed by Barney Barnato and Joel. This concern could alone supply twice the number of diamonds the world could absorb at paying prices.

But Barnato was the exception to Rhodes' rule that, approached on a basis of equality and with all cards face up on the table, any man could be brought to fair terms. With Barnato there was no *modus operandi* save brute force.

Rhodes learned it. He knew that he must hold a pistol to Barnato's head. In 1887, on one of his flying trips to England, he persuaded the Rothschilds to back him in his merger scheme. He returned to Kimberley and bought up Kimberley Central shares at any price. Still Barnato controlled the majority stock and refused to yield.

Then nature took a hand. Heavy rain fell and washed into the DeBeers workings. Rhodes and all his friends got down into the mud and harvested diamonds to the extent of over 12,000 carats. He carried them to Barnato, poured them on the table, threatened to throw the whole output on the market at once . . . and still the stubborn Cockney refused to yield.

Rhodes was worried. But not for long. He told Rudd:

"Every man has a vulnerable spot. I shall find Barnato's."

He found it. It was a mean, snobbish spot. But it did the trick. For Barnato, despite his wealth, had never been able to achieve the social recognition which his East End soul craved. The Kimberley Club, rendezvous of the local Bourbons, had rejected him time and again. Rhodes called on him. He told him bluntly that, as a director of his new company, he would not be blackballed. And Barney Barnato gave in, was elected to the Club, and the DeBeers Consolidated Company was formed . . . a company fated to make history, and based on a comic little parvenu's comic snobbery.

Into its articles Rhodes wrote provisions hopelessly beyond the narrow, money-grubbing visions of Barnato and his associates. For from the profits funds were to be reserved for the construction of a Bechuanaland railway and the acquisition of territories to the north, by government charter which permitted to colonize, develop, and protect it by a standing force.

Thus, with the formation of the *"bread and butter"* company, new means came to Rhodes for transmuting dreams into realities.

The "acquiring of territories" clauses Rhodes inserted because of an event of the previous year.

For in 1887 the Portuguese had thrown a bomb into African affairs by depicting, in their official map, the western boundary of Portuguese East Africa as running inland to include Matabeleland, ruled by Lobengula. Inspired by Rhodes, Downing Street protested. Lisbon agreed to keep their claims within the 32nd degree of east longitude. But the direction of the wind had been indicated. Rhodes knew it was time to act if he was to get his red map. Everybody was beginning to scramble and bicker for the African loot. Kruger had obtained hunting permits for his Boers in Lobengula's domain. The Germans were working over into Matabeleland from their Southwestern colony.

Moffat, Resident at Bulawayo, Lobengula's kraal, heard about it. He trekked south to make report. He advocated a Protectorate. But, as always, the Cape politicians were short-sighted. They refused to act.

So did the Imperial officials who had their eyes on the cash box.

Then Rhodes met Moffat. He told him he would be responsible for all expenses, and sent him back to Lobengula. The latter, having been assured that a treaty undertaking not to grant concessions without the approval of the High Commissioner of Cape Colony would protect him from pestering, unscrupulous adventurers, placed his mark on the document which, when ratified by Sir Hercules Robinson in April, 1888, gave to Cecil Rhodes virtually an option on Matabeleland for the Empire. This experience, atop of the Bechuanaland affair, convinced him that the only way for him to acquire the *"balance of the map"* was by private effort.

Still, despite the "Moffat Treaty," Portuguese and British concession hunters poured into Matabeleland. Too, advices came that Kruger was planning a great Boar trek across the Limpopo. Thus, if Rhodes' efforts were to bear fruit, he must at once follow up his advantage. So he despatched a well-organized party, under the leadership of Rudd, to Bulawayo with instructions to obtain at any cost concessions of all mineral rights in Lobengula's country.

Rudd arrived only just in time. All the major claimants had agents on the spot. They plied Lobengula with champagne. They talked by the hour. Either Rudd's champagne was more potent or his arguments more convincing. At all events, Lobengula granted Rhodes' mineral concessions for a consideration of £100 per month and one thousand rifles with one hundred rounds each.

After a terrible trek south, leaving his companions to sit on the nest, Rudd met Rhodes in Kimberley and handed him the paper which was a certificate of progress in the materialization of his dreams of

Empire. Both men were jubilant. The scheme promised well. But, almost, it failed at the outset. For
the remaining members of Rudd's party fell foul of
native etiquette. Lobengula grew angry and started
dickering with the agents of the Cawston Exploration
Company, with headquarters in London, who were
spreading the rumor that they alone were the favor-
ites of the *"Great White Queen."* But Rhodes' representatives were not easily foiled. They fought rumor
with rumor, actually whispering where it would do
the most good that no *"Great White Queen"* existed,
that good old Victoria was a myth; that there existed
only one Great White Sovereign—by the name of Cecil
Rhodes.

Lobengula was bewildered. But he was shrewd in
his way. He sent a minor chief to London to find
out the truth. This minor chief saw Queen Victoria
in the flesh at Buckingham Palace. She sent gracious
messages to Lobengula.

But, in the meantime, Rhodes, too, acted. He embarked for London. He interviewed the Cawston
people and absorbed their concern.

Even before his London trip, before his Matabele
interests had become secure, he had been looking beyond the further borders of that tract. In the north
was the Mashona country. It was best to peg down
a claim or two there against future eventualities. He
talked to Dr. Jameson. Would the latter undertake
an up-country trek? Jameson had a thriving practice.
His common sense told him to cling to the Cape Town
flesh pots. But he never could resist Rhodes' enthusi-
asms. He trekked the next morning—fifteen hundred
miles to Bulawayo, since he needed Lobengula's permission to cross his territory into Mashonaland.

He delivered the first lot of rifles under the Rudd
treaty; cured the chief of an attack of gout which had

nonplussed the medicine men; and the grateful Lobengula allowed him to proceed north, while the other
concession hunters were still bickering about the opening of Matabeleland.

It was typical of Rhodes, the dreamer and doer.
Here, as always, he was hundreds of miles ahead of
his rivals in terms of geography—and terms of the
spirit; was already laying more phantom outposts in
the north—on the road to Cairo.

With Jameson on the way to Bulawayo, he had taken
ship for England.   There, while absorbing the Cawston concern, he also looked after the home end of
the Mashona venture.   F. C. Selous, the big-game
hunter and explorer, was in London.   He, too, had
ideas about Mashonaland; had already started a company.   Rhodes made friends with him, bought him
out, attached him to his chariot of victory.

In addition he met several men prominent in finance
and politics.   He invited them to join the board of
the British South African Company he was about to
form and applied for a Government Charter, assuring Downing Street that any further extension of
Empire northwards from Bechuanaland would be carried out without expense to the Imperial exchequer.
He undertook to furnish, from his own pocket, £30,000
required for the construction of a telegraph line and
£4,000 a year for the maintenance of a British representative at Bulawayo.

With negotiations for the Charter under way,
Rhodes—since waiting was never his *forte*—returned
to South Africa.   At Kimberley he learned that his
remaining agent at Lobengula's kraal, Thompson,
with shaky nerves and the memory of a father murdered by savages, had fled Bulawayo.   Nothing could
have boded worse.   For a white man to show fear

before natives was to give a dangerous blow to the
interests he represented.

Here was another task for Jameson. Hurriedly
he trekked back to Bulawayo to find the chief over-
loaded with gifts from adventurers and mixing his
drinks—figuratively and literally. A fortunate recurrence of the royal gout gave Jameson a lever to repair
the damage. Lobengula was cured and immensely
cheered.

On the 29th October, Rhodes was granted the
Charter for the British South African Company, with
Imperial sanction to develop, exploit, and police an
area which, in his lifetime, was never completely de-
fined. Jameson heard the news. At once he asked
and obtained Lobengula's permission for gold prospecting to commence, in order that the provisions of the
Charter might be speedily put into effect. Then he
returned to Kimberley to join his triumphant chief.

The latter, as soon as he had the Charter, became
busy pushing his side of the bargain, settling details
with the new High Commissioner, Sir Henry Loch
relative to the telegraph line it called for, getting the
Kimberley-to-Mafeking section under way, and gathering a band of explorers, tried hunters and pioneers to
open up the north, sending them on their allotted trails
to Lobengula's country to plant the first seeds of development.

The Mashonaland situation was puzzling him. It
promised to be more expensive than he had figured.
One morning, on the *stoep* of the Kimberley Club,
he complained about it to Johnson, one of the members of Selous' absorbed company. Johnson assured
him that he could clean up the entire area with 250
men at a cost of £87,000. Rhodes took him up on
this, giving him three months to pick and equip his
expedition. In the meantime Selous was held up on

the Matabele border waiting for the working party
promised by Lobengula for the construction of the
road through to Mashonaland. Tired of inaction, he
trekked alone to Bulawayo to find that Lobengula had
again gone back on his word and insisted on seeing
Rhodes himself before having any more parleys.

Selous notified Rhodes who, on this occasion, wasted
no words, merely informing Lobengula that, unless
he observed the terms of the treaty, troops would be
sent immediately to enforce it.

At this moment, with all set and moving forward,
news reached Rhodes that Kruger was planning a
great trek into Mashonaland. He sent an official protest; then, together with Sir Henry Loch, met the
Transvaal President on his own ground and made a
settlement with him. If Kruger kept away from
Mashonaland, the British would not interfere with
his trekkers to the east of the district. It was a fair
exchange. Kruger agreed.

At this meeting another matter was settled, one
which contributed its share towards bringing on the
difficulties of later years. Kruger told his visitors that
against his wishes the Pretoria *Volksraad* or Parliament had approved the extension of what was nicknamed the *"Rhodes Railway"* into the Transvaal.
The only condition upon which he would not veto the
bill was that the Transvaal section should be under
control of the Netherlands Railway Company.
Rhodes considered communications more important
than mere control. He agreed to Kruger's proposal.

By late June Johnson's Mashonaland party was
ready for the road. It consisted of 200 picked men
from all necessary professions and occupations.
Jameson joined the expedition up-country, with Selous
in the advance guard, cutting a way through the jungle. They moved 400 miles from the Bechuanaland

border to hoist the flag, on the 12th September, at a place they called Fort Salisbury—to-day the capital of Southern Rhodesia with a white population of over 8,000.

Rhodes heard the news. He said:

"I am the happiest man in South Africa."

Happy—but weighted down now with greater responsibilities than ever.

For Sir Gordon Sprigg had returned to the Premiership in 1886—as short-sighted as before, again squatting on the money bags; while Rhodes, with his pioneers off and the Mafeking line under way, clamored for more railway mileage within the boundaries of Cape Colony. For once the House agreed with him and, with Sprigg voted out of office, there was but one man whom Loch could ask to form a ministry: Cecil Rhodes.

He accepted. At the age of thirty-seven, with projects involving tens of millions of pounds sterling to keep him as occupied as any normal man could wish, Rhodes, on the 17th July, 1890, formed his first cabinet as Prime Minister of the Colony of The Cape of Good Hope.

Power—and wealth—and *"to render myself useful to my country"* . . . his Trinity.

He had almost achieved it.

Heretofore he had lived the life of a well-to-do bachelor, with rooms at the Kimberley and Cape Town Clubs. Now he set to establishing a home on lines matching his position. He bought and developed the Great Barn, the famous *Groote Schuur,* an ancient 17th Century Dutch farm building on the slopes of Table Mountain, rebuilding it with lavish care in Huguenot style, importing teak from the Orient for the interior

woodwork, crowning it with an eminently generous
and suitable thatch, filling it with unique treasures of
old Dutch glass and silver and earthenware, reminiscent
of the past of the Colony. On its 1500 acres he
planted every tree that could be found to flourish in
the climate, built roads and winding mountain paths,
and laid out an immense, private zoo.

De Groote Schuur! A name nearly as closely linked
to Rhodes' as Kimberley—as the Rhodes Scholarships.

Here he expanded from a public character into a
great human being, exercising loves and tastes that a
busy life had denied him. Here he brought his tired
henchmen for recuperation. Here he entertained his
friends with regal hospitality. Here, to lessen the tension of conflicting ideas, he talked to his political and
financial enemies. Here, too, often, he was host to
the less fortunate of the Colony that they might share,
to some extent, in the colossal stake he had pegged out
in South Africa.

Not that all was plain sailing.

For, in October, 1890, with High Commissioner
and Prime Minister on a tour of inspection to Bechuanaland, news came that the wily Lobengula had
granted an hundred-year concession, covering all the
Matabele territory, to Lippert, a German financier,
thereby repudiating everything he had traded to
Rhodes. "Never fight where any other settlement is
possible," he told Sir Henry; and he approached Lippert and, by paying several times the sum it had cost
the latter, obtained the actually illegal concession for
the Chartered Company together with the good-will
and coöperation of the German financiers.

On his way back to the Cape, he stopped at Pretoria
where he had a significant though barren interview with
Kruger. He suggested that the Transvaal required
a seaport and hinted in the direction of Portuguese

territory. Kruger scorned bargaining for *"stolen goods"* and, inconsistently, considering his own frustrated attempts to help himself to native land, berated Rhodes for robbing him of the northern country.

After Rhodes' departure, he said to Joubert: "I do not like this young man. He never sleeps and will not smoke. He goes too fast for me."

Meanwhile the Company pioneers were reporting progress. Unable to affect the Portuguese influence east of Mashonaland and being forestalled by Belgian interests in Katanga, Loch had found the Barotses willing to accept a Protectorate, while Johnson had proclaimed the Makololo and Shire districts of Nyasaland under British control. Satisfied, Rhodes made for London to discuss Charter details with the Colonial Office.

There he met the Prince of Wales—later King Edward VII—and earned his friendship and admiration.

On his return to the Cape he was greeted by conflicting accusations, the English denouncing him as pro-Boer and the Dutch as too English. He replied to the double attack by declaring in the House that he was trying to steer a fair course between English Jingoism and oversensitive Dutch prejudices, and by stating:

"Union under the same flag will not be easy. I am not prepared to forfeit at any time my own flag . . . and I can well understand the feelings of others for the flag they have been born under."

During the same session of the House a Boer raid into Mashonaland required his attention. Five thousand armed Boers were reported ready to move to the Limpopo Drifts. Kruger, for once, was not enthusiastic. But Joubert was all for the trek "to found a new Republic where genuine Afrikander nationality could be developed."

Imperial troops were ordered to Mafeking while, in Mashonaland, Jameson marched the Company police to cover the fords and while Rhodes sent Kruger warning of the welcome prepared for the raiders. Before the President's proclamation providing heavy fines and imprisonment for trekkers could be published, some of the latter crossed the Limpopo to find themselves disarmed and put under arrest.

Jameson talked to the prisoners. For hours he argued on the folly of their enterprise and offered them Rhodes' terms: "land for *bona fide* settlers willing to accept Chartered Company rule." His tact and cleverness prevailed. The invasion was over.

Kruger was not pleased—and he was afraid.

"Rhodes," he complained, "is putting a ring fence round me, and that is why I must fight him."

But Rhodes, just then, was not thinking of strife, but of peace—and the profitable blessings of peace. He decided to take a trip of inspection through the new Empire he was building for Britain, the new markets he was developing for British labor. His tour was almost a royal progress. Disgruntled settlers and chronic grumblers approached him at every halt, always to ride off satisfied. Round the circuit he went over the new roads built by his orders, returning to Kimberley on the 23d November after a 4000 mile trek, convinced that before long the new territories would be supporting rich farms and wealthy towns.

Of one more thing his tour convinced him: that the time was ripe for the active pushing of his next dream, a further step toward his red map. So, toward the end of 1892, he went to London where, addressing the directors of the Chartered Company, he insisted on the necessity for a Cape-to-Cairo telegraph line. The di-

rectors agreed, and Rhodes drove the first nail in
another important Empire link.

Among additional details for which his first
Premiership may be noted is the fact that he took the
first steps toward convening an Inter-Colonial Conference. It had always been his idea that the British
Colonies should coöperate in the matters of cable
routes, trade, preferential tariffs and diplomatic rela-
tionships with London. His initial appeal went out in
1891. It bore fruit in 1894 when the Canadian Government issued an invitation to representatives from
all the Colonies to meet in Ottawa.

In the meantime the Mashona settlements were
steadily developing under Jameson. Solid buildings
rose where a few years back the land had been empty
of everything but negro kraals. In new little towns
banks were establishing branches; printing presses
were roaring to send the news of the world to small
circles of intrepid adventurers; the Empire was on the
march, keenly, riotously.

It had been Rhodes' conviction that, pleased with
his monthly payments, Lobengula would behave himself. But he had made this calculation without reference to the minor Matabele chiefs who were getting
nothing out of their ruler and who, for generations,
had been permitted to go on the rampage now and
then, to *"wash their spears"* and burn up a little excess
vitality. They were getting tired of this perpetual,
enervating peace and clamored to be let loose on the
Mashonas. Lobengula, knowing how his bread was
buttered, tried to calm them, but only succeeded in losing their respect.

So raids commenced. A few Mashonas on the border were murdered on the pretext that they had stolen

royal cattle.   Too, native servants of white settlers
were killed.

Jameson wired to Rhodes that it seemed to him time
to take the initiative, strike a blow at the border raiders, and march on Bulawayo.   Rhodes wired back to
go ahead, and Jameson sent an ultimatum to Lobengula . . . and was amazed by the latter's counter-
ultimatum demanding a certain number of Mashonas
for execution.   The Company immediately raised
volunteers; Sir Henry Loch dispatched 200 Bechuanaland Police; and Rhodes sold 50,000 of his own
Chartered Company shares to provide funds.

So came the Matabele War.   In two major encounters small British parties routed ten times their
number of natives, and Lobengula fled his kraal behind the screen of his younger warriors.   Shortly
afterwards he died from smallpox, ordering his *impis*
back to their village with his last breath.

Rhodes was almost in at the death.   Trekking fast
from the south to join Jameson, he arrived only just
in time to disband the troops and to tell them, before
they scattered to their farms, his attitude toward the
future:

"I regret standing in what I may call stolen clothes.
Everything in this campaign has been done by Dr.
Jameson and yourselves. . . . Now it is for me to use
my brains in getting capital to build railways and public
works, to found a state south of the Zambesi which I
hope will be the largest and richest in South Africa."

Such was this man: looking ahead; never looking
back . . . yet a man to whom, as in the career of every
great man playing for stakes worthy of himself, there
came a time when he found the spectre of his own
achievements facing him, threatening to drag him
down, to destroy him.

For, in founding the wealth to weight his political opinions and in acquiring the political power to further his dreams of Empire, he had drawn a vicious circle about him—a vicious circle in treading which no man could have remained above suspicion.

The passing years had found the Transvaal *Uitlanders,* the foreigners, two-thirds of the white population of the Republic, being pushed into an increasingly impossible situation. Kruger looked to Germany for capital. This prompted him to grant resident Germans something like equality with his burghers. With the British, however, he would have no truck. They were unwanted and might return under their own flag—and leave the Rand Gold Fields for the Dutch! If, though, they chose to remain, they must put up with whatever treatment the *Volksraad* cared to give them.

They were denied all political rights. They were grossly overtaxed. Government monopolies hindered their every venture. Yet they were required to take up arms whenever called upon for the suppression of native uprisings. They protested. The *Volksraad* would not listen.

Trouble was in the air. It was unavoidable.

Other things happened.

Rhodes moved in the Cape House that the Colony should annex British Bechuanaland and procure the consent of Her Majesty's government to this end. The motion was carried. On the same day Rhodes made a speech declaring it impossible for the Chartered Company to administer Rhodesia permanently and promising that at a future date it would be united to the Cape.

A Federated South Africa—under British rule. His old plan.

Kruger, too, remembered his old plan: a Federated

South Africa—under Boer rule. He moved; signed a treaty of alliance with the Orange Free State.

To intensify the situation things were happening in England. Lord Rosebery's government went down. Lord Salisbury, Tory of Tories, was called to form a ministry. Joseph Chamberlain was appointed to the Colonial Office, and an era of Imperial unity was inaugurated.

Sir Hercules Robinson was again High Commissioner at the Cape. He set out on a tour of the Transvaal. There the Boers received him with heavy courtesy and the *Uitlanders* with a certain uneasy expectation. In careful speeches the High Commissioner stressed the importance of Dutch and British working together in South African harness. The *Uitlanders,* who had elected a Johannesburg Reform Committee, saw hope in this. Again, immediately upon Robinson's return to the Cape, they presented a petition to the *Volksraad.* But again they were rebuffed with ridicule and contumely, one member of the Transvaal Parliament daring the strangers within the gates to "come and fight these matters out."

Other events increased the tension.

During September, Colonel Frank Rhodes, Cecil's brother and his liaison officer with the Johannesburg Reform Committee, appeared at Ramoutsa, on the Transvaal border, negotiating with the tribal chiefs of the Mamaliti and Bora-Isile Baralong for a concession. He was successful; and so the Chartered Company acquired another territory. A small territory— yet one more log in the ring fence of which Kruger was complaining.

Not that the latter was still at the time. To help the Delagoa Bay Railway he instructed the Rhodes section of the Netherland Railway Company to place prohibitive rates on its line. Rhodes, seeing a yearly loss of £15,000 to the Cape treasury, struck back by installing a fleet of ox carts to take his railway's freight from the border to Johannesburg, thus dodging the expensive stretch of line. Kruger replied by closing all the Drifts—passes and fords—into the Transvaal from the south. From British and Dutch alike rose a storm of protest. The High Commissioner, backed by Joseph Chamberlain, informed Kruger that the closing of the Drifts would be regarded as a declaration of war. Kruger gave in. But the Transvaal Boers were furious and vented their spleen on the *Uitlanders*. Insults and threats were exchanged in Johannesburg. Colonel Frank Rhodes was at work firing the enthusiasm of the Reform Committee and began smuggling rifles across the border, acting on his brother's orders.

It was the beginning of that black chapter in South Africa's annals known as the Jameson Plot. A misnomer. It should have been called the Rhodes Plot.

For C. J. Rhodes, Managing Director of the Chartered Company of South Africa, of the DeBeers Consolidated Mines, of the Consolidated Gold Fields of South Africa, Multimillionaire, Empire Builder at large, had evolved an amazingly complicated plan to force a situation into which might step The Right Honorable Cecil John Rhodes, Prime Minister of the Cape of Good Hope, as mediator and spreader of the gospel of coöperation, the greater gospel of a Federated South Africa. No one but himself, not even his confidential secretary, knew all the varied ramifications of this plan during the hatching.

This was how he calculated:

As a private citizen he would furnish the *Uitlanders* with funds and weapons necessary to insure their chances in the eventuality of open strife. With this secret security behind them, they would present another petition to the *Volksraad*. Its rejection was a foregone conclusion. Immediately they would occupy Johannesburg and march on Pretoria to seize the seat of government and the arsenal and to submit their wrongs to the vote of the entire white population of the Republic. Of course the Boers would resist. They would ride in from their farms. There would be fighting, property in danger, people killed, and, at the invitation of the Reform Committee, a British force would be justified to move into the Transvaal. War would be imminent. And, at this precise moment, Cecil Rhodes would come to the rescue, act the *deus ex machina*, pour oil on troubled waters, pacify both Dutch and English, and bow to the applause of the admiring multitude.

The plan seemed feasible to the inveterate dreamer. But, unfortunately, the man of multiple personality and office could not be in more than one place at a time.

Besides, he had reckoned without Dr. Jameson, whose success in the Matabele War had turned him into that most dangerous of mortals: a once victorious amateur soldier. Where care and subtle caution were essential, Jameson saw only the opportunity for another military triumph and a dramatic political coup.

He was waiting at Mafeking, with a mere handful of men, for orders from Rhodes, in his pocket an undated letter, signed by the chairman of the Johannesburg Reform Committee, which asked for protection for the women and children on the Rand. The writer, after sending the appeal, had seen his error and endeavored to get it back, only to be told that it had already been forwarded to Cape Town as a matter of record. He hurried south to explain the state of affairs to Rhodes. It seemed that the Committee was divided against itself, that the time was not yet ripe. Rhodes understood that postponement of his plan was necessary. He offered to keep Jameson on the border for six months if need be, hoping for a peaceful solution. Sir Hercules Robinson informed Chamberlain that the threatened rising had fizzled out.

But Jameson and his irregulars became impatient. In spite of Rhodes' orders he wired him that he was going forward, cut the telegraph lines, and set out from Mafeking.

This news came to Rhodes as a devastating blow. Without the internal incentive, Jameson's raid was unjustified. It was criminal—and easily traced to Rhodes' inspiration. With Jameson's last message, which reached him at 11 P.M. on the 29th December, he went in search of the High Commissioner, could only find the State Secretary, explained what had happened, and vanished.

Few knew his whereabouts during these critical days. Of course there were all sorts of tales: he had gone with Jameson; he had committed suicide; with unbalanced mind he was wandering over the slopes of Table Mountain; this and that and the other thing. . . .

But actually he was confined to *De Groote Schuur* with a severe heart attack.

Lightning had struck; had set fire to the building of his dreams—the building of Empire, of British domination from the Cape to Cairo . . . and his own fault— dear God—his own fault!

Thus the bitter thoughts coiling in his brain . . . and what was he to do?

For five days and the greater part of five nights he paced his bedroom, reading letters and telegrams, putting them on an ever-growing pile, picking them up again, again reading them, afraid of being left alone, more afraid of seeing people, of having to talk, fretting, seeing no end, no way out.

Friends came. They offered him help; all on the same terms: he must repudiate Jameson.

He could not make up his mind. He paced his bedroom, up and down, up and down, with a mask-like face that held the coldness of death, cloaking whatever emotions were in his soul.

Something seemed to have broken in his brain . . . and his enemies triumphed. Kruger was jubilant. So were the Germans. So were the Little Englanders. So was every mean, small, envious man between London and Chicago, between Moscow and Valparaiso.

A great man had been pulled down!

Wasn't it glorious?

And still Cecil John Rhodes did nothing, nothing . . . except, perhaps, to dream other dreams . . . to plan already how he could change them into reality . . . ?

The Raid itself was foredoomed. Jameson pushed to Johannesburg. In face of discouragement and inertia on the part of the men to whose assistance he was supposed to be moving, he advanced; was led by a treacherous guide into a Boer trap; was crushed by superior forces; surrendered on the 2nd January, 1896.

On the same day Rhodes tendered his resignation from the Premiership of the Cape. He was succeeded by the ever-present Sir Gordon Sprigg.

Once more he was a private citizen. He proceeded to his familiar, beloved Kimberley. There his friends gathered about him. They gave him an enthusiastic welcome. He had regained his self-composure.

He told them, arrogantly, magnificently:

"My enemies are wrong. My career is not over. It is only just beginning."

But there were stockholders and officials to be faced

in England. So, a week late, he embarked. There
were a busy six days in London, spent with the board
of the Chartered Company and the Colonial Secretary,
Joseph Chamberlain.

The two men understood each other. They were
Empire builders both; had the same slogan:

"Try again!"

A Federated South Africa?

They would achieve it yet.

Cecil Rhodes returned to South Africa. He landed
at Beira, in Portuguese territory. He had gauged, no
one more accurately, the effect of Jameson's surrender
upon the Matabele mind.

Jameson, "Rhodes' younger brother and first *in-
duna*," he who had smashed Lobengula's *impis,* whose
word had been absolute law . . . and defeated by the
Boers! What dangerous thoughts this happening
would give to warlike Matabele, even to cowardly
Mashonas!

There was no time to lose. Up country was Rhodes'
place, and he trekked the 200 miles beyond Portuguese
railroad to Salisbury in ten days from his landing. The
journey revealed another catastrophe. Some weeks
before rinderpest had broken out in the Company's
territory and was decimating the cattle of the natives.
The latter were blaming the whites; had begun to
massacre them, men, women, and children.

Over corpse-strewn paths Rhodes reached Salisbury.
He took matters in hand. Action first; policy next.
He was shaken by a terrible attack of malaria. But,
with one hundred and fifty armed settlers, he marched
to the relief of the Matabeleland colonists, fighting his
little band through innumerable skirmishes and three
serious actions toward Bulawayo.

The news reached Cape Town. It enthused his

friends; enthused even his foes. Friends and foes,
Dutch and British politicians, urged him to return to
the House, promised him a generous majority on
arrival.

The Imperial government, too, moved. Troops
were sent to the aid of the Chartered Company. General Carrington marched his soldiers from Mafeking
to join Rhodes. The Matabele, beaten in the open,
retired to the Matoppo Hills. There the Mashonas
made common cause with their hereditary foes against
the white men. But by July peace discussions were
under way.

Peace finally came . . . and it was due to one man;
one man who, during these days in the Matoppos,
proved that he was more than a mere multimillionaire,
a mere successful politician; proved that his soul was
as great as his head.

The position in the Matoppos was difficult. The
Matabele were playing an endless game of hide-and-
seek, promising everything, doing nothing.

Then, almost naïvely, Cecil Rhodes expressed his
idea:

"Surely there must be reasonable men among them
who will listen to me when they know I will meet them.
At any rate let us find out."

Camping with his personal party two miles ahead
of the outpost line, he sent word to the fugitive chiefs
that he was ready for parley. Babayan, who had been
a councilor of Lobengula and one of the emissaries
sent years earlier to London to find out the truth about
the *"Great White Queen,"* came in. Rhodes chatted
with him, but did not rush matters. Babayan spoke of
Lobengula's last hours, of the foolishness of his own
people, and how he had not dared to tell Lobengula
of the wonders of London for fear he would be
stamped as a liar. Two weeks he pottered about

the camp and left finally to persuade other chiefs to come in.

A day or two later, assurance was sent that some chiefs were willing to confer with a party of not more than seven, six miles beyond the British lines. Rhodes chose six and rode forward. At the indicated point five hundred fully armed natives rose from the bush and surrounded the white men.

Rhodes walked up to the chiefs. He demanded:

"How can I trust you? You asked us to carry no guns, and what do I find? Until you lay down your weapons I will not discuss a single point with you."

The chiefs were forced to confess their weakness; they complained that they had no influence over the young warriors. He replied that they must enforce their orders, adding:

"Otherwise I shall go back and the war will begin again."

There were no white eyewitnesses to what followed. For Rhodes had told his white companies to stay back. But in ten minutes they heard loud yells as the young warriors pressed around *"U'Rhodes"* and hailed him as *"Father, Great Chief, and Separator of the Fighting Bulls."*

Still, they were not to be let down as easily as all that. Before entering into any discussion, Rhodes had to be assured that there were no murderers of defenseless settlers in the party. The Matabele gave their word of honor to the effect; and then he spoke for two hours, listening to their complaints and reiterating, as was his old habit, simple points he wished to impress upon them until at last they gave in.

An old chief said:

"We shall always call you Separator of the Fighting Bulls. Now that we have no longer Lobengula, you

are our father, our friend and protector, and to you we
shall look in the years that are coming."

The return to camp, to the bewildered astonishment
of Colonel Plumer, O. C. Troops (now Field Marshal
Lord Plumer, lately commanding Haig's Second Army
in Flanders), was in the nature of a triumphal progress, as Rhodes, in the usual crumpled white flannels,
riding carelessly as he ever did, walked his horse in the
midst of some hundred young Matabele warriors.

During the following weeks, pitching his camp in the
Matoppos, he declared open house to all chiefs, summing up grievances in simple sentences and, through
long hours of conference, establishing lasting under-
standings. All the settlements and provisions made
were scrupulously adhered to, and the warrior clans
never regretted adopting *"U'Rhodes"* as successor to
their hereditary chief.

During these negotiations Rhodes came upon that
bowlder-strewn hill top which at first sight he selected
as the site of his grave.

On his return trek he was met by ill news. His home,
De Groote Schuur, had been burned to the ground.
Nothing had been saved of his great collection of ob-
jects of art.

He shrugged his shoulders; said to Lord Grey who
had brought the news:

"Oh—is that all? I thought you were going to tell
me Jameson was dead."

A couple of days later he overtook Baden-Powell
who was heading in the same direction and told him:

"Providence has not been kind to me this year.
What with my house burned, Jameson's Raid, rebellion, famine, rinderpest, I feel like Job, all but the
boils."

And, back at the Cape, he declared:

"I honestly believe that my years of trouble have made me a better man. I am determined to go on with my work—the work of forming a railway junction with Egypt and the work of closer Union in South Africa."

Not for a moment did he try to dodge his share of the misfortunes arising from the Jameson Raid. His comment, when he heard that Jameson had been sentenced to fifteen months' imprisonment, was that it was a tribute to the "upright rectitude of my countrymen." Back at the Cape he spent a busy ten days going into all the details of rebuilding *De Groote Schuur*, outlining and financing a scheme for building up the fruit production of the Colony, and founding a concern for the local manufacture of industrial explosives and fertilizers; then took ship to appear before the Select Committee of the House of Commons which was to inquire into his responsibility in the Raid.

The result of the inquiry was a minor triumph for him. The Little Englanders, chiefly Labouchere, editor of *Truth,* who had been his most persistent detractor, spared no pains to attack and discredit him. He replied to all questions and hecklings with a chilly, consistent candor that impressed every one. Even Labouchere was forced to admit that the *"African demon"* was a far better type than he had imagined, and he voiced his conviction that Rhodes, whatever his mistakes, had never worked for his own ends nor to increase his private wealth.

Rhodes did not make the slightest effort before the Committee to whitewash himself. He answered truthfully; then, the examination ended, he did not wait for the publication of the findings, but sailed back to South Africa.

His reception at Cape Town was tremendous. He

was greeted by deputations, both British and Dutch, from all over the Colony. In a speech to the gathering he informed South Africa that he would strive for equal rights for every white man throughout the Continent, adding, as though thinking of the impending decision of the Select Committee in London:

"I shall fight constitutionally."

On the 13th July, 1897, the Select Committee presented its report. It decided that, however great the justification may have been for action by the Johannesburg *Uitlanders,* there was none for the behavior of a man in Rhodes' official position. It added that any insinuations that Rhodes had acted with the intention of benefiting the Chartered Company or enhancing the stock of any private concern were absolutely groundless.

In the meantime Sir Hercules Robinson had resigned. He had been succeeded by Sir Alfred Milner. At first Rhodes saw in him something of an opponent. But the years were to bring these two very closely together on Imperial matters.

The Afrikander Bond, the Dutch party, was having its annual meeting at Malmesbury. The leaders were for Rhodes. The mass of the party, remembering his share in the Jameson Raid, trusted him no longer. But he lacked no support and encouragement from other quarters. Letters from Boer and Briton alike insisted that he should return to active political work, assuring him that, before long, he would regain the Premiership.

But, just then, his heart was up country—and from up country he received a pleasant surprise. For the settlers there, for some time, had been in the habit of referring to the Chartered Company territories as *"Rhodesia."* Now Her Majesty's Government legalized the name.

Rhodesia! A monument, covering thousands and thousands of square miles—for a man not yet old, still alive . . . but a man far from well.

Up country he suffered a severe heart attack. And, because of it, because of the fear that he might not live long, he worked harder than ever for the good of Rhodesia, always looking forward to the Grail of a United South Africa and realizing that, the stronger Rhodesia's position at the time of Federation, the better terms she would get from her sister states. He wanted no loafers there; and every laborer was worthy of his hire and a little more than his hire. He drove others as he drove himself. His associates and friends complained bitterly of the relentless machine. Sixteen hours a day he worked; insisted on every one keeping pace with him. Stragglers received curt dismissal. Many were on the point of revolt. But he carried on.

It was at this time that he broached his favorite scheme to those who were to put it into practice for him: "a great educational plan to apply to all the English speaking portions of the world." He said:

"I consider the education of young colonists at one of the Universities of the United Kingdom is of great advantage to them for giving breadth to their views, for their instruction in life and manners. I do not want simply the book worms. . . ."

And, in his confession to Rosebery, this lonely man "with the mien of a Roman Emperor, born to rule," exhibited for a flashing moment what was at the core of him:

"When I find myself in uncongenial company, or when people are playing their games, or when I am alone in a railway carriage, I shut my eyes and think of my great idea. . . . It is the pleasantest companion I have."

Beyond picking his men and laying the bare founda-

tion of the plan there was no time that year to go further.   He was too busy looking into farming and
mining problems, and all the while messages from Cape
Town arrived asking him to return and throw his
weight into the scale against the growing partisanship
of the Afrikander Bond, and, once again, to interest
himself on behalf of the sorely tried *Uitlanders* of the
Transvaal.

Before returning he put under way the Rhodesia
Dam project.   Understanding the necessity for con-
serving some of the tremendous Matoppo rains against
the dry season, he specified for a billion-gallon reser-
voir on which work was at once begun.

Shortly after his arrival at the Cape, with elections
pending, he preached unceasingly for his old dream:
Federation.   If the two *"stiff-necked races"* could be
brought to pull in the same harness, all troubles would
evaporate.   But the elections disappointed him.   While
his party polled a clear majority of 14,000 votes, he
found it with one seat less than the Bond, and so he
had to go into opposition with the question of a
redistribution of seats a burning one in the new
House.

By the early weeks of 1899 the telegraph line had
nearly reached Tanganyika, with Kitchener working
down the Nile to meet it.   The time had come for
Rhodes to take a look at the farther end of the red
map.   In February he took a trip to Egypt, summed
up the situation, saw that not only the telegraph but
even the Cape-to-Cairo railway was beginning to change
from a dream into a reality, and proceeded to Berlin
—where he shocked the Kaiser by his South African
informality.   For, during an audience, noticing a clock
over his Imperial host's shoulder, he suddenly rose,
extended his hand, and said:

"Well, good-by. I've got to go now as I have some people coming to dinner."

His stay in England on this occasion was chiefly important for the side lights cast on his general acquaintance as a great force in the Empire. Long past were the days when Lord Salisbury, asked who Rhodes was —Rhodes who, at the time, had made some singularly tactless and forceful statement about British Imperial politics,—replied: "Oh—some cypher!" The "cypher" had become famous; had become the greatest single influence in the Empire; and Oxford honored her son, in company with Kitchener, by conferring the degree of D.C.L. upon him.

"Don't look so bored, Rhodes!" called an irrepressible undergraduate from the gallery during the ceremony; and the man who had successfully faced so many antagonistic crowds on the edge of civilization, who had bullied Kruger and fought the warlike Matabele, blushed and stammered like any shy freshman.

During his return voyage he came into contact with Princess Radziwill who was en route to the Cape as the representative of several European papers. They saw a great deal of each other; and there was, of course, gossip. People rolled scandal under their tongues. What happened is anybody's guess. Nobody knows for certain. But it is a fact that, back in Cape Town, the careful Rhodes refused to see her without a witness being present.

The Cape was now a cauldron of trouble. War with the Dutch Republics was inevitable. But Rhodes would not take part in the negotiations. He said:

"I made a mistake with regard to the Transvaal once. A burnt child dreads fire. No one will be able to say if things go wrong that Rhodes is in it again."

But this calm attitude did not preclude his indulging in a bit of irony which did not go unnoticed. Hear-

ing that the Pretoria Zoo had lost its two lions, he
presented it with a fine specimen of a young lion—
"British lion" he called it in his letter—which, however, was refused by the Boers since a sense of humor
was never their *forte*.

There was laughter throughout South Africa. The
last hearty laughter for quite awhile.

For tragedy—war—was on the march.

On the 9th October hostilities were obviously ahead;
and Rhodes, worried about his Kimberley miners in
their unprotected proximity to the Republics, caught
the last train from Cape Town to reach the diamond
town before the invading Boers cut off its communication with the outside world and laid down the siege.

He found his *"place of destiny"* happily reveling in
the novelties of war—and badly equipped for long
resistance. As usual, people mistook enthusiasm for
strength; and Rhodes knew that, once the truth found
its way home to them, the corresponding reaction
would be dangerous. There was a shortage of regular
troops. Colonel Kekewich with half of his North Lan-
cashire Battalion and some light artillery was confronted with the task of defending a rather large-sized
town on a lengthy periphery. But his ideas of the Boer
military qualities made him confident.

This view was not shared by Rhodes. The moment
he arrived in Kimberley he made all possible preparations to help in a situation which he, for one, did not
underestimate. But, with the declaration of martial
law, he became nothing more than a private citizen and
found his influence and power sadly curtailed by
Colonel Kekewich who, bearing the responsibility of the
defense on his shoulders, did not care to entrust deci-
sions to a man notoriously interested, financially, in the
district.

There was the matter of Kenilworth. Going his decidedly unofficial rounds, which went a long way toward keeping up the morale of the citizens, Rhodes discovered at Kenilworth a spot which obviously required protection for which no provision had been made. He approached Kekewich and was told that headquarters had no intention of diverting soldiers to the point in question. Rhodes lost no time. He found money for the work and enrolled a citizen contingent of one hundred to hold it. Later on, the place, rechristened *"Fort Rhodes,"* became a key situation, and its defense undoubtedly saved Kimberley from Boer invasion.

In the meantime the enemy wasted no efforts to take the town. Rhodes' presence was an even greater incentive than the diamond fields. Proclamations were issued to the commandos urging the capture of this man who had so consistently opposed Oom Paul's schemes of expansion. There were rumors that, once he had fallen into their hands, he was to be paraded through the chief towns in a cage for the delectation of his Boer enemies . . . a form of simple, rustic entertainment which Rhodes gave his opponents every opportunity to carry out. For, day after day, clad in conspicuous white flannels, he visited exposed positions —a perfect target which, somehow, was never hit.

Providence?

Not according to the Boers—whose God was strictly Dutch Reformed and vengeful.

Artillery was the great trouble. The Boers possessed two long-range guns which they could place out of range of the field pieces of the garrison. After two months of siege Rhodes consulted with one of his mining engineers, Labram, an American, and urged him to construct a gun. With no knowledge of requirements and only the tools available in the DeBeers workshops, but with the amazing mechanical genius of his race, Labram went to work with the result that by the middle of January heavy shells were being lobbed into the Boer lines. It was one of the tragedies of the siege that Labram was killed shortly afterwards.

Another of Rhodes' activities was the organization of his soup kitchen. To it thousands came daily to receive their ration of broth, made on a horse bone basis and messed up with any available greens. The threat of scurvy brought the kitchen into being—and by it was laid.

But his handling of the natives inside the lines will be longest remembered. With the cessation of work in the mines ten thousand unemployed negroes came in to swell the black population to close on twenty-five thousand. Rhodes took hold of the problem. The natives presented a danger. It was as much because of this danger as for safety from shells that he opened the diamond workings as a place of refuge for the white women and children. Then he put the blacks to work on road mending and building. *"Siege Avenue"* remains to this day the *"show"* street of Kimberley, constructed under Rhodes' supervision and mostly at his expense.

But England—as is England's habit—was beginning to muddle and worry through its war. On February 15th, with no advance signs to herald him, General French's flanking movement brought relief to Kimberley . . . and so Cecil Rhodes was not put into a cage after all, but returned to Cape Town, with headquarters at *De Groote Schuur,* reassuring the colonists and pointing to the golden future.

He had erred, he admitted. For years he had imagined Kruger to be bluffing. But in his miscalculations he found the basis for increased optimism. The war could only help Federation. The hands of the clock had moved forward.

Ten days sufficed to show him that, with hostilities still going on up country, he could spare the time for a hurried trip to London where he preached the new gospel to the board of the Chartered Company and adjusted the temporarily disrupted affairs of the DeBeers interests. He worked quickly. A few weeks later, he was back at the Cape and ready for a tour of inspection through Rhodesia.

His trip seemed to justify his highest expectations. In five months he covered 1600 miles. His railway was now paying as far as Bulawayo. But, in his dreams, it was already running through-trains to Cairo:

"Not just so that I can say that a man can climb aboard at Cape Town and get off in Egypt. But because I know the vast resources it will touch on the way."

The discovery of the Wankie coal deposit had made the existence of the whole line possible. He said:

"We now propose to cross the Zambesi just below the Victoria Falls. I should like to have the spray of the falls over the carriages."

On his round he was accompanied by a few friends, the party taking with them six riding horses and three mule wagons. Thirty miles a day was the average trek, the wagons sticking to the roads and the riders flanking it about a mile, ready to shoot their evening meal, and closing in on the scattered settlements where Rhodes interviewed farmers and did his best to adjust their difficulties.

But the trip came to an end. Cape business called. He set off south.

Kimberley then. Then the Cape. Again Kimberley. Back to Bulawayo, to look after the railway, the telegraph line, the Rhodesia dam.

Again Kimberley. Again the Cape. Always on the trek—always working . . . this man who had not ceased from trekking and working since, so many years earlier, because of an affected lung, he had first landed in Durban.

Then London.

Here he was busy with his will, the final document of which had been completed the year before; giving instructions to his executors and making various detailed provisions for the future administration of its terms . . . *"to render myself useful to my country"* . . . useful indeed!

Jameson was with him. They went to England; thence to Egypt to see how the other end of what he called his hobby was keeping pace: Cape-to-Cairo.

But he suffered from the heat. His heart hurt him. He wrote to a friend:

"The great thing is rest."

Rest? He could not afford it. They wrote to him from South Africa that he *"must* return" . . . that he alone could "end the war quickly and not disgracefully."

So it was London in December with innumerable, maddening odds and ends of politics and finance. Then the Cape.

An interlude there. Princess Radziwill was trying to blackmail him. He refused to have matters hushed up. It came to a trial. And the Princess received a sentence of eighteen months' imprisonment.

He was staying at Muizenburg, several miles from Cape Town, on the sea, where he had built a smaller house for relexation.

He needed relaxation—needed it badly.

He was so sick; so tired; was drifting toward the end.

It came on the 26th March, 1902, at half past four in the afternoon.

He turned to Jameson.

He said in a whisper:

"So little done! So much to do!"

Then, for awhile, he sang to himself—a thing he had never done during his lifetime, a thing for which, perhaps, he had never had time . . . and so he died.

From Muizenburg the body was removed to *De Groote Schuur* to lie in state. There, for two days, tens of thousands, Dutch and British, passed his bier, in complete silence, while, up in the Matoppos, arrangements were going forward for his burial.

They took him there. They paid the dead man— "the greatest Englishman in modern times"—high honor; higher honor than they had paid the living man.

Thousands and thousands made the long, weary pilgrimage into the far Matoppos, accompanying the coffin.

The cortège neared its end. It was greeted by more thousands and thousands. Black men this time. Matabele warriors in full ceremonial dress, shaking their spears, bestowing on the dead Briton the royal salute which never before had they bestowed on any one but their own kings.

He lies there . . .

> *"There, till the vision he foresaw*
> *Splendid and whole arise,*
> *And unimagined Empires draw*
> *To council 'neath his skies,*
> *The immense and brooding Spirit still*
> *Shall quicken and control.*
> *Living he was the land, and dead,*
> *His soul shall be her soul!"*

RICHARD FRANCIS BURTON

[1821–1890]

who dreamed in seventeen languages

RICHARD FRANCIS BURTON

RICHARD FRANCIS BURTON

THERE is no psychological or ethnological riddle as hard to solve as that of the Bedaw, the desert Arab. In practical shrewdness, when forced by circumstance or by his own will to enter the arena of competition, he compares favorably to the Scot, the Jew, the Yankee. Almost invariably, whenever he wanders forth from his brittle, yellow homeland, he succeeds: as merchant, statesman, missionary, and, oddly enough, as sailor. Nobody reaches the heights of power as fast as the Arab political intriguer in Constantinople or Cairo, at the courts of Central Asian Khans or at those of semi-independent Malay Rajahs. No European trader penetrates further into Central Africa or mulcts the natives more profitably. No Christian clergyman *in partibus infidelium* has ever made as many and as faithful, even fanatical, converts, though the preacher of Islam works alone, without a central organization to prepare him for his task and to send him financial assistance, and without machine guns to second the word of God in tight corners. No western mariner has ever outdone in bravery or love of adventure the burnoosed sailing-masters who cruise their riotous, careless sea way between the Persian Gulf and Hongkong, between Rangoon and Zanzibar, between Sumatra and Port Said.

In innate, racial culture he is not much behind the Frenchman, the Chinese, and the Virginian of a past generation; is far ahead of the Scandinavian, the Italian, the man from the English Midlands, and the man from Tennessee or Kansas or Maine. A peasant or, more often, a nomad, without schools, without newspapers, without railways, without radios, without anything except crude tools for a most miserable existence, he speaks, in his black felt tent, the language of classic poetry. He expresses keen and noble thoughts, keenly and nobly. He is familiar with the glorious traditions and achievements of his people, passing on its epic deeds by word of mouth, from father to son. He possesses an amazing capacity for clean-cut, logical argument. He is to this day a gentleman reminiscent of the age of chivalry, where his European or American prototype is a yokel—a yokel who votes, who has open plumbing, electricity, Ford cars, rural free delivery, and the telephone—but still a yokel whose mind is more manure-caked than are his boots.

As a soldier the Arab equals the Anglo-Saxon and the German; is surpassed only by the Turk and the Japanese. Three times his race, numerically so weak, founded far-flung Empires. He met the steel-clad legions of Rome and defeated them by sheer bravery. Again and again, without armor, he vanquished the armored barbarians, the Crusaders, the picked warriors of a dozen Christian lands. Within our living memory we have had an Osman Digma and his illy armed tribesmen charging crack British troops, Berkshires and Marines, and breaking the famed "square."

In art and literature it is enough to point at the Alhambra, the great Mosque of Cordova, the Koran, the poems of Zohair, Imr al-Qais, Abu'l-Ala, and Abu'l-Atahija.

Yet, having all these gifts of body and soul and brain, he prefers, nearly always, to seclude himself in his sterile, monotonous desert, living there a life of material poverty such as few Occidentals can conceive, but living it with a perfected balance of mental and spiritual content which asks no favors from anybody, not even from God—living it until death comes, and accepting death as an ordinary fact, neither to be sought nor feared.

Such is the riddle of the Arab. Many have tried to solve it. Only one has succeeded.

Not one of the large shoal of more or less negligible small-fry: the André Chevrillons, the John Foster Frasers, the Marmaduke Pickthalls and Niebuhrs and Burckhardts, the Sadliers and Wellsteds and Halévys, the Hubers and Guarmanis. Not a Charles M. Doughty who, when all is said and done, explored no more than a very limited district of the enormous Arabian peninsula and was too wrapped up in his particular brand of medieval, narrow, intolerant Protestant Christianity and too busy with Elizabethan tricks of diction to get at the roots of an alien faith and civilization. Not even H. St. J. B. Philby, our finest living Arabicist, more important than Doughty, but who, so far, given his official and scholastic duties, has perhaps not had the time to record the true, full tale of what he knows, what he has seen—and felt.

What he has felt. . . .

It is that which counts—more than minute observation and academic digging—when one wants to solve the riddle of the Arab: the feeling, the instinctive, almost psychic reaction and perception. And there was one man, England's greatest traveler and linguist, who had this quality.

Sir Richard Burton. Who else?

Sir Richard Burton . . . a queer, reverberating ring to that name—a name to this day affectionately remembered in Mecca, in Baghdad, in the Street Called Straight. . . .

He saw eye to eye with the Arab. He needed no lancets or scalpels or bone-scrapers of psychological vivisection to comprehend the immemorial, unbending haughtiness of a man who prefers material poverty to spiritual poverty and, by the same token, prefers spiritual riches to material riches.

Perhaps this instinctive understanding and sympathy was partially due to the racial mixture of which he was the result. For on his mother's side he was a Highland Scot of the lawless, landless clan of Rob Roy M'Gregor; a descendant from that bitter, proud, tense Gaeldom which, a century or two ago, was pistoled and legislated out of existence by the German, to-day so English, Hanovers' red-coated soldiers and black-coated judges. His father's stock was English. There is no truth to the old scandal—spread, in ironic mood, by himself—that this English blood was tainted by intermarriage with gypsies. On the other hand, there was a left-handed Bourbon trickle from the veins of King Louis XIV.

In this last he took a sardonic pride, often relating the romantic episode of *"La Belle Montmorency"* carrying her illegitimate son to Ireland.

"I should have thought," commented an English nobleman, stiffly starched with Victorian prudishness, "you would be glad to forget your descent from such a dishonorable union."

"I would rather be a king's bastard than the son of an honest man," came Burton's reply.

A thoroughly un-English reply—un-English, that is, from the accepted John Bull point-of-view . . . as Cecil Rhodes was un-English, Wilfrid Scawen Blunt, Sir John Fisher, Lord Byron, Labouchere, "Chinese" Gordon . . . all so typically un-English as to be typically British. . . .

He was born at Torquay on the 19th March, 1821,
the son of a lieutenant-colonel on the retired list who
divided his time between looking up cures for his
mostly imaginary ailments, making unsuccessful though
excessively smelly chemical experiments, and grumbling
over the legal provisions of his wife's dower money
which rendered it impossible for him to double the
capital, as he was convinced he could, on the stock
exchange.

Early in life Richard Francis Burton was ear-marked
for Oxford and the Church.

He never cared for the latter.   Dislike of Christianity—even before, civilizationally more than re-
ligiously, he became to all intents and purposes a
Moslem—was congenital with him.   He considered its
preachments wishy-washy and milk-soppy; considered
the result of its preachments hypocritical and mendacious.

He did reach Oxford—and cared for it as little as
for the Church.

This was, possibly, the fault of his father whose
hypochondria, for years, had taken him all over western and southern Europe, from doctor to doctor, from
nostrum to nostrum, from spa to spa—wanderings
which changed Richard into a second-rate Frenchman
and a third-rate Italian; which taught him two foreign
languages better than his native tongue; which, too,
taught him enough foreign deviltry to astonish and
shock his fellow-undergraduates when he went up to
Trinity College in October, 1840.

By this time he had lived, loved, lied, and been a
pest to successive tutors in Tours, Blois, Pisa, Siena,
Perugia and back in Richmond.   He had ridden out a
cholera epidemic, during which he sneaked out in his
night shirt to carry a torch and help pile the day's
corpses on the death carts; had witnessed, as a reward

for lessons unusually well learned, the guillotining of a
woman; had had a brace of mistresses; had whipped a
couple of maids out of his mother's service; had become a gourmet as well as a gourmand; had trained
a subtle, strong wrist for both broad-sword and rapier;
had developed a remarkable love for animals and,
paradoxically, a passion for cock-fighting; had smashed
a violin over the pate of the unfortunate Italian who
arrived intent on giving him his first music lesson;
had reached the conviction:

"Of all the various countries I know, I hate England
most."

Nor did Oxford in the least temper his early opinion
of his native land. He found the undergraduates unbearable snobs, the dons smug, snuffling and dull, and
the college accommodations frowsy.

Oxford returned the dislike.

For he arrived among the dreamy spires behind
magnificent, Mediterranean mustachios which he ob-
stinately refused to shave off until, finally, his tutors
appealed to the highest university authorities. He
complained formally of the incessant bell ringing from
the towers. He waited for a ragging party with a red-
hot poker. He made lewd puns, to that worthy's face,
on the name of his tutor—The Reverend Mr.
Havergal.

Disgusted by an educational system which he described as worthless, he spent most of his time shooting
protected birds, fencing, drinking, sharing his affection
between an amazingly beautiful gypsy fortune-teller
and an amazingly ugly bulldog, and breaking as many
university rules as he could.

But he grew bored. He decided to leave Oxford;
decided, too, that it would be more amusing to be sent
down than to go of his own will. He succeeded, the

last straw after many straws being his attendance at a banned race meeting.

So he received his notice of expulsion and bade a characteristic farewell to Oxford by driving down The High in a tandem with a couple of spirited bays between the shafts, extravagantly dressed, tootling a noisy horn, and kissing his hand right and left.

He had not wasted the eighteen months entirely. For he had begun to teach himself Arabic. Unable to get individual instruction and finding classes too slow for his remarkable gift, he devised a method of his own—a method which, later on, he used for all the many languages that he acquired.

First he reduced the principal rules of grammar so that he could write them upon a card small enough to be carried in his pocket and looked at whenever he felt like it. Then, day after day, he learned by heart as much vocabulary as possible, usually from three to four hundred words a week, and then commenced reading, making annotations where peculiar construction occurred. "The neck of the language was now broken," he put it. Strange words he would repeat, over and over again, for an entire day, until his ears and throat had become familiar with the alien sounds. But apart from this particular lingual drill the most time he ever spent at a study on a stretch was fifteen minutes.

"After fifteen minutes the brain loses its freshness," he used to say.

To ease his return to the bosom of the family he informed his father that, having broken all scholastic records, the university had granted him a special vacation. Promptly the proud parent organized a banquet in celebration of the event, including an academic gentleman who knew the truth and did not hesitate to spring a bomb at the feast.

There was a scene. The father roared and cursed. So did the son. Perhaps the latter roared more loudly and cursed more profanely. At all events, he got his heart's desire: release from a cleric's future and purchase of a commission in the service of the Honorable John Company—the *United Company of Merchants Trading to the East Indies.*

So, on the 18th June, 1842, certain pompous directors swore young Richard in as ensign in their 18th Bombay Infantry Regiment and dispatched their newly acquired treasure to his post.

Despite his burning desire to arrive in time to assist in visiting revenge on the belligerent Afghans who had just murdered Sir William MacNaughton, had smashed the punitive British columns and forced them on their terrible retreat from Kabul, the four months aboard ship did not pass too slowly. There was Hindustani to be learned. There were various women to be made love to. There was a series of fist fights with members of the crew.

At last Bombay was reached. Too late. For, by this time, the British had somehow white-washed their faces; and, for the nonce, all was serene on both sides of the Afghan border.

Burton's regiment was stationed at Baroda. But he did not proceed there immediately. Nor did he show his white gloves, as a proper griffin should, in Bombay's social salons which have not changed in pristine starchiness since, in the year 1663, Mr. Humphrey Cook took possession of the town in the King's name. Instead he plunged into the exotic, forbidden delights of Black Town, of Bycula, Mahaluxmee, and the Docks—specializing for awhile in native liquor, native drugs, and half-caste women, with the result that, for some weeks, he was laid up in a sanatorium.

But when, finally, he reported to the adjutant, he got down to work quickly, attending to drill and wearing out two native teachers in daily twelve-hour sessions and sitting, metaphorically speaking, at the feet of his *"bubu"*—for *"bubu,"* comely and young native women, were, in those far-off, less hypocritical days, considered necessary for the education of an East Indian cadet and were, in fact, chosen, almost appointed, by John Company in person—a *"bubu"* who, Burton confessed with his usual double meaning, "gave me an interest in local manners and customs and taught me thoroughly the language."

Customs, second to tongues, attracted him. He did not altogether specialize in young native women. On the contrary—old native women found great favor with him. He would squat by the hour beside some ancient hag; would "follow her speech by eye and ear with the keenest attention" and repeat words and sentences until his accent and intonation were indistinguishable from the native. Too, he would ask questions, questions, questions—learning India by heart as he learned her languages.

His quick understanding was amazing. So was his sympathy with the Indians—so much so that, in the mess of the 18th Foot, he was nicknamed *"The White Nigger"* . . . so much so that, before the end of the year his Hindu teacher granted him officially the holy Brahminical thread, while the directors of the Honorable John Company presented him with a certificate of having passed in Gujarati with distinction.

During a regimental move to Karachi—where Burton's chief excitement consisted in baiting the sacred crocodiles attached to the temples and taking dangerous rides astride their scaly backs—he met a captain of sappers, Scott by name, who applied for the subaltern's attachment to his company. The application

was allowed, and, presently, Burton was surveying in
the neighborhood of Hyderabad.

He found it a dull grind. So, combining, as was
his wont through life, pleasure with hard research,
he devoted part of his spare time to the ancient sport
of hawking and part to the study of India—looking
more and more deeply into her dark, brooding soul.
On his return to his regiment he demanded and received leave—went on leave, not to the flesh-pots of
Bombay, but taking the road in the disguise of a half-
breed Arab from Bushire, observing Indian life and
customs from the peculiar vantage point of a peddler
of things dear to the garrulous, female heart.

This was his first venture into serious fancy-dress.
It was not very risky, since he did little beyond bargaining with and entertaining the ladies. But it taught
him some of the finer points so useful in his later, romantic escapades. He made, furthermore, innumerable jottings of odd, invaluable information to be used,
some day, in his recognized *magnum opus*.

Sir Charles Napier, commanding in Scinde, heard
about the queer young subaltern. He saw in him good
material for the Intelligence Service and offered to
send him on special duty, to find out the exact nature of the goings-on in certain notorious Karachi
bawdy-houses.

Burton accepted the task. In native guise, he discovered all there was to be known; made a complete
report—not only of the political intrigues but, in the
thorough way he had, of everything else he had seen,
and adding a lengthy theory as to the nature of sex-
perversion, as studied in the Karachi houses, which
acted as a boomerang. For frequently, in after years,
the manuscript was dug out from the Bombay ar-
chives; was used to blacken his character; and, in one

instance, was made the basis of a demand to the Company for Burton's dismissal from the service.

Ill health now forced him to rest—to rest, that is, from his official duties, since little of his furlough was actually spent at the sanatorium in the Nilgherries to which he was sent. Instead he explored the back alleys of Goa, Calicut and Panany; and, between attacks of ophthalmia, he devoted himself so seriously to languages that, on his return to Bombay, he sat for examination in Persian, passing brilliantly, and was presented by the Board with a gratuity of one thousand rupees. During the convalescent period he had also mastered Arabic, Telugu and Toda.

Back in Karachi, with little to interest him in the routine barrack life, he conceived the idea of a pilgrimage to Mecca. He buckled down to preparatory work, soundly and thoroughly as always: commencing to study Islam; learning much of the Koran by heart; becoming an expert in the correct ritual and delivery of prayers; discussing the deeper aspects of Islamic theology with great Moslem doctors.

Then news came that trouble was brewing in Multan and that an expeditionary force was being made ready.

At once he gave up his work. For he had always longed for active service. His regiment was not slated to go to the front. But he was certain that his linguistic attainments would earn him an appointment to headquarters as interpreter. He made his application. But some creeping file-comber attached to it Burton's papers on the Karachi houses together with some damaging comments on the author's character—with the result that the latter's application was turned down and the post was given to a man with a bare smattering of Hindustani.

The disappointment, the injustice, was a terrific blow
to Burton's tired, overworked brain. He understood
that the John Company did not reckon merit as he
himself reckoned it. He collapsed completely.

He went to Bombay; embarked there for the homeland he so heartily loathed. He was sick in soul and
body—but not too sick to indulge in a few strenuous
flirtations aboard ship, and well on the road to physical and spiritual recovery when, at Pisa, he joined his
parents who were still wandering at large over Europe.

Back in England he settled down to work. But, as
always, England was too much for him. So he crossed
the Channel and took up residence in Boulogne where,
at least, he could get the sort of food which he liked.
He hated English cooking; agreed with a famous
French philosopher that the English had too many
religions and too few sauces; would point out that no
such thing as a dyspeptic Frenchman existed.

During his voluntary exile he prepared three books
for the press: *Goa and the Blue Mountains, Scinde;
or the Unhappy Valley,* and *Sindh, and the Races that
Inhabit the Valley of the Indus;* and within the year—
the which would have broken the heart of almost any
modern publisher insisting on paucity of output and
on safe and sane sameness and standardization of sub-
ject-matter on the part of his author—followed these
books with two entirely different volumes: *Falconry
in the Valley of the Indus* and—of all things—*A Complete System of Bayonet Exercise.*

Not that writing took up all his time, nor that he
sacrificed entirely his avocation to his vocation.

At the time several English families lived in Boulogne, and they had—as is somehow usual with English families—a plethora of unmarried daughters. Of
course Burton paid ardent court to a number, chiefly

to a certain Louise. Very successfully he explained to her his conscientious scruples against monogamy; was suspected and finally most embarrassingly cornered by the girl's mother, a female, red-faced John Bull who demanded straight out:

"I would like to be quite certain as to your intentions toward my daughter."

"Strictly dishonorable, madam, I regret to say," came his reply; and he left that house and looked for other amorous adventures, at last meeting Isabel Arundel whose golden hair stood out in a family noted for their looks and who, later on, was to become his wife.

He fell in love with her, romantically. She with him, quite as romantically.

But she would not listen to anything except marriage.

Here was a facer for Richard Burton.

Marriage? Well—perhaps. But he was not to be rushed in such matters.

Writing and flirting were not enough for his restless body and mind. So, in the intervals, he attended M. Constantin's Academy where he laid the foundations of the reputation held later of being the best swordsman in the Army. He defeated all the local talent and earned his official brevet of *Maître d'Armes,* furthermore gathering knowledge for his future book: *The Book of the Sword.*

Writing. Flirting. Fencing. Still not enough. The lusty, adventurous blood coursed hotly in his veins. He remembered plans laid before his illness: Mecca!

He made up his mind to cross Arabia from the Red Sea to the Persian Gulf. But first had to come careful preparations, and France was not the right place for these. His parents were living now at Bath. He settled near that city of fading renown to put the last touches to his equipment, a process including the mastery of the blacksmith's trade and the polishing of his Oriental languages.

Ready then to proceed, he made representations to the Royal Geographical Society, offering "to remove that opprobrium to modern adventure, the huge white blot which our map still notes—the eastern and central regions of Arabia."

The Society was impressed, but not so Burton's employers, the Honorable John Company. To a distinguished deputation from the former body the Chairman of the Board of Directors of the East India Company refused to grant Burton the suggested three years of leave, allowing instead an additional twelve months of furlough "to study Arabic in the lands where best learned." The enterprise itself the Board condemned as hazardous, remarking that "nothing but a string of fatalities had resulted from the travels heretofore undertaken in that region."

Burton was aware of this. For—remember!—all this happened over seventy years ago, before the days of the airplane, the automobile, the radio, the cable— in the days when a man who went into the wilds had to stand squarely on his own two feet. Nor was the reward, in case of success, so much to look forward to. There would be no immense sale of books with royalties pyramiding. No newspaper publicity. No hailing as *"hero"* and *"the world's most romantic adventurer"* from pulpits and lecture platforms. No syndicated newspaper articles with obligato pictures of the reckless traveler, in the rather theatrical costume of an Arab Shaykh, to cause matronly and flapperish hearts to skip a beat.

Burton was not looking for reward; was not trying to *"épater les bourgeois."* He went because of the dream he had of doing what nobody else had done before; perhaps also—illogically—to burnish the fame of that England which he so cordially detested.

So, liberally supplied with means by the Geographical Society, tired of material progress and civilization, eager to see with his eyes what others were content to hear with their ears, he resolved to assume his old disguise and make the journey.

Until the eve of his departure he made frequent visits to his parents, without divulging his plans. He slipped off, leaving behind a letter to his mother outlining his program and giving directions for the disposal of his small estate in the event of his not returning.

So, on the 3rd April, 1853, Richard F. Burton vanished somewhere in the port of Southampton, while a certain Mirza Abdulla of Bushire, a devout Moslem, howling his prayers and reading the Koran, came to life.

At Alexandria he led something of a double existence, staying secretly with English friends, but sleeping in an outhouse where he could revel in the utmost freedom of life and manners, brushing up the intricacies of the Islamic faith, reviving his knowledge of ablutions and prostrations and similar religious rites, attending the Mosque, and pitting his patience against bazaar vendors whilst picking their brains of the lore he had to acquire. His stay convinced him of the efficacy of his disguise—a conviction amply proved by the insults meted out to him in his character as half-breed Arab by the employers of the British Consulate during a three days' hunt for passports.

But in a month he was tired of inaction . . . *"the man wants to wander, and he must do so or he shall die."* So, carefully covering his spoor, he bought a traveling kit consisting of a rag wrapped about a tooth-

stick, a bit of soap and a wooden comb, stuck into his
waistshawl a brass inkstand, an illegal but useful
dagger and a gigantic Moslem rosary for defense as
much as for devotions, and boarded a boat for Cairo
as deck passenger.

He might have traveled openly, as an English con-
vert to Islam. But as such he would have had to submit to suspicions and not a little disdain, as a renegade
from another cult. Only disguised as a born True
Believer could he hope to unveil Islam.

The Cairo trip was disappointing. Grounding five
times a day regularly, the boat passed through scenery
dully reminiscent of Scinde. But the tedium was somewhat relieved by his meeting with Kudabakhsh, a pleasant merchant from Lahore, and Haji Wali, who traded
in shawls and had a nasty bit of litigation on his hands.
Under the brazen, broiling sun he spent many hours,
conversing with both in Persian and Hindustani.

The two men liked him—so much that, arrived in
Cairo, Kudabakhsh offered him the hospitality of his
house. But the merchant was partly westernized. He
preferred sitting on chairs and discussed Liberalism—
things from which Burton was fleeing. Therefore,
after ten days, he moved to a public caravanserai
where, by singular good fortune, he found Haji Wali.

It proved providential. For Haji Wali advised
Burton, who, heretofore, had traveled as a doctor of
medicine, to teach languages instead; and, over many
a hashish pipe, in return for some assistance which
Burton had given him in the British Consular courts,
explained to him the drawback of being a Persian in
Arabia—since the Persians are of the Shia sect of
Islam and as such despised by the orthodox Sunni—
and prevailed upon him to become a Pathan, an In-
dian-born Afghan, educated, so as to avoid all chance

of detection through a slip of the tongue and the rare mispronunciation of a word, in Burmese-speaking Rangoon.

But Burton still practiced medicine; bickering, to the increase of his Islamic knowledge, with natives as to their ailments, remembering many a nostrum from the days of his youth when he had gone from spa to spa with his hypochondriac father; and, with Haji Wali acting as his publicity agent and lauding him in and out of season as "the very phœnix of physicians," Burton distributed such prescriptions as:

"In the name of Allah, the Compassionate, the Merciful, and blessings and peace upon our Lord the Apostle, and His family, and His companions one and all!

But afterwards let the patient take bees-honey and cinnamon and album græcum, of each half a part, and of ginger a whole part, which let him pound and mix with the honey, and form boluses, each bolus the weight of a miskal, and of it let him use every day a miskal on the saliva. Verily its effects are wonderful. And let him abstain from fish, flesh, vegetables and sweetmeats, flatulent foods, acids of all descriptions, as well as the major ablution, and live in perfect quiet. So shall he be cured by the Help of the King, the Healer.

And the Peace!"

Perhaps the prescriptions did good—one of Burton's most successful cases being his curing a slave-dealer's female stock-in-trade from the price-lowering habit of snoring.

As the great Moslem feast of Ramazan approached, he devoted himself to pious exercises, screeching endless prayers and reading assiduously in the Koran. He became known as a Holy Man—until he was the victim of an "accident."

For he had a run-in with Ali Agha, a swaggering, enormously red-mustachioed and red-nosed captain of Albanian Irregulars who lived at the same caravanserai. There was an exchange of insults; then of blows. Finally they made friends, and the Albanian asked him to seal the friendship by handing over a little poison "that would not lie" and "would be useful on a certain person." The poison given by Burton consisted of five grains of calomel. But he had no time to learn the sequel. For, that same night, perhaps to celebrate the "certain person's" early demise, the Albanian asked Burton to a drinking bout. Not only drinking. There was, too, talk of hashish and dancing-girls—hashish and dancing-girls and forbidden, fermented spirits in a caravanserai for pious pilgrims!

The scandal was great. It ruined Burton's reputation. He decided that the time to leave Cairo had arrived.

Sending ahead his servant with the baggage, he followed to Suez on a camel through the wilderness—"a haggard land infested by wild beasts and wilder men" —and set about looking for fellow-pilgrims bound for Mecca. He discovered a motley crowd planning to sail on the same boat and attached himself to them, commencing operations by acceding to the general request for small loans. But Burton was Pathan as to outer man; Pathan, too, as to inner man, deliberately, to identify himself completely with the rôle which he was playing. Thus he made the loans at a high rate of interest; though—again to be the perfect Pathan who blends pulling avarice with reckless munificence— he meant to remit both capital and interest when due, so that his fame as a man *"of seven hearts"* might be early established.

He succeeded; was dubbed a *"generous beard"*; was also, by reason of the grandly untrimmed, hirsute growth on his upper lips, nicknamed *"The Father of Moustachios."*

To relieve the tedium of waiting for the pilgrim ship to sail, he carried on a heavy flirtation with the plump wife of a bazaar merchant.

"Be mine, O Fathma, O delight!" he would commence his serenading in the morning; until on an evening—a too successful evening—he sang in another key: "I will away, O Fathma! Marry you? *Wah*—by the honor of my nose—I would rather marry a yearling camel, O ancient and decrepit female!"

So once more there was scandal in the tents of Shem; and the pilgrim was glad when at last the ship sailed.

Built barely to accommodate sixty, this vessel took on ninety-seven assorted devotees. Burton and his friends established themselves on the raised poop, the choice spot, after a Homeric battle with a party of Moroccan roughnecks.

The filth and stench aboard was indescribable. A jaunt ashore at Mahar resulted in nothing more than a poisoned foot. At last, after twelve days quite different from those spent on a Cunarder, the passengers disembarked at Yambu where Burton set about hiring camels, purchasing an Arab outfit, and attaching himself to a caravan leaving for Medina the next evening.

The desert journey was little improvement on the sea trip. There was, day after day, the same sun, brazen, pitiless; the same sands spawning their yellow eternities; the same wretched food and brackish water; the same bickerings with the other pilgrims who had the temerity to call him—the lusty Pathan—a Hindu, despising him as such, mocking and baiting him as such. Perhaps the resulting fights broke the monotony. At all events Burton maintained his high humor, though his sore foot festered, though the sun blistered his shaven poll and his right shoulder exposed to the heat in correct pilgrim fashion; and, straight through, he watched, observed, took copious notes whenever he could.

He had made elaborate preparations for this note-taking, remembering others who, bound on the same Arabian adventure, had had their scribblings discovered by the suspicious True Believers—and had paid for it with their heads—these same heads rolling on the ground like rather ghastly pumpkins. To guard against such a misfortune, he had provided himself with a box holding compass, watch, pencils and small scraps of paper, and designed to look exactly like the traveling Korans carried by pilgrims. Rough notes were hastily written on these scraps and later transferred to a diary, also specially designed to nestle in the lining of his flowing robe. Where transcription promised to be difficult, he cut the scraps into yet smaller pieces, numbered them, and secreted the indexed parts in the canisters of his medicine chest.

Arriving at Medina—where Mohammed's earthly remains rest in the Hujrah—he lodged with Shaykh Hamid, a lazy old man of filthy habits, but an excellent guide, and a mine of information. Here Burton lived for close on five weeks; talking, thinking, even dreaming in Arabic; fulfilling all the required religious exercises of the *Hajj,* the pilgrimage, with diligent exactitude; finding a wealth of information for generations of western students and strong food for his own, broadly Rabelaisian sense of the ridiculous.

The Tomb of the Prophet disappointed him. He thought the outside lacking in dignity and beauty, described the inside as resembling "a museum of second-rate art, an old Curiosity Shop, full of ornaments that are not accessories and decorated with pauper splendor."

Time and time again he visited the edifice. Between prostrations and proper prayers he paced and measured the distance which went into his survey plan of the Hujrah, the first genuine one of its kind. And, at the end of it all, he reported his conviction that:

"Although every Mohammedan, learned and simple, firmly believes that Mohammed's remains are interred in the Hujrah at Al-Madinah, I cannot help suspecting that the place is as doubtful as that of the Holy Sepulchre at Jerusalem."

The Pathan pilgrim became quite a figure locally. The town-bred Arabs liked his wit, his recklessness, his knack of reciting classic Islamic poetry. He rejected invitations to open a shop near the Hujrah, where *"thou wilt eat bread by thy skill, and thy soul will have the blessing of being on holy ground."* He performed a final obeisance and, on the last day of August, joined a caravan for Mecca.

The same desert journey. The same flayed, brittle wilderness, hour after hour, day after day. Aridity. Vacancy. Immense, crushing solitude. The same sneering sun, poised like a great balloon, melting all colors into a swimming milky-white. The same wind, hot as the blast of a lime-kiln. The same occasional attacks by nomad robbers.

The pilgrims were silent; they saved their breath to curse the heat; and there were no sounds except the groaning of the camels, the lonely tinkling of bells, steel and wood and leather rubbing together discordantly, once in a while the staccato tapping of a signal-drum and, more faintly, the answer from the next down the line of the trek.

Then, at last, Mecca jumping into the focus—a

monochord—a point of dazzling white far off—dissolving on approach into a maze of low houses, a confused labyrinth of uneven roofs skirting the ground except where the minaret and the palm rose and united it to heaven. . . .

And then the first sight of the Holiest of Holies, the Sanctuary.

"The Sanctuary! The Sanctuary!" shouts bloating and shrilling on every side. And all the pilgrims, of a dozen races, nobles and commoners, men and women, throwing themselves flat on the ground; some sobbing as if their hearts would break . . . and a chant welling forth, a prodigious sound of countless voices whose volume was the volume of the ocean:

> *"Labbayk' Allahumma Labbayk'!*
> *La Sharika laka, Labbayk'!*
> *Inna 'l-hamda wa 'l ni'amata laka wa 'l mulk!*
> *La Sharika laka, Labbayk'. . . ."*

Burton himself was strangely affected. He felt the elemental power, the elemental, burning, vital energy of the *Hajj*—this hodge-podge of races drawn, year after year, to the city in the heart of Arabia by a gigantic, irresistible will, a gigantic, irresistible faith. . . .

"Labbayk' Allahumma Labbayk'!" he yelled with the best of them—he, the lone Englishman, surrounded by Arabs, Persians, Indians. Moroccans, Negroes, Tartars, Turks. . . .

But the frenzy passed. He was the student, whose duty it was to observe and record.

On the following morning he hurried his ritualistic ablutions to join the crowd pressing into the Prophet's Mosque where he caught his first view of the huge trapeziform Kaaba . . . "there at last it lay, the bourn of my long and weary pilgrimage." Struggling forward with the worshipers who pressed their beating hearts against the Black Stone of the Kaaba, the place of answered prayer, praying as loudly as the others, he kept his eyes open, observed the stone narrowly, became convinced that it was an aerolite.

The water of the sacred well of Zem-Zem, that which Allah indicated to the saving of Hagar's life, was unpleasant to the taste. But what matter? The seven traditional circuits around the Holiest of Holies were difficult of completion through the enormous, fanatical throng. But he succeeded—and made his measurements and took his notes. It was for these he had come.

Two days were occupied in minor pilgrimages, including attendance at a sermon on Mount Arafat where, amongst the loud *"Amins!"* and *"Labbayks!"* of the True Believers, he succeeded in gaining the attention of a young Meccan girl . . . "about eighteen years old, with regular features, symmetrical eyebrows, the most beautiful eyes, and a figure all grace."

The second day—of praying and love-making—was interrupted by the news that the Kaaba itself was open, and, fighting his way back from Arafat with fifty thousand frantic pilgrims, he entered the sacred interior— the first European to set foot inside—doubtless a little frightened since discovery would mean instant death— but coolly observing that the pavement was composed of vari-colored slabs of fine marble, that the ceiling and upper walls were covered with handsome, red damask flowered over with gold, that the flat roof was upheld by three cross beams supported in the middle by columns, and that between these columns bars of metal anchored many lamps said to be of solid gold.

The fifty-five other wonders of holy Mecca being visited, he sent his servant ahead to Jeddah and fol-

lowed leisurely the next day when, after the customary,
final celebrations and prostrations at the tomb of Eve,
Mirza Abdulla of Bushire, Pathan, and *"Father of
Moustachios,"* proceeded to the port, embarked on the
British ship *Dwerka* and vanished.

That same evening at dinner, a quiet Englishman,
one Richard Francis Burton of the East India Company's service, last seen in Southampton some months
before, unostentatiously entered the first-class saloon,
slipped into a vacant chair at the skipper's table, ordered a gin and bitters, and, to a careless question
where he had been, replied in deliberate ha-ha army
accents:

"Oh—just kickin' about a bit, y'know!"

If Richard Burton had not been Richard Burton, he
would have gone straight to London to become the
hero of the hour. But, *being* Richard Burton, he went
to Cairo, settled there for awhile, wrote his epochal
work: *Personal Narrative of a Pilgrimage to Al-
Madinah and Meccah,* and then took ship for Bombay,
traveling as an Arab. During this trip he made the
acquaintance and earned the admiration of Mr. J. G.
Lumsden, Senior Member of the Bombay Council,
whose friendship, later on, was of great value to the
wanderer. For he was still, would always be, a wanderer. Quickly, despite the almost regal hospitality of
the councilor's Bombay establishment, he tired of contact with accepted civilization and contrived a new
scheme.

He had solved the mystery of Mecca; had lifted its
veil.

But there was another mystery, another veil: the
forbidden Abyssinian city of Harrar.

Natives along Africa's northeast coast shuddered
when Harrar and its bloodthirsty tyrant were men-

tioned. Even Arab traders fought shy of the place.
Burton decided to go there and take a look. If the
Board of John Company had considered Mecca too
perilous an adventure, what chance of obtaining permission for this second escapade? But Lumsden used
his authority, and Burton received not only the sanction
of his employers, but also the promise of aid.

At once he embarked for Aden to complete his
preparations. His plan was to cross from Aden to
Zeila, thence to Harrar, find out there what he might,
and push south to the coast at Zanzibar. But the Company's assistance was limited to the sending of three
lieutenants from its army—Speke, Herne and Stroyan
—to Berbera, in the hopes of giving the impression
in the district that Burton had power behind him. So
the latter reluctantly curtailed his program, deciding
to return direct to Berbera instead of venturing south
from Harrar.

His stay at Aden was fruitful. For Dr. John
Steinhauser, an old friend, was stationed there as
medical officer. The two men had the same admiration
for things Oriental, and, in casual discussion, decided
that the world needed a full translation of *The Arabian
Nights*. They arranged a tentative division of work.
When Steinhauser died, twelve years later, whatever
work he had done was lost, and even Burton's share
had progressed only slowly. But during the interval
they corresponded regularly on the subject, and doubtless Burton's eventual production of an unmatched
edition found its seed in these interviews and in this
correspondence.

On the 29th October, 1854, Burton sailed for Zeila
with his staff—a rather questionable staff consisting
of a dragoman called *"The Hammal,"* a lanky police-
man from the Aden force, and a thorough rogue of a

Moslem priest whom—since he appeared to be the visible sign of a certain Koranic prophecy: *"At the end of time the priesthood shall become terribly corrupt"*— he christened *"The End of Time."*

Burton had assumed the disguise of an Arab merchant. As such he spent three weeks at Zeila, in hard bargaining for camels, studying local conditions, and making the usual pious demonstrations. But if the people of Zeila were impressed by his stout orthodoxy, they were in grave doubts as to his sanity. To run the gauntlet of the desert robbers—to go to Harrar— why—it was impossible! But, impossible or not, Burton trekked, adding to his party a petty chief who knew the best route, two picturesque if fat Somali women whose precise duties he had trouble to explain, and himself bringing up the rear encouraging his companions with obscene bazaar songs and, at night, around the campfire, with equally obscene tales from *The Arabian Nights.*

The predicted attack by robbers was not a success. Received by Burton's double-barreled gun, they protested that their attack had only been meant as a practical joke. For a day or two they joined the caravan, Burton gaining their admiration by his profound lore of certain things about which Occidentals usually are silent—if enviously so.

The Somali ladies—for reasons never precisely discovered—were left behind at Wilensi. Thence the party proceeded to Sagharrah where Burton made a firm friend of the local ruler. But when spies arrived from Harrar, demanding that the person of the daring Arab merchant be handed over to them, the native prince, though refusing to do so, backed out of the half-promise he had made to escort Burton to Harrar.

So Burton—"there was nothing to do but face it out"—gathered his small caravan, minus *"The End of*

Time" who did not choose to trek further, and departed into the unknown.

He reached Harrar. Explaining at the city gates that he came as an emissary of the Governor of Aden, he was admitted, with little parley, to the unventilated, red-clay edifice which did duty as a palace. Adopting his most arrogant Arab air—and nobody can be quite as superciliously arrogant as an Arab—and with a revolver in his burnoose to clap to the Amir's head in case of trouble, he marched with a strut and a swagger down the lines of lanky warriors to have his audience with the most barbarous and cruel of African potentates.

The latter did not look the part. He turned out to be a rather gracious, sallow-faced youth of twenty-five. Still—there was the fact that his dungeons were notorious and generally full; that his executioners had few hours of leisure; that he hated all foreigners; that he took a sadistic delight in watching tortures.

For some reason or other, some quirk in his savage brain, he treated Burton with kindliness, though the latter never got rid of an eerie sensation of insecurity during the time he spent in Harrar. As always, he observed, asked questions, investigated, wandered about, made notes which, subsequently, he recorded in his book: *First Footsteps in East Africa.*

But the town got on his nerves. It was mean, foul, filthy, inhabited by people specializing in narcotic drugs, aphrodisiacs, sex perversions, and the worship of flea-bitten household saints; and he was glad to leave—with another leaf added to his laurel wreath— to trek to Berbera, across a brittle, waterless desert, to find there the "support," the trio of lieutenants, which John Company had so generously provided.

The adventurer decided that he needed a rest—and he spent it with Steinhauser at Aden, planning a new

and gigantic enterprise: the discovery of the source of
the Nile.

Arrangements included an extension of the loan of
the three John Company lieutenants, the hiring of
forty-odd black auxiliaries, and the establishment of a
fake trading post near Berbera which would mean the
support of the guns of H.M.S. *Mahi,* stationed in
those waters.

Plans progressed well when, suddenly, the skipper
of the gunboat departed on a coastal cruise. No
sooner was the *Mahi* hull down than things began to
happen. Several hundred blood-thirsty Somalis appeared on the scene; and, immediately, the native contingent took to the bush, leaving Burton, Speke, Herne
and Stroyan to fend for themselves against impossible
odds. Stroyan went down early. The remaining three
fought like wild cats. In a rear-guard action, Burton,
wielding an Arab sword with telling effect, a javelin
striking him and piercing both cheeks as well as removing four of his teeth, carried Stroyan's body to the
beach where they embarked on a rickety native boat.

The Nile expedition had to wait. They headed for
Aden and disbanded, Burton leaving as soon as possible for England—where, in the meantime, his mother
had died—to have proper treatment given to his
wound and to submit an account to the Royal Geographical Society which had never failed to help him,
where possible, in his exploration schemes.

During Burton's Harrar escapade, the bickerings of
Greek and Latin monks over the Holy Places of Palestine, the territorial ambitions of the Tsar, the military
aspirations of the lesser Napoleon, and the stupid behavior of the British Government resulted in the tragi-
comedy called the Crimean War. Burton made up his
mind not to miss this brawl. Aided by the commission

he held in John Company's army and his reputation
for daring, he was gazetted into the home army, with
a gorgeous uniform blazing with gold as Chief-of-
Staff to General Beatson.

Commanding Officer and Chief-of-Staff quarreled at
once. The latter, with the former's hearty concur-
rence, attached himself to Britain's ally, the Turk,
levying and drilling a unit of Turkish *bashibazouks* or
irregulars. Too late to take part in the final operations in the Crimea, he planned a personal campaign,
with his *bashibazouks,* for the relief of Trans-Cau-
casian Kars where a beleagured Turkish garrison
was making a heroic stand against superior Russian
forces.

But the diplomats, that being their trade, had already smelled peace in the offing; had, by the same
token, set aside Kars as a consolation prize for the
Tsar. So, when Burton hurried to Constantinople to
submit his plan to the British envoy, he was denied permission; talked back, expressing his disgust with England's diplomatic methods; and was treated to a furious
tirade during which he was called "the most impudent
man in the army."

Promptly Burton resigned his commission and returned to England—to discover that, during his absence, his name had become the current synonym for
everything malodorous.

There were all sorts of scandalous tales about him:
how he had robbed a post office in Egypt; had basely
murdered a native fellow-traveler to obtain possession
of his wives; had done this and that and the other
nefarious thing . . . all sorts of highly spiced gossip
rolled over thick tongues and whispered from Apsley
House to Lambeth Palace, from the Horse Guards'
Tilt-Yard to Rotten Row. A pariah they made him

out; a Bluebeard with a dash of Nero. He did not care; was really amused; did not try to deny the rumors; in fact exaggerated them by insisting he had murdered two, not one, husbands defending their honor.

Only one story made him furious: the one relating that he had been caught in the harem of an eastern princeling who had punished him in the accepted manner. This tale he denied fiercely and vituperatively; was wont to declare loudly that he was physically intact in every detail.

In London he met again golden-haired Isabel Arundel. This time he proposed marriage and was accepted. She put a chain with a medal of the Virgin about his neck. He protested, declared it was similar to any witch-doctor's amulet, but wore it.

Isabel's mother objected to the match, saying he was "a heathen of the lowest grade with no prospects." There the matter rested. Nor did Burton exactly mind. For he was again dreaming of lifting the veil of Isis, of discovering the source of the Nile; and, in October 1856, he sailed for Bombay and there embarked, in company with Speke, on a British man-o'-war for Zanzibar.

What followed constitutes both the triumph and the tragedy of Burton's full life. For, in the next two years and a half, whilst playing the part of a dry-land Captain Cook, he misjudged his findings, failed to gauge an opportunity to realize the aim of his expedition and gave the world sure ground from which to misjudge him.

After a couple of preliminary canters a hundred-odd miles inland, from which he and Speke returned almost beaten by fever, the great expedition to Tanganyika got under way. In his book, *The Lake Regions of Central Africa,* he recorded his impressions, and there we learn of the pestilence, the tribulations and dangers which beset the intrepid explorers as they marched to their goal.

Attempts at murdering them were frequent. Burton fought back in kind. He killed—instead of being killed. Over hundreds and hundreds of miles he carried on; crossing a broad stretch of land foul with small-pox where the corpses festered in heaps; going out of his way to help a peaceful tribe against slave-raiders; spending weeks with aborigines of the lowest human type who divided their spare time between intoxication and the use of powerful narcotics; trekking through immense jungles, great seas of vegetation, an exuberant entangling of leaves and odorous, extravagant, waxen flowers, a throbbing surge of green life, but life that seemed incredible, exaggerated, innately vicious and harmful; gathering a mass of ethnological and scientific material; and, straight through, conscious of a sort of guilty feeling—like a Peeping Tom—that he was not wanted here, in the bitter, tense heart of the Black Continent, that he was trespassing on the destinies and the brooding energies of this Africa which hated him and his race, which would kill him given the chance. He was happy when, at Unyanayembe, he fell in with some Arabs—the folk he loved—and who loved him, received him hospitably. "What a contrast!" he wrote. "Here were comfortable homes, luxuries." Here, too, were women . . . chiefly three local beauties who smiled at his advances.

Again they trekked, Burton shaking with malaria, Speke almost blind—until, on the 13th February, 1858, they looked down upon a vast expanse of water—Tanganyika, obviously the head of the Nile.

For fifteen weeks the two explorers continued their

work, sailing the five-hundred-mile stretch of the lake
and penetrating some two hundred miles westward
from its southern point. At last, with exhaustive notes
and proofs of their discovery, they started back for
Zanzibar.

The return journey promised to be much like the
advance. But presently the unforeseen swooped down
upon their tracks. A batch of news from the coast
told Burton that his father had died. Too, they heard
of the existence of a still larger expanse of water lying
to the north. Speke was eager to find it. But Burton, considering his task accomplished, decided to live
for a while with the friendly Arabs of Unyanyembe
and there put his notes together, while his companion
made the side trip alone.

When Speke returned the friendship between him
and Burton was over. The younger man had discovered Lake Nyanza; insisted that here was the source
of the Nile—discovered by him, not by Burton, who
held out for Tanganyika. On their trek back to the
coast Speke, in fever delirium, cursed and accused Burton of being a charlatan and a stealer of reputations.
Burton paid no attention; hardly bothered to contra-
dict the charge.

They reached Zanzibar. There Burton made his
old mistake: he lingered, instead of proceeding straight
for home. Speke, on the other hand, took the first
boat, making London two weeks ahead of Burton and
working so quickly that, when the latter arrived, he
had not only the seal of the Royal Geographical Society upon his version of the exploration, but also the
promise of the Society's assistance for a second journey.

Burton was coldly furious. The future proved him
in the wrong as to his theory about Tanganyika. But,
at the time, Speke had no proof on his side; and, to

discredit Burton, went to the extent of inventing the non-existent *Mountains of the Moon* to prove that Tanganyika's outlet could not run northward, could therefore not be the source of the Nile.

There was, too, the old campaign of lies and scandalous gossip against Burton, with Speke helping the good work along . . . so much so that when Burton again proposed to Isabel Arundel, her mother was even more opposed to the match. Burton wanted to marry without her mother's consent. Isabel refused. There was a scene . . . he said to her:

"You and your mother have one characteristic in common; you are both as obstinate as mules."

For the next year he was busy with his courtship and the writing of his books until again he tired of civilization. On an April morning Miss Arundel received a short note that he had left for Salt Lake City and would be abroad for nine months.

Since, in Mecca, he had worn the costume of a Shaykh of the Moslem faith, he saw no reason why, in the City of the Saints, he should not don the garb of an American preacher. He did. His frock-coat was long and black; his silk tile was impeccable. Thus arrayed he made quite an impression amongst the Mormons. But Brigham Young, in the thick of his ethical, almost political, fight with the United States, was suspicious. He received Burton without enthusiasm and denied his personal application for admission to the Mormon Church, though the other pleaded that he had crossed the ocean and the broad American land to join a colony "sensible enough to permit polygamy." Brigham Young had heard about Burton's escapades in Mecca; refused to show his Holiest of Holies to curious eyes; remained adamant.

There was an intermezzo with an amorous Mormon lady which caused Burton to leave in a hurry—

by stage to San Francisco, thence to England by way of Panama.

Back in London Isabel Arundel decided to wait no longer for her mother's consent, afraid her lover might once more slip away without warning. Burton argued —perhaps marriage seemed less rosy as the day approached—but she had her way. On the 22nd January, 1861, Isabel being unable to face the registry office which he would have preferred, they were quietly married at a Catholic Church. So, as Burton expressed it, the "strong-willed woman had her way," after ten long years . . . and so, too, the most peculiar of unions was effected.

It would have been difficult for Burton to find a wife more seemingly antipathetic. Belonging to one of Britain's oldest, Catholic and baronial families, of a religious devotion which amounted at times to a lack of tact equal to that of a fanatical Christian Scientist, she had wedded a man who ridiculed and despised Christianity. Strait-laced to a degree, she had become the wife of a man who had loved profusely in four Continents and who considered chastity a comic virtue.

Still, she adored him. She admired him wholeheartedly; she moved heaven and earth to help him; and though at times the persistency of her efforts to explain him and obtain recognition of his talents did his credit in men's eyes less good than harm, no one could accuse her of anything except an obstinate enthusiasm for a difficult cause.

Burton refused to go on a honeymoon, considering it "a barbarous and indelicate exhibition." He continued in London lodgings, to complete his book, *The City of the Saints,* while strong-willed Isabel had to battle valiantly to drag him through what, naturally, she described as a "brilliant season."

She had friends at court and never hesitated to extol her husband's qualifications for political preferment. But the old stories about Burton persisted. He did not trouble to deny them; indeed loved to color them; and was always congenitally unable to be civil to people whom he did not like. So all she could extract from the kindly disposed Lord Russell was the offer of a seven hundred pounds a year Consulship at Fernando Po, off the African West Coast, where white men found it hard to keep alive for more than five years.

Burton swore his enemies were trying to kill him, but vowed in the same breath that he would disappoint them all. In August, 1861, he left for his post, leaving his wife behind.

His first stay in Fernando Po lasted sixteen months during which he did much to put the Burton mark on the settlement.

For instance—for he held the theory that "the negro is always eight years old and his mind never develops, belonging to an inferior race that neither education nor anything else can raise to the level of the white"—objecting to the familiar back-slapping of a swaggering mission-bred, mission-spoiled black, he had him pitched out of the Consulate window by a couple of Kaffir boys. A week later, on the arrival of the mail boat, he threatened to have the vessel blown up if the skipper did not adhere to his contract and remain at anchor for eighteen hours of daylight.

The frightful climate could not dampen his ardor for exploration. Whenever he could steal the time, he was off on trips to the mainland, finding out about that in those days almost mythical animal, the gorilla, and investigating the life of cannibals, nor neglecting the love life of cannibal ladies. During this time faith-

ful Isabel kept on pestering the Foreign Office, finally
obtaining for her husband a four months' furlough
which he spent pressing Lord Russell for the Governorship of the Gold Coast—"make me Governor, and I'll
send you home a million pounds a year"—and, together
with some kindred spirits, forming the Anthropological
Society.

His second period as Consul in *The White Man's
Grave* was brought to an end in a way that heartened
both husband and wife.   In 1863 he was appointed as
Commissioner to bear gifts and a plea to abandon
slave-selling and human sacrifice from Queen Victoria
to Gelele, King of Dahomey.   Alone, but for the doctor of the ship which carried him to Waydah, the port
of Dahomey, he started out.   Once ashore he indulged
in all the display he could afford, hiring a native bodyguard of one hundred armed ruffians.

His fame having preceded him, his reception at
Gelele's kraal was regal.   The King, as always, was
half drugged.   But there was his famous battalion of
Amazons, notorious for their extreme ugliness as well
as for their extreme bravery, shaking their spears.
There was singing, dancing, mock-fighting, and a long
gala program—Burton drawing the line at the *pièce de
résistance,* the slaughter, some weeks ahead of the
proper time, of the annual batch of eighty of Gelele's
subjects.

In his two-volume work, *A Mission to the King of
Dahomey,* he could write no word of good about the
potentate or his domain, describing incredible brutality
and filth as the chief characteristic of the land.   But,
on his return to England, maddeningly perverse as always, he got himself into hot water by pretending to
defend the race which he had so completely damned in
his report and book.

"The customs of Dahomey are no worse than those of England," he assured Froude.

"But why, if he is such a paragon, does Gelele not stop his barbarous practices—murder and sacrifice?"

"Would you have the Archbishop of Canterbury alter the Liturgy of the Church of England?"

"But you admit that eighty persons are sacrificed at the annual celebrations."

"True, and Dr. Lancaster has estimated the number of people killed each year in England, through the custom of wearing crinolines, at seventy-two."

In the meantime Speke had come back from Africa convinced that, as was subsequently true, his contentions about Lake Nyanza were correct. Burton read his former lieutenant's reports. He hated him personally, though—let there be no mistake about it—he admired his pluck. Nevertheless he maintained his position as to Tanganyika being the source of the Nile.

To give both men a chance to state their claims, the British Association arranged for them to debate the matter before its council at Bath on the 15th September. Burton was delighted. He took his place on the platform, armed with a bulky sheaf of notes. There was delay. Speke did not come. Burton grew restive. Presently news came that Speke had shot himself—accidentally, it was said. Burton was overcome, was unable to make any statement to the gathering. Finding, however, that the council still considered his case as unproved, he flew into one of his violent rages. Speke, he announced, had preferred suicide to being proved wrong.

Burton gained nothing from this—except the ever-growing hate of his many enemies.

Another tragedy that happened to him at this time

was his loss, by fire, of his priceless collection of Arabic and Persian manuscripts.

That same year Burton was transferred to the Consulate at Santos, Brazil. After a couple of months in Portugal, polishing the new language, Burton proceeded to his post, his wife following him shortly after.

He did not like Santos; thought it had too many signs of western civilization and too large an English colony. But he did not waste his four years there. At the time a most sanguinary and unjust war was being fought by Paraguay, Brazil, and Argentina against the tiny, brave Republic of Uruguay, and Burton was ordered by the Foreign Office to report the conditions. His report, as always, was voluminous and thorough. He crossed the Andes—many, many years before the railway—to accumulate a mass of facts which he published in his book, *The Battlefields of Paraguay*. In 1869 he returned to England where he finished and published his next two volumes: *Exploration of the Highlands of Brazil*, and *On an Hermaphrodite*.

In London, for once, he was made much of, being greatly in demand as a speaker before learned societies, while his wife had the social flutter which she craved. By the end of the year he was appointed to the Consulate at Damascus where, in a suburb, he settled down to what was in the main a pleasant two years.

Had he in any way posed as a diplomat, the Damascus interlude would have amply disproved his claims. He could never refrain from speaking his mind or acting directly on its dictates. Nor, which made matters worse, did he ever interfere with the actions of his wife whose lack of tact was even greater than his and who had an amazing gift of taking up with the wrong people.

Besides, there was his pet dislike: Christian mis-

sionaries. He obstructed them in every way he could
—and, true to form, the missionaries, forgetting their
Savior's lessons, fought back, with lies, vituperation,
false accusations. But the most unfortunate affairs in
which he busied himself were those relating to the
Shazlis, a Moslem sect, and the Jewish money lenders.

The Shazli matter showed exactly the way in which
the minds of both Burton and his wife worked. In a
state of religious ecstasy, one of the sect had seen the
vision of an old man beckoning him along the true
path of heaven. Later the victim of the visitation
identified his mysterious apparition as a Spanish priest
serving in a nearby monastery. When Isabel Burton
heard this, her Catholic soul was vastly pleased. She
considered it a miracle and immediately distributed
piles of rosaries and crucifixes to the Shazlis. Burton
himself, in Arab disguise, attended the Shazli séances
and became convinced that, whatever his belief as to
the errors of Christian doctrine, these people were
sincere.

But Wali Rashid Pasha, the Turkish Governor-General of Syria, differed. He was an orthodox Moslem.
He jailed a number of the Shazlis, whereupon Burton,
furious at the injustice, bombarded the Foreign Office
with protests and denounced the Pasha in no uncer-
tain terms, even protecting personally some of the renegades—which brought him into disfavor with the
Sultan.

So, again, he made enemies; made yet more enemies
by the Jewish incident. He had always been incredibly
prejudiced against the Chosen Race; so much so that,
amongst his many books, the one dealing with the
Hebrews is absolutely worthless, gives the impression
of having been written by an illogical child.

The incident began over the attempts of Jewish
money lenders, charging a minimum of sixty per cent

compound interest and, claiming British citizenship, trying to enlist the Consul's official aid in the matter of collections. Burton was furious. He threw the usurers bodily out of his office and commenced a campaign against them. The Syrian Jews complained to their rich and powerful co-religionists in England.

Thus—organized Jewish opinion and organized Christian missionaries' opinion . . . finance and religion . . . had ever a man two more dangerous, more implacable enemies?

Not that Burton cared. He continued his official work, his private investigations, making voluminous notes for his greatest work, the translation of *The Arabian Nights*. Besides, he made frequent, perilous trips of exploration into the interior, accumulating a mass of priceless archæological data and trophies.

In the meantime the mails to and from London were hot with complaints. The Reverend So-and-so, the Reverend This-and-That combined with Millionaire Moses and Millionaire Jacob. The Foreign Office wrote to Burton—who, in his short replies, showed beyond the shadow of a doubt that he had acted on the side of justice and to the enhancement of British prestige.

But the Church, ably assisted by Lombard Street, won.

Burton was dismissed . . . dismissed at fifty, because he had been right and just—because he had not permitted the Hebrew usurers to rob the Arabs of their poor all; had not permitted the Christian missionaries to proselytize.

He was embittered—and he was almost broke. There was only one consolation: the innumerable letters of praise and gratitude written him by the Arabs . . . for instance the one which said:

"You have left us the sweet perfume of charity and noble conduct in befriending the poor and supporting the weak, O warden of the seas of knowledge, O cistern of learning exalted above his age!"

The couple arrived in London. They were down to their last fifteen pounds. But Burton still maintained his uncompromising attitude.

—Say *pater peccavi?* Not he!

He had been right, he insisted, and the others, the missionaries, the usurers, had been wrong. He was a gentleman, he declared, so why should he truckle to knaves? To the devil with them!

A Scot, Mr. Lock, came to temporary rescue. He was the possessor of a sulphur concession in Iceland upon which he wanted an expert opinion. Burton— expert on almost everything, thus why not on sulphur? —went to Iceland, found the mining impossible, but collected material for a book. The trip took him out of his black mood; and he returned, looking fifteen years younger, to hear that in his absence his mother-in-law had died in the odor of sanctity, protesting to the last that "Dick Burton is no relative of mine"— to learn, too, that strong-willed Isabel had again been active on his account, obtaining for him the Consulate at Trieste, at seven hundred pounds a year . . . "a come-down after Damascus," commented Burton, with his Islamized fatalism, "but better than nothing."

Thus the foremost traveler of his day, when travel meant something else beside the ability to pay for it and the trick of having it blared about in the newspapers, took his thirty-odd languages, his unequaled powers of observation, his literary genius, his knowledge of the Orient and his high, clanking courage to an apartment at the top of a dismal building behind the railway station in a third-rate Adriatic port; took the apartment because, with all his amazing attainments, he lacked the smallest notion of that dingy, middle-class quality called tact and compromise; took it to the triumph of his enemies—who are to-day forgotten.

The place, where Mrs. Burton entertained "seventy of her very best friends at a weekly magpie sanhedrin," became at once notorious for its typical Burton atmosphere. The Crescent, as represented by the husband's curios and ethical convictions, competed for supremacy over the Cross, as represented by the wife's Pope-touched and Pope-blessed relics and candle-lit shrines— though, possibly, the altar at which she paid her most solemn devotions was the case containing the fifty-odd volumes he had published up to that time.

In one room eleven rough tables were strewn with papers and implements of the writer's craft, each carrying the making of one book. Rising shortly after four every morning, he worked at one or more tables until noon when physical exercise, a swim in the sea or a bout with the foils, prepared him for a short session at the Consular office. Of course he explored the neighborhood as well as the back alleys of Trieste; made notes; read voluminously. He ate heartily as ever—English in this one respect: he wanted his food and lots of it.

During a leave of absence in London he decided to make his fortune, by putting on the market *Captain Burton's Bitters*—a tonic which failed completely to establish itself in the livers of his countrymen. Then he sailed to India with the idea of surveying the deserted mines of Golconda.

India!

Memories of his youth!

He took Isabel on a grand tour, showed her the India he had promised her so often. It had not changed. Bombay was the same old hodge-podge of forty dialects, the same old tulip garden of vermilion turbans, yellow and pink turbans, cloaks and trousers in purple, scarlet, grasshopper-green. Jaipore was the same old excessive, flamboyant rhapsody of color and sound. Karachi was the same old blending of pomp and poverty, of stench and cloying odors. Hyderabad was the same old jingling of silver anklets and trumpeting of majestic elephants, picking their way, with ludicrous daintiness, among gayly painted carts drawn by sleek bullocks.

Only Golconda was a disappointment. Burton himself believed that the ancient mine workings there might be made profitable. But he failed to convey his optimism to the financiers whom he had hoped to interest.

Returning poorer than ever to his eleven tables in Trieste, he received an item which, since he was never the forgiving sort, caused him fiendish joy; received, too, fruitless, but highly appreciated, recognition for his past work.

As to the latter, General Gordon, "Chinese" Gordon, about to take up his duties as Governor of the Soudan, offered Burton the governorship of Darfur at more than double the Trieste salary, writing:

"Now is the time for you to make your indelible mark in the world."

But Burton refused, though he was gratified. He knew that Darfur would mean a renewing of his former hopeless fight—against missionaries, usurers, concession-hunters, all the wire-pullers of the Foreign Office. He would not be able to help the Moslems whom he loved; would only hurt them.

The other news, which he so fiendishly enjoyed, was that of the assassination of Wali Rashid Pasha, Governor-General of Syria, at Damascus. He considered it a personal triumph, while his wife's animosity faded at the Pasha's death and her forgiveness of "the fat, indolent, purring, well-fed cat" ran parallel with her regret that, according to her husband, she had not been on the spot to push a holy wafer down his throat as he passed to his fathers.

Presently Burton's thoughts turned to the ancient gold mines of Midian, in the Syro-Arabian desert. Hundreds of thousands, in former days, had lived on their produce. Could they, with their primitive methods, have exhausted the deposits? The Khedive of Egypt, as well as Captain Burton, needed gold. The former, interviewed in Cairo, was ready and willing to finance the expedition. In Cairo, too, Burton met again his old friend Haji Wali, of Mecca days, who, despite his seventy-odd years, was greedy enough to shake his rickety bones for the sake of a little money.

Burton made one of his "preliminary canters," became convinced that the enterprise was feasible, but not during the hot weather. So he spent the summer at Trieste where he wrote: *The Gold Mines of Midian and the Ruined Midianite Cities.*

Back in Cairo, at the end of the year, he got together his expedition and set out, with the Khedive's formal blessing, with a French engineer, some Egyptian soldiers, Haji Wali, and the divining rod which he expected would amply make up for the lack of a mineralogist.

Establishing a base at Moilah, he trekked with his caravan on three journeys of discovery. The first was headed for Ptolemy's Madiana and Makua where excavations yielded ruined cities, a bag full of ancient coins, and the Tombs of the Kings—long ago rifled by Arab nomads. There were, furthermore, some mar-

velous inscriptions and many quaint drawings on the
monoliths dug up—but not a speck of gold. The next
trip was due east to Hisna where there were more
ruins, no coins—and no gold; and the third was fully
as disappointing—but not to the Khedive who, a Moslem, loved Burton, promised further aid which only his
death prevented, and celebrated the explorer's return
with magnificent pomp by opening a *"Burton Exhibition"* at Cairo.

The next year, 1878, Burton spent his leave in England. There, during a meeting of the British National Association for Spiritualists, husband and wife
clashed. The talk was on "Spiritualism in Foreign
Lands." Burton was interested in the question. Before a sympathetic audience of respectable, middle-aged
seekers for truth, refusing to catch the eye of his
spouse, he related incident after incident of what he
had observed and capped them by his own ideas. He
finished, bowed, resumed his seat—already the chairman of the meeting had opened his mouth to express
his thanks . . . when Mrs. Burton jumped up. She
told the startled hearers they were not for a moment to
believe that her husband was so crack-brained as to
take this matter seriously; told them, furthermore,
that, having been born and brought up in the bosom of
the One and Only True Faith, she was confident that
eventually the captain would give up all perverse heresies, reform, and return to the Mother Church.

Strong-willed Isabel had had her say—and for once
Richard was silent.

Shortly afterwards, they left England and went to
Cairo. There Burton spent the rest of the winter
chatting in coffee-houses and on door-steps with disreputable native friends and making a brilliant translation of Camoën's *Lusiads,* besides beginning an English rendering of the same Portuguese poet's lyrics and

his *Life and Commentary,* and putting the finishing touches on his *Kasidah of Haji Abu El-Yezdi*—an original work tower-high above Fitzgerald's adaptation of Omar's *Rubáiyát*.

On returning to Trieste, he busied himself at various of his eleven tables until August when, after his wife had offered due prayers for him and for herself, they went to Oberammergau to witness the Passion Play. He reached the conclusion that the Mecca scenes were far superior to the European religious masque and published his findings for the delectation of the world at large.

After a short stay in Venice—where the International Geographic Society was in session and where, to the laughter of the gods on Olympus, the conference took particular pains to snub Burton, the greatest traveler and linguist of his age, but where, on the other hand, he made friends with Lovett Cameron who had crossed the Dark Continent—he went back to his Consular post.

There, in 1881, he read a newspaper announcement that John Payne was about to publish a translation of *The Book of the Thousand Nights and One Night*— *The Arabian Nights* in other words—the great Islamic classic which, heretofore, in emasculated versions, was known to the western world only as a collection of nursery tales—the classic which he had hoped to issue with the help of Dr. Steinhauser, now dead, and about which he had accumulated a mass of notes, chiefly marginal notes, given his unexcelled knowledge of the Orient.

But Burton, whatever his faults, never envied another man's honestly merited achievements. At once he wrote to Payne, an acknowledged scholar, wishing him all success, offering to help him, mentioning that he, too, had labored for years on the Arabic master-piece.

In the meantime, his friendship with Lovett Cameron bore fruit. Together they interested a financier in the possibilities of the Gold Coast which, earlier in his career, Burton had failed to impress upon the Foreign Office.

They proceeded to West Africa to advise on a projected mining venture. There seemed to be much of the precious metal to be had for the asking, and the explorers returned to England to complete arrangements with their principal which were destined to come to nothing.

In London Burton met Payne who, his first volume already out and making a stir, suggested collaboration. Burton was willing. For months he worked with the other, lending him his invaluable knowledge of Arabic and things Oriental, but finally refused to go on. Nor would he accept any renumeration for what he had done. There was no quarrel between the two men. But Burton, who had a horror of sham and cant and hypocrisy, insisted that Payne—though too outspoken for Britain's contemporary Mrs. Grundys, the prurient Pecksniffian horde, the garbage-sniffing Comstocks of a past generation who did not differ from the present one in ignorance and impudence—was not outspoken enough in the translation of daring, yet essential passages of *The Arabian Nights*. Personally he would not sacrifice one iota of beauty or truth on the altar of mendacious fundamentalism. So he bade Payne good-by and went back to his Consular post.

Shortly before, the battle of Tel-el-Kebir, decisive of Egypt's future, had been fought. England was anxiously awaiting news from Professor Palmer, who

had been sent into the Sinai Peninsula to attach the
tribes to her cause for the safety of the Suez Canal.
Unaware that Palmer had been murdered, the Foreign
Office wired Burton to go and find him.

He arrived in Egypt ready to adopt Arab disguise
and play his favorite game. But Sir Charles Warren—the same stiff-necked martinet with whom Cecil
Rhodes had his memorable run-in in South Africa—
was the commanding officer. He and Burton almost
came to blows, and the latter returned promptly to
Trieste where, financially more secure, thanks to ac-
cruing royalties, he moved from his dingy apartment
to the Palazzo Gosleth, the finest house in town.

Here, in the lovely garden overlooking the sea, he
settled down to his perpetual writing: busying himself
with his translations of *The Arabian Nights,* not, as
he had promised Payne, a popular edition to compete
with his, but a complete rendering, to tell the full tale
in defiance of Anglo-Saxon prudishness; finishing his
volume, *The Book of the Sword;* and doing his share
in the work of the Kama Shastra Society in which he
was associated with Rehatsek and Arbuthnot and
which proposed to make a number of erotic Oriental
books available to European scholars.

At this time, though still a powerful, upstanding,
wide-shouldered man, he was subject to attacks of gout.
He was no longer *"The Father of Moustachios,"* these
famous appendages having dwindled somewhat to gray
wisps which barely covered his upper lip. Generously wrinkled by time and life, the spear wound in
his cheeks still was the most conspicuous mark on his
features. Occasionally he would wear a beard, changing its cut from week to week, often from day to day.
He had developed into an eccentric, with a terrible temper. Jews, missionaries and waiters were the people
he hated most. Next came Baptists and professors.

But to his wife he was ever indulgent, treating her as though she had never emerged from her early teens; allowing her—the typical Victorian busy-body—to keep herself occupied making plans for this and that, but invariably, when it came to the point, ignoring what she had done and completing all arrangements himself, as he considered they should be made.

His work continued steadily until, early in 1884, he was taken seriously ill. He recovered; carried on, applying himself more and more seriously to his *magnum opus,* issuing circulars announcing that the work was under way, without benefit of publisher or agent, and receiving a gratifying number of subscriptions.

At last he not only had enough to do, no new thing for him, but there was actually wealth in sight. He went at his task like a beaver, not alone with the translation itself, but with the marginal notes which are an encyclopedia of priceless Oriental lore.

In January, 1885, the news of "Chinese" Gordon's death reached him and drove him to one of his typical, vituperative outbursts against the British Government which "employed donkeys and rejected or allowed to be massacred men with any talents at all."

His remarks about Gladstone, the Grand Old Man, though according to others the Grand Old Mischief-maker, were epic; and it is interesting to conjecture how he might have improved on these remarks had he known, as we know to-day, that when Gladstone assured the House of Commons of Gordon's absolute safety and maintained there was no necessity for particular precautions, the sleek old man had the telegram giving the actual facts of Gordon's impending doom in his pocket!

In May, 1885, Burton applied for leave and went to England to work day after day at the Athenæum Club. An English resident of Trieste, not sharing the general sentiment, since Burton was very popular there, wrote to the Foreign Office, complaining of the Consul's slip-shod manner, and suggesting that the Consular post devolve entirely upon the Vice-Consul—in theory as well as in practice. To the eternal credit of the Foreign Office, against which Burton loved to rile, the objector was curtly informed that, in view of Burton's services to his country, the Consulship was regarded as a free gift to him.

Burton stayed in England until November. In September his first volume appeared. The success was immediate and enormous. So was the success of the entire work. It gave him a definite place in literature. It enhanced his reputation as an Oriental scholar. And—as sweet to Burton as delayed recognition—it netted him nearly ten thousand pounds, more money than he had seen in many a moon.

He set off alone for Tangier. He was in high spirits. He continued his work at *The Arabian Nights;* commenced a translation of the *Pentameron*, never to be finished; and, in February, 1886, joined his wife at a hotel in Gibraltar where a telegram was delivered to him addressed to:

"Sir Richard Burton."

He was certain some practical joker was in back of it; refused to accept the envelope. But his wife tore it open, to find that it was from Lord Salisbury announcing the bestowal of a Knight Commandership of St. Michael and St. George. At which the new Sir Richard grumbled—remarking it had taken England a "damned long time to make an honest man of me."

So they returned to Trieste where the indefatigable man continued to pore over his manuscripts, until the time for the annual summer trip took the ménage to Innsbruck, Zurich, Basle, Boulogne, finally to England to celebrate his sixty-fifth birthday. He applied to the Foreign Office for retirement and a pension. His request was refused. Instead he was granted what amounted to perpetual leave—on full pay.

He decided at this time to prepare a new and thoroughly annotated edition of that erotic Oriental classic called *The Scented Garden*. But in Cannes he was taken seriously ill. Slaving for hours each day at his desk, one morning Lady Burton noticed that he was unable to find the ink pot with his pen. Convulsions followed. He was put to bed. The doctors decided that he could not live. But they were mistaken. Within a few weeks he was up and about, and back in Trieste, back at work, the next year transferring his activities to the milder climate of Abbezia.

In July, 1888, he was once more in England, meeting old friends—Lovett Cameron, Swinburne, Sir Henry Irving—and participating in the foundation of the Gypsy Lore Society. He had long had the makings of a manuscript on the Romany folk, and with the idea of the Society came the desire to complete the book. During the next few months he worked at the manuscript, but was unable to complete it before his death.

Not that he thought of death.

He had too many things to do—working, working, working wherever he went—in London, Boulogne, Switzerland, during a trip to French North Africa which he described as "dead and damned, dirty as ditchwater," and back again in Trieste—working at *The Scented Garden,* at a translation of Catullus, and at *Priapeia, or the Sportive Epigrams of Divers Poets on Priapus* . . . carrying the manuscript of the last-named contribution to human knowledge under his arm and, greatly to the annoyance of the dignified Lady Burton, reading aloud choice if risqué passages at meals in public places, always insisting that the matter was "of tremendous interest to anthropologists and humanists."

But, most of all, he loved *The Scented Garden*. He worked at it "twenty-five hours a day," as he expressed it. He considered it an invaluable contribution to literature and knowledge. Returning from Mass early in the morning of Sunday, October 19th, Lady Burton was greeted with the news that Chapter XX had been completed. He was busy with its revision and happily announced that, on the next day, he would commence his autobiography.

A bird hopped on the window ledge and pecked at the glass. It flew away; returned a second time and repeated the slight taps. Burton laughed. It flew away again. The bird returned and tapped for the third time.

"This is a sign of death," announced Sir Richard and went back to his writing.

After breakfast he asked for a novel—a most unusual request. He made a heroic effort to return to his desk; was not able.

In the evening he complained that his foot hurt him —"a touch of my healthy gout," he called it—and retired to bed. After some time he spoke of the lack of air, asking the doctor shortly after midnight for chloroform or ether, while Lady Burton was busy loudly praying that the soul might remain long enough in her husband for a priest to arrive.

But—with a sudden "I am dying; I am dead!"—he grew heavier in her arms; and passed on.

The priest did not arrive until daylight. He would not, at first, administer the sacrament. But Lady Burton kept on insisting two things: that her husband had abjured all his heresies and belonged to the Catholic Church, and that he was still actually alive.   At last, to her "tremendous joy" as she put it later on, and, doubtless, to the dead Sir Richard's intense, sardonic amusement, the priest administered the last rites.

And so strong-willed Isabel won out in the end . . . more than won out.   For, with her husband forever silent, she went over his manuscripts, reading them, censoring them, going over all his enormous mass of notes . . . invaluable notes, the result of a lifetime of study . . . and consigning them to the flames . . . reading and consigning to the flames, too, his last finished work, *The Scented Garden,* upon which he had labored so proudly and happily almost until the hour of his death . . . consigning it all to the flames because "it shocked me."

And—once more she won out: she had him, the doubter, the almost-Moslem, buried in a proper English cemetery with proper Catholic rites.

Thus, after death, Captain Burton was cheated by his wife; as, during life, he had been cheated by his country, by envious, mean-souled cavilers, by dirt-sniffing hypocrites; as, to this day, he is cheated by that sheepish thing, called Public Opinion, which, forgetting him, sits, gaping and gullible, at the feet of lesser men, of self-seeking, self-advertising, self-romanticizing explorers. . . .

But he was not cheated in his high dreams—nor in his high deeds!

JOHN NICHOLSON

[1821–1857]

who, great in war,
dreamed greatly of peace

A good many of the historical events which form the background to the biographies of Henry Lawrence and John Nicholson overlap. Therefore they have not been repeated in detail; and it is advisable to read the two biographies together.

JOHN NICHOLSON

JOHN NICHOLSON

A WOMAN in charge of certain Irish parish work was going her rounds, accompanied by her ten-year-old son. They passed a house without making the usual visit.

"Why don't you go in there, mother?" asked the boy.

"Because bad people live there," was her reply.

At which Young Hopeful exclaimed:.

"Oh—mother dear—God made His sun shine upon the evil as well as the good!"

A wretched little prig! A lad of such regrettable, goody-goody precocity, such meretricious religiosity that, had he gone to Eton, he would have been ducked in Cuckoo Weir immediately upon his arrival and would have had red ink poured down his neck during service in Lower Chapel! Incredible to relate that this Sunday-schoolish young ass was destined to grow up into the same John Nicholson, the bravest of the brave, who, in the full course of time, was acclaimed a Warrior Saint by that honest, forthright fighting race, the Sikhs; in whose memory they chant, in the Punjab to this day a stirring dirge with the refrain:

"Nikalsain is dead!"

Yet his early boyhood was full of instances of a similar, objectionable, moral exhibitionism . . . rather strange, considering his recent family history. For his father, Alexander Nicholson, had been a promising young Dublin surgeon; a Quaker, of Scotch-Irish descent, he had married Miss Clara Hogg of Lisburn,

111

a communicant of another Christian sect; had promptly been expelled from his church with the quaint, sadistic ceremonial used on such occasions; had been deprived of his family's social and professional support; and— his Keltic blood popping up rebelliously—had told his relatives to go straight to hell and had turned on his unregenerate way, rising in his chosen profession, achieving an excellent reputation for medical skill though not very much money, scalpel and forceps paying for a deal of pot-still whiskey but not always the butcher's and greengrocer's bills.

Just the type of cheerful, optimistic idiot to have a lot of children: seven—of whom John, born at Lisburn on the 11th December, 1822, was the oldest.

To his father's disgust he developed, soon after reaching if not the thinking then at least the prating age, the peculiar, disagreeable, moralizing tendencies mentioned above. He might have broken his parent's heart entirely by going into the Church, by becoming a Pecksniff in Holy Orders, dusty black coat, dusty side whiskers, and dusty hypocrisy. But—and, unfortunately, the doctor did not survive long to see and applaud—he was rescued from such a fate by an Irish drill sergeant who looked after the pupils' discipline in a Delgany County day school which John attended. A ribald, riotous man was this sergeant, telling ribald, riotous stories of campaigning in the Peninsula, in Flanders, in the Indies, firing John's imagination . . . so much so that his mother objected to her first-born's barrack-room viewpoint and diction and bundled him off to another, more refined, seat of learning: a boarding school, at Dungannon.

There he remained until his sixteenth year. He showed no intelligence above the average, no particular distinction except a glorious temper, a strictly Irish temper . . . "if ye see a head, hit it!"

He left school. He had absorbed, more or less, the usual, useless knowledge: he could stammer a few words of bad French, decline seventeen irregular Greek verbs, and quote: *"Tempora mutantur, et nos mutamur in illis!"*

What next?

More useless knowledge, of course. More schooling.

Where?

Trinity College, Dublin, he suggested; and his mother agreed—not very willingly, since she had so little money.

But, after all, it was not Trinity. For destiny intervened—destiny in the rotund, rubicund person of John's uncle, James Hogg, a man with a long Indian record and a great deal of Indian gold, who had come home, endeavoring to get himself elected to the Board of Directors of the Honorable East India Company.

A typical Nabob was James Hogg. A Nabob of the days when, to be a Nabob, one had to have a *zenana* filled with Hindu women and to breakfast on curry, chutney, Bombay duck, and seven ponies of three-star straight. A specimen of that picaresque age when trading in the far corners of the earth was still a swaggering, clanking adventure, a spirited gamble with fate, a high-hearted, red-blooded, two-fisted romance; when Gulf Arab shaykh and Malay prince and Deccan Rajah and Rajputana thakur and English merchant met behind tightly closed rattan shutters, the velvet punka flopping lazily overhead, and dipped their disreputable noses in the same cup of honeyed, spiced wine, and winked at one another as Greek is said to wink at Greek, and played hide-and-seek with Her Britannic Majesty's inquisitive red-coats and inquisitive men-of-war; when the men of the outer seas and the inner lands preferred a handful of Maria

Teresa dollars and Chinese candareens and Moghul muhrs and shoe-shaped, archaic Mandarin ingots to a draft on the Old Lady of Threadneedle Street or a certified check signed by all the Rothschilds and all the Morgans; when yellow men and gold disputed the eternal Asian trade balance with white men and blood; when a merchant-prince was still a swashbuckler upon the blue seas and the gray hills, and not a swag-bellied, asthmatic, guinea-coining automaton, safely ensconced behind a mahogany desk, a steel filing cabinet, and an army of immaculate, almost sacerdotal private secretaries.

Real Nabobs. Brothers-in-spirit to Job Charnock, Stringer Lawrence, Warren Hastings. And James Hogg, if not the best known of them, was not the poorest, not the least influential.

He swore strange curses in a mixture of Hindustani and Persian when his sister told him that John was going up to Trinity.

Trinity?

Poppycock!

"The Indies for you, my boy!"

And, pulling strings here and there, he secured for John Nicholson a cadetship in the Bengal Infantry, without the usual, time-wasting trouble of competitive examination or months spent at the Company's training college at Addiscombe.

So, in February, 1839, John Nicholson sailed from the Thames for Calcutta, aboard the East India Company's vessel *Camden*.

His first trip. A long trip, around the Cape of Good Hope. An uneventful trip, with Nicholson just one of a number of cadets going out on the same adventurous errand.

In July, Calcutta was reached. Not the City of

Palaces which it is to-day, glorious with the beauties of the Maidan, the Chowringhee, Dalhousie Institute, the United Service Club, Belvedere House, and Metcalfe Hall. But a miasmic town that, except in wealth and imperial importance, had progressed amazingly little since the day, almost two hundred years earlier, when Aurangzeb, the Grand Moghul, instructed Ibrahim Khan, his Bengal Viceroy, to invite the Rt. Worshipful Job Charnock, John Company's head agent, to return from Madras and reopen the Calcutta establishment.

There, for nearly a month, Nicholson remained, taking lessons in Bengali, getting his first taste of goat masquerading as lamb, beginning to learn that India was not all beer and skittles, was not entirely composed of Rajahs, heat, gold mohurs, nautch girls, and elephants, beginning to understand that the "sceptr'd race," to keep this same scepter steady, had to do a lot of hard work. Finally, on August 12th, 1839, he embarked on a Ganges river boat for Benares, that palimpsest of India's motley religions which, beside being the holiest of cities to Hindus, has been in turns a center of Vedic thought, of Buddhist preaching, even a local Mecca for Moslems—that huge expanse of clouted stone which is considered deified in its whole material mass and which claims that all those who die within its boundaries "be they Brahmins or low castes, Moslems or Christians, be they liars, thieves, or murderers, are sure of admittance into Siva's heaven."

Immediately upon arrival, John Nicholson received his first appointment, to the 41st Sepoys . . . and an excellent time it seemed to an imaginative young subaltern to join the army.

For the Afghan border—then, as to-day, as always, as long as Afghans are Afghans and will insist on behaving as such—was in a turmoil. Up in the north, beyond the Khyber Pass which was not yet British, the hillmen's broad-bladed butcher knives were at the stabbing and slashing and British bullets at the popping and screaming, since England was engaged in helping the former Amir, the pusillanimous Shah Shujah ul-Mulk of the Durani clan, back on the throne from which Dost Mohammed Khan, that hook-nosed, red-bearded, ruffianly adventurers of the Barakzai family, had kicked him.

Britain's interest in the north was vital. For at this time the Russians were advancing rapidly in Central Asia, threatening China on the east as well as India on the south. A Persian army, with Muscovite support, was besieging Herat, Afghanistan's traditional bulwark toward the north. Lord Auckland, the Governor-General, sent Captain Alexander Burnes to Kabul to negotiate with Dost Mohammed Khan, to find a mutual *modus vivendi* against the common enemy. The Khan gave a dozen solemn promises—and broke every one of them. Forthwith Lord Auckland resolved on direct, if rather dangerous, action. He made up his mind to oust the Khan and to replace him by the more subservient Shah Shujah who was an exile at Ludhiana, in the land of the Sikhs. In those days both Sind and the Punjab were independent kingdoms. The former being the less powerful of the two, a British army, escorting Shah Shujah, was despatched through its territories into southern Afghanistan by way of the Bolan Pass. Kandahar surrendered. Ghazni was taken by storm. Dost Mohammed Khan—though strictly temporarily—fled across the Hindu Kush. And Shah Shujah, flanked by British rifles, was led back in noisy triumph into the Bala Hissar at Kabul.

Thus there was a good show in the north; plenty of fighting and, by the same token, plenty of chance for

distinction and promotion; too, plenty of heartburn
for more than one young officer, including John Nicholson, when, instead of being sent on active service,
they were put on the square under a brass-voiced drill
sergeant and set to learn their martial profession—
to learn, furthermore, the time-honored lesson of the
British army: that there is no existence quite as dull
as that of a subaltern *in partibus infidelium* who has
to live on his pay, to whom a brace of double-whiskies
is a social experience and a polo game a fata morgana.

At last, late in the year, he received orders to join
the 27th Native Infantry at Ferozepore, and he went
on his long, solitary journey to his new station by way
of Meerut and Karnal.

Fate did not seem to be on his side. For, en route,
his quarters were broken into, and he was robbed of
most of his camp kit as well as of a most important
£10 which loss threw his finances out of gear for several months to come; and, during a short turn of duty
to which he was assigned at Karnal, he had an alter-
cation with a superior officer. The latter found fault
with the manner in which the other handled his Sepoys.
John Nicholson flew into one of his murderous Irish
tempers. Nothing short of a duel with pistols would
satisfy him, and it required the advice of several big-
wigs on the local staff to make him change his mind.

Toward the end of March, 1840, he reached Ferozepore and settled down, as best he could, to life with
his permanent regiment. The remainder of the year
was not pleasant. The land was bare, yellow, dusty,
heat-baked, unattractive. The station itself was new,
and, since no pioneer troops were available, the men
and officers of the 27th had to pitch in and erect their
own quarters. They did so grumblingly—and were,
presently, a little cheered by rumors of strife that
drifted down from the frontier.

Dost Mohammed Khan, after one more brave struggle, had surrendered and was on his way to Calcutta as a State prisoner. But the Afghan show, it seemed, was not yet settled. The British, while able to put Shah Shujah ul-Mulk back on the Durani throne, could not win for him the hearts of his countrymen who considered him a degenerate exile thrust upon them by alien arms.

Besides, for good measure, trouble was brewing in the Punjab. For Ranjit Singh, the founder of the kingdom of the Sikhs, or the "liberated," in the Punjab, had died. During his lifetime, thanks to Metcalfe's diplomacy, he had been a good friend of the British. But he left no son capable of wielding the scepter. The court at Lahore, the capital, was torn by dissensions between rival ministers and generals and queens. The only strong power was the army of the *khalsa,* or Central Council of the Sikhs, warriors unequaled for steadiness and religious fervor since Cromwell's Ironsides. They were eager to cross steel with the British Sepoys. They ousted the late Ranjit Singh's European generals, Avitabile and Court; vested supreme military power in a series of *panchayats,* or elective committees of five; and were evidently in a threatening mood, ready to go on the war path, to cross the Sutlej where British dominion hemmed them in on the east.

Yes—the whole north was smoldering—was ready to burst into flame. So regiments were being shifted here and there; the 27th, in October, receiving orders to proceed via Peshawar and the Khyber Pass to Jalalabad, a rather charming town, Afghanistan's Windsor, near Kabul, where Shah Shujah was in residence.

Welcome news to John Nicholson—then seventeen years of age and so proud of his glistening sword—and his brother-officers. They marched away, drums

beating, colors flying, rifle barrels glistening in the
sun; marched away, cheering and eager, meeting other
troops on the road: horse, foot, not to forget the
guns—the light guns of the Indian army, drawn by
buffaloes, rumbling along to the lilt and roar of the
ancient song, most rollicking of all the Anglo-Indian
army tunes, known and yelled and hummed to this day
from Cape Comorin to Mandalay, from the Coro-
mandel Coast to the snows of Simla:

"I love to hear the Sepoy with his bold and martial tread,
And the thud of galloping cavalry reëchoes through my head;
But sweeter far than any sound by mortal ever made
Is the tramp of the Buffalo Battery a-going to parade.
   For it's 'Hanya! hanya! hanya! hanya!'
     Twist their tails and go!
   With a 'Hathi! hathi! hathi! hathi-oh!'
     Elephant and buffalo!
   With a 'Chow-chow! chow-chow! chow-chow!'
     'Teri ma!' 'Chel-lo!'
   Oh, that's the way they shout all day and drive the
     buffalo. . . ."

Up in the hills above Jalalabad was plenty of work
for the guns; plenty of work, too, for scouting parties
of the 27th, since the clansmen were squatting behind
every rock, ambushing convoys, cutting off stragglers,
and, with their women's enthusiastic help, mutilating
the prisoners after the time-honored Afghan habit.

John Nicholson mentioned these amenities of border
warfare to his youngest brother, Alexander, who was
due in Calcutta in a few months. Not that John encouraged him to come. For the other's besetting sins
were laziness and bad manners; and John wrote him
that, unless he got over both these faults, he would be
decidedly out of luck in India. He wrote very curtly
and to the point—this young subaltern who was fighting Afghans at an age when the average Eton boy's

highest ambition is to see his House get into the ante-final.

A short time later, the 27th received orders to return through the Khyber Pass and to assist in bringing up Shah Shujah's rather extensive harem to Kabul. The regiment had hardly reached the border when news came that several thousand Sikhs were on the warpath, loudly declaring that they were *"singhs"* or "lions" and not *"sahijdharis"* or "livers at ease" and were more than ready for the *"Khanda-di-Pahul"* or "Baptism of the Sword." But, to John Nicholson's freely expressed disgust, Major Broadfoot's diplomacy, at least for the nonce, quelled the trouble, and the 27th continued on their way, escorted Shah Shujah's veiled ladies to Kabul, and were thence moved to garrison the riotous southern Afghan town of Ghazni.

They arrived there in July of the following year, about the time that Sir William Macnaghten, the British envoy at Kabul, who did not know his Afghans as well as he might have, reported that "all is perfectly quiet from Dan to Beersheba."

So, indeed, it appeared—until John Company decided that, for the future, the Ghilzai tribesmen were to be paid no more subsidy, *anglicé* for bribe, for allowing the free passage of merchants and caravans through their lands. The Ghilzais' answer was prompt. Within a week they had plundered a caravan, put a dozen peaceful Indian traders to the sword, and placed themselves astride the road between Jalalabad and the Khyber.

It was the spark needed for the explosion. Within the next few months, all along the border, hell broke loose.

Shah Shujah was murdered by the followers of Dost Mohammed Khan; so was Sir Alexander Burnes, the

political agent; so, during an interview with Akbar
Khan, Dost Mohammed Khan's oldest son, was Sir
William Macnaghten. The British army in Kabul
was commanded by General Elphinstone, a doddering
old man not to be confounded with that great explorer
and statesman, the Honorable Mountstuart Elphinstone. He was unable to make up his mind what to do.
For a number of weeks the soldiers lingered in their
cantonments. At last, in the hard depth of winter,
under a lying guarantee of free passage granted by
the Afghan chiefs, the army set off, to find its way
back to India through the snow-bound mountain passes.
Sixteen thousand men, including civilian camp followers, and, too, a number of English and Hindu women
and children, started on that tragic journey. A single
survivor, Dr. Brydon, who saved himself by giving a
Masonic sign to the chief who was about to kill him,
reached Jalalabad where General Sale was making a
gallant stand, to tell the tale of the terrible catastrophe:
the army trusting the safe-conduct promised them,
caught in the icy, slippery defiles of Khurd-Kabul and
Jagdalak, unprepared and unable to defend themselves,
butchered by Afghan matchlocks and broad-bladed *che-
rays,* only a few, mostly women and children, taken
alive by the mountaineers and sent back to Kabul
where, by orders of Akbar Khan, they were treated
considerately enough.

In Ghazni, too, was trouble. Persistently, in spite
of most anxious recommendations, John Company had
refused to appropriate funds for the defense of the
town. There were a few guns in the open, no artillerymen, no proper escarps or glacis. It was now too late
to mend matters. So, as best they could, the 27th got
down to digging themselves in; and, when the Afghans
came, they found themselves faced by a make-shift
system of breastworks and outposts.

The first phase of the siege did not last long. Before it was seriously laid down, news came from Jalalabad that a relief force, commanded by Maclaren, was en route. So the besiegers left their prey, while the garrison stretched its limbs and waited. But snow and ice impeded Maclaren's column; the Afghans returned; and, a fortnight later, carried the outposts, rushed into Ghazni with the crimson sweep of their long knives, and confined the British garrison in the inner citadel.

The winter that followed was strenuous. The cold was intense; the rations grew slimmer day by day, since John Company had been economical even in the matter of supplies; the clansmen squatted on their haunches, calmly waiting for the inevitable.

It came, after three months, on the 6th March, 1842. The British demanded and received terms. They marched out of the citadel, colors flying, drums beating, officers retaining their swords, to take up the quarter of the town to which they were relegated as prisoners of war. There was keen regret amongst them that they had not been given a chance to do more than crouch behind walls and take pot-shots at fur-capped or turbaned heads. To be starved out without coming to close quarters was a disappointment.

But from this disappointment they were not to suffer long. For, on the day after the surrender, whilst the troops were cooking their midday meal, the Afghans —being Afghans—decided to forget parole given and accepted, and swept into the quarter with the swish of naked steel.

Fast cut and drive it was then, quick flash of the saber, with the palm up and the hand low to find the groin, and a long reach with the short dagger, and the choked breath hissing at teeth and nose. Afghan

treachery it was—death, moist and sticky and red and
sudden; and the British defending themselves, mostly
with their bare fists, since all weapons, except the
officers' swords, had been given up. John Nicholson
and two other subalterns, with a couple of hundred
Sepoys, found themselves isolated in a house which
was soon set afire. They digged and sapped their way
through the back. After two days of house-to-house
fighting, with the help of matchlock and pistol picked
up here and there or wrested away from some bearded
mountaineer in body-to-body struggle, they rejoined
their comrades; where, with the survivors of the
Ghazni garrison, bottled up in a single building with
hardly a chance of getting out of it alive . . . since the
Afghans, now in control of the citadel, turned the guns
on them and were raking them with shot.

Again, after a day or two, Shamsuddin, the Afghan
commander, proposed surrender on parole. His offer
was rejected, since he had broken his word once. But
the Sepoys were getting desperate. A number of
them made a sally from the house, in a mad attempt
to fight their way through the ranks of the besiegers
and to reach the passes—to return to their Indian
homes.

Then, understanding the position was hopeless either
way, Colonel Palmer of the 27th decided to take another chance on Afghan honor. On the 20th of the
month came the second surrender. Palmer, accompanied by his officers, went out to meet Shamsuddin,
to throw his sword at the feet of the man who had
broken his promise once.

Shamsuddin—since Afghan charm is quite as potent
as Afghan treachery—almost succeeded in persuading
Colonel Palmer that the recent breach of faith had
been nothing but an unfortunate misunderstanding.
This time—he gave solemn oath on the Koran—the

British would be treated fairly and honorably, as prisoners of war; and he had them escorted to the safety
of the citadel.

But, again, this decent treatment did not last long.
For there was yet another Afghan characteristic to be
reckoned with: cupidity. Thus, gradually, the hillmen's attitude changed until one day the British were
searched for any valuables they might have. Everything except the clothes they stood in was taken from
them, and the officers, ten of them, were herded together in a one-windowed room 18x13.

During this search John Nicholson earned some
distinction by one of his exhibitions of Irish temper.
In his possession was a locket containing a wisp of his
mother's hair. When an Afghan chief added this to
the little pile of penknives, keys, pencils, collar studs
and similar trinkets, Nicholson jumped up, grapsed
the man's wrist, and took the locket away from him.
There was a tussle. Nicholson was overpowered by
half a dozen clansmen. But he held on to the locket.
Threatened with death unless he gave it up, he flung
it full in the face of the Afghan chief. The latter
laughed, slapped him on the back, and returned the
locket.

During the first week of April news of Shah Shujah's murder reached Ghazni. At once the treatment of the prisoners became more severe. Their
food rations were reduced to a minimum; all light was
excluded from their cell; nor were they allowed to
leave it except once, when they were forced to witness
the torture of Colonel Palmer who was given the
Afghan equivalent of the medieval European "boots."
For their jailers were convinced that, before the surrender of the citadel, the officers had concealed four
lakhs of rupees. The "boots" did not work; Colonel

Palmer survived; but, day and night, the Afghans pestered and nagged their captives with questions about the apocryphal treasure.

By the end of April news reached Ghazni that a British relief expedition was headed up from the passes. At once the treatment of the prisoners changed. From their cell they were taken to more roomy and airy quarters with a courtyard in which to exercise, but not before one of their number had died of typhus in that first, filthy, vermin-ridden hole.

The rumor of the relief expedition turned out not to be true. But the more humane treatment of the British continued; and, finally, one night, after four months, they were taken out without notice, packed on camels, and hurried off on a three days' journey to Kabul. There they were kindly received by Akbar Khan, given the first square meal they had seen in many weeks, and provided with fresh clothes—exceedingly welcome to John Nicholson—since cooties were not a *schrecklichkeit* invented by the Germans during the Great War and since he had worn the same shirt for the last four months.

Other surprises followed. After a banquet presided over by Akbar Khan, the party were driven out to a fort near Kabul and united with some other prisoners, including Lady Sale and Sir George Lawrence. The latter was permitted to receive mail; and the acquaintance established between him, his brother Henry and John Nicholson was destined to become of enormous, almost epic, importance to Britain's dominion in the Indies.

In the meantime troops were advancing from the south under Pollock and Nott. After hard fighting and hard marching Kabul was reached and conquered;

the great bazaar was blown up with gunpowder to fix a stigma upon the city; the British prisoners were recovered; and—a gigantic jest on England, a more gigantic jest on bombastic, vain-glorious Lord Ellenborough who had superseded Lord Auckland in 1842 —Dost Mohammed Khan was left to take undisputed possession of the Afghan throne.

Thus, ironically, ended Britain's Afghan adventure —with the Afghans, as before, squatting on their hills, making jeering remarks, and thumbing their noses at British and Hindu alike—and with John Nicholson, for one, hating the Afghans because of their treachery, yet admiring them because of their hardy, ferocious bravery; liking best the Afghan aristocrats of whom he said: "I was never in the company of more gentlemanly, well-bred men; they have more innate, natural politeness than any other people I have ever seen"; and, as to the Afghans of the border clans, rather agreeing with Mountstuart Elphinstone's opinion that they "have the finest physique and the worst morals in the world."

More fighting had to be done on the march south which was consequently slow. Nicholson helped in the demolition of the Jalalabad defenses and did a like duty at Daka, at the northern end of the Khyber. There, among the replacements arriving to Pollock's army, he was surprised to meet his younger brother, Alexander. There was only time for a brief conversation and the promise of meeting in Peshawar.

This promise was not to be kept.

For, two days later, as John Nicholson was trailing with the rearguard down the Khyber, he noticed a naked body just off the road. With a fellow-officer he rode over to inspect. The dead man—really only a boy—was his younger brother, mutilated after the Afghan custom.

John Nicholson prayed. Then he shrugged his shoulders and rode on.

Blood—and death! Britain's price for dominion! A price that had to be paid—in full. . . .

At last the troops reached their side of the border. John Company and England had burned their fingers badly. It would be some time before they tried meddling with the Afghans again. But Nicholson, now turned twenty, had received a liberal education in his chosen profession. He had suffered hardships and dangers innumerable, had learned to study territory and to lead men.

Neither he nor his fellow-officers were too much pleased when, back in Ferozepore at Christmas, they received a *communiqué* from England which included most scathing remarks from the Duke of Wellington as to the manner in which they had done their work. It was not fair, they thought, for they had done their best, handicapped by John Company's dilatoriness and parsimony; not fair when, in January, 1843, the 27th regiment was ordered to Meerut, taking with it its colonel—under arrest, to be courtmartialed for neglect of duty.

The courtmaritial was hectic and lengthy. Palmer, on evidence from his companions, chiefly a vehement and fearless tirade by Nicholson, was exonerated; and the Afghan intermezzo, for the latter, was closed.

But he was furious at the comments of the mutton-fed, armchair gentry safely ensconced in England; at "Pagett, M.P." back home—Kipling's "Pagett, M.P." who was "a liar and a fluent liar therewith"—immortal, never-changing "Pagett, M.P." who, as long as England will be England and the Anglo-Saxon, at a secure distance from the scene of strife, a sentimentalist, will speak of his countrymen in the far corners of the earth as "bloated Brahmins" and of their miserable stipend as "princely pay"—"Pagett, M.P." who, the minute things go wrong and his money bags are threatened, demands investigating committees, courtmartials, and what not.

"The ideas of people at home," Nicholson wrote at the time, "concerning the late war fill me with bitterness. I am sorry now that we have left Kabul while one stone remained on another."

Sorry—afterwards. Sorry not because of honest hate for an honest enemy. But sorry because of dishonest criticism by dishonest countrymen. . . .

An old, old English story!

The Afghan activity was followed by two years of inaction which John Nicholson spent in assiduous study. At Meerut and Moradabad he applied himself first to languages and then, on account of encouragement received from higher up, to the details of his trade. He was regarded as a rather austere young man with no interest beyond the barrack square. But his letters home tell a different story. By avoiding all social functions and keeping well within his shell, he hoped to be out of debt soon and, within six months, to remit £100 to Ireland for the education of his youngest brother, also destined for the John Company army. His evident interest in things military earned him the appointment as adjutant with his regiment and the promise of transfer to the staff corps so soon as he could satisfy the examiners. But, though it brought him extra and very welcome pay, the position as adjutant handicapped him in his studies; and it was not until November, 1845, that he sat for the examination—which he passed without any particular distinction.

His consequent transfer to the Commissariat De-

partment occurred almost simultaneously with the
Sikh outbreak.

Tired by John Company's high-handed methods,
the Sikhs at Lahore declared war, and, on the 17th
December, crossed the Sutlej with 60,000 men and
150 guns, invading British territory to defend the ap-
proaches to their own land. The British, led by Sir
Hugh Gough, hurried up. There were pitched battles,
with heavy British losses, at Mukdi, Firozshah, Aliwal,
and Sobraon. But the last engagement was a decisive
victory for John Company; the Sikh warriors were
driven back across the Sutlej; and Lahore surrendered.
By the terms of peace, Dhulip Singh, supposed to be
the son of Ranjit Singh and a dancing-girl, but in
reality of decidedly dubious parentage since the dancing-girl had been notoriously unfaithful, was recognized as Rajah; the Jalandar Doab territory was annexed; Henry Lawrence was appointed resident at
Lahore; and a British force was sent to garrison the
Punjab for the next eight years.

Nicholson's work during the campaign was well regarded by his seniors. It brought recognition and
reward.

Very recently Gulab Singh, a Mian Rajput and ruler
of Jammu, had become Maharajah of Kashmir by purchasing the territory from the British who considered
that the presence of a friendly power on the flank of
the Sikh confederacy would be a valuable asset. Kashmir had known many masters; amongst others the
Moghuls; the rapacious Afghan wolves from Kabul,
who, under the name of *"Shanhani Durani,"* are still
remembered with a shudder between the Indus and the
Ravi; finally the Sikhs. After the latter's expulsion a
Rajput tribe, though not numerically, became the leading race: the Dogras, a hard, proud breed of hillmen,
an unruly clan finding a great deal of fault with Gulab

Singh, their new overlord, who applied for the loan of
two British officers, capable of training the mountaineers.

John Nicholson, on the nomination of Gough supported by Sir George Lawrence who recognized his
fellow-prisoner of Afghan days, received the appointment. On April 2, 1845, with Captain Broome, the
officer seconded for the work, he arrived at Jammu
and reported to his new employer.

The program advocated by Gulab Singh in his corre-
spondence with John Company had seemed simple.
For a few months the two officers were to train his
Jammu troops; were then to lead them across the
mountains to establish his authority in Kashmir.
Nicholson and Broome started in with enthusiasm.
Soon, however, they found their hands tied. Gulab
Singh was a shrewd politician and an opportunist who
might have shared honors with Lloyd George himself.
His application for British officers had been nothing
more than a diplomatic trick to curry favor with John
Company. Presently he told Nicholson and Broome
that he was entirely satisfied with the *status quo* and
informed them that they were excused from all duties,
condemning them to a life of monotony only relieved
by linguistic studies.

In July, 1846, Gulab Singh decided to move to his
new capital, Srinagar. He took the two British officers
with him.

A glorious journey. A glorious land. When
Jehangir, the great Moghul emperor, lay dying and
was asked if there was anything he wanted, he replied:
"Only Kashmir!"

And Kashmir had not changed since the days of the
Moghuls. There were still—will always be—the
towering, snow-clad mountains, the amazing fields and

slopes covered with a motley of flowers that puts California to shame, the lovely, fair lakes studded with lotus, blue and white and pink.

John Nicholson, for all his austerity, enjoyed it; did not enjoy Srinagar itself where the same routine, the same deadly monotony of doing nothing awaited him. Then news came, welcome to him; news brought by the gossip route, by what is known to the garrulous folk of Kashmir as the *"hawa kadal"* or "bridge of air"; news that swords were at the sharpening from hill to hill and that the Dogras intended to rise and send Gulab back to Jammu—"with his tail between his legs and eating his fill of dirt," as they expressed it. Nicholson advised this and that. But Gulab would not listen. Quickly the revolt ripened, finding the Maharajah unprepared. He told Broome and Nicholson to shift for themselves, while he, leaving his soldiers under their native commander, made for the border. Broome and Nicholson, forbidden to take part in civil warfare, made their way alone across some two hundred miles of savage and unknown country. They found Gulab Singh already at Jammu, chewing betel, drinking Persian wine, supinely accepting the news that his troops had been completely routed by the insurgents, and, urged by Nicholson to do something, quoting trite Hindu philosophy: *"Muala par kodo dare aile"*—in other words, that it was useless to grind corn wherewith to feed the dead.

To Captain (afterwards Sir Herbert) Edwardes and Henry Lawrence went the onus of reëstablishing order in Kashmir, whilst Nicholson remained with Gulab Singh, busy passing up soldiers to the north. At last the rebels were subjugated; Edwardes, Lawrence, and Broome returned south; and Nicholson was left by himself beyond the mountains, to chafe at the drab monotony of life, to eat the Kashmir lotus nor to care

for the cloying taste of it.   But Lawrence had his eyes
on the rising young man; and, until such time as he
could find something more suited to his proven genius,
a peculiar mixture of hard courage and hard efficiency,
he obtained for him the sinecure of political agent on
the Northwest Frontier.   Finally, toward the end of
the year, Captain Lawrence, having received his appointment as sole regent of the Punjab, caused John
Nicholson to be gazetted as assistant resident at the
court of Lahore.

Trouble was in the wind.

For the Kashmir revolt had been traced directly to
intrigues of the Lahore court which, having been defeated in its own recent war, was only too glad to fish
in muddied water, to cause all the annoyance possible
for John Company.   Lawrence understood this.   In
his new position he treated the Sikhs with scant consideration.   He deposed Lal Singh, who had been at
the root of the conspiracy, from his advisory office and
did not permit the Queen-Regent to have any future
voice in the affairs of government.

Heroic measures—that boded little peace for the
new administration; and so Nicholson took up his
duties with the certain knowledge that, sooner or later,
the lid would blow off.

After a lengthy tour of inspection of the Punjab—
picturing the land, in his report, as a "wretched country, a poverty-stricken acquisition"—he proceeded to
Lahore where his brother Charles, who had obtained a
Company appointment, was waiting for him.   They
had not seen each other for eight years; and Charles
did not recognize John.   The latter, now six foot four
inches in height, was gaunt, hawkish, tanned to a deep
mahogany.

For India had set her mark heavily upon him—as

he, in turn, was destined to set his mark heavily upon India. . . .

For some weeks he was attached to Henry Lawrence's personal staff. In daily contact with his indefatigable chief, he learned much of the policy of the administration—learned so quickly and thoroughly that, in a short time, Lawrence decided the other was ready to try his own wings and appointed him to full political control of the Sind-Sagar Doab, between the Jhelum and the Indus. These duties he took over in June, 1847, with very definite ideas as to how he was to act. His task was to cultivate cordial relations with the native rulers, protect the poor from the ravages of the tax collectors, and maintain an efficient army.

Here he commenced to build up that extraordinary reputation with the natives which marks him as unique among the men who, in serving India, in lifting her out of the medieval slough, have made her an integral part of the British Empire. Soon he discovered that the method in which taxes were collected was the chief cause of possible civil trouble. An assessment was nothing more than an armed raid during which the collectors used any and all means, from threats to thumb-screws, to force the unfortunate peasants to pay the land revenue in full, and an equal amount, as bribe, to the collectors themselves. At once John Nicholson prepared plans to rectify matters.

Within a month, too, he was called upon to use his military force. Captain Abbott, the administrator in the north, was having a rough time bringing order in his area. Summoning certain chiefs before him to answer for corruption and maladministration, Abbott found himself treated with scorn. Those were the days when an Englishman, in the far corners of the earth, had to use his own initiative, to act quickly. So, immediately, Abbott called for help from adjoining departments. Three small armies trekked, to meet at a given point, and to make a combined attack on the fort of Simalkand. Though he had to march the longest distance, Nicholson reached the junction first and, finding no one there to meet him, led his men at once to the attack. Already his name was becoming known to the Sikhs. When the rebels in the fort heard it was *"Nikalsain"* who was opposing them, they evacuated their position, and Nicholson was able to turn over the empty stronghold to Abbott without the loss of a single man.

For the remainder of the year he applied himself to his own domain with surprising results. He protected the villagers against cattle thieves who roamed about taking what they could find and against the tax collectors who traveled abroad followed by small bands of ruffianly soldiery. With heavy prison sentences, with whip and, occasionally, the executioner's blade, he made examples of the most flagrant cases of oppression, earning the respect of both sides to such an extent that, before he left on a short Christmas furlough, the cattle thieves were exercising their peculiar gifts in a different part of the country, the tax collectors, touring their routes without armed attendants, were content to assess the legal dues and no more, and the smallest differences were being voluntarily referred to him for adjudication.

The first three months of 1848, throughout the Punjab, saw peace progress still further. The two Lawrences, Henry and John, thought they saw light ahead. But the tranquillity of this period was only the lull before a great storm.

It came suddenly.

Mulraj, the governor of Multan, applied for per-

mission to resign from his post. Two Company
agents, Anderson and Agnew, were sent to establish
his successor. There was a misunderstanding—a row
—they were murdered—and Mulraj, upon whom suspicion for the assassination settled, became panic-
stricken and in the last week of April declared Holy
War against the British.

The Sikh warriors gathered. They chanted their
battle hymn: *"Wahguru ji ka khalsa, Wahguru ji ki
fatah"*—"The covenant of God, victory to God!" Unfortunately, Henry Lawrence was away on sick leave.
His brother John took his place, summoning Nicholson
to the office of chief assistant. Quick action brought
the early defeat of Mulraj; but, soon, the revolt
spread; the resources of the Company were not immediately equal to the strain. Afghan tribesmen, forgetting for the nonce their ancient feud with the Sikhs
in their common hatred of the British, rode down from
the north with steel and torch and the nasal, sardonic
drone of the drums.

Lahore was about to explode. Chatar Singh, the
old Sikh chieftain who time and again had been foiled
in his intrigues for replacing the Queen-Mother, was
beginning to show his hand more and more; was doubtless on the verge of joining the rebels. Murder started
in a nearby village. Momentarily Lawrence was nonplussed. But Nicholson had learned his Asian lesson
—to strike rapidly and decisively. He took a handful
of loyal Sikh troopers, marched over to the village,
confiscated a considerable quantity of arms and ammunition, and punished the headman severely. Hereafter he became a power with Lawrence who depended
on his junior's advice and assistance in all matters.

When the news came that Chatar Singh had engi-
neered a bloody outbreak at Haripur, Nicholson was
laid up with fever. He insisted on leaving immediately

for the scene of trouble. Lawrence refused to let him
go, arguing that, in the sick man's condition, it might
be fatal to move. He recommended other available
officers to head the enterprise. But Nicholson would
not listen. That same night he set out with sixty
Pathan horsemen, gave orders for two companies of
infantry to follow as fast as possible, and, riding fifty
miles before morning, was at the gates of the citadel
before the insurgents had had time to close and barri-
cade them.

Thirty of his Pathans, seeing likely cattle that
waited for the stealing, had straggled during the advance. The whereabouts of the infantry was entirely
unknown. But, daring the keepers of the gates to
touch him, with a lordly mien imitated from what he
had seen amongst the Rajahs, he went inside and addressed the rioters. He spoke well, this lean, handsome, bearded Irishman, then twenty-six years of age.
Using an alien tongue, he blended threats and florid
cajoleries. For twenty minutes he talked—and he
won. He won, by the sheer power of chilly brain and
chilly pluck, as, many years later, for the pride of that
same British empire, Cecil Rhodes won in the Matoppo
Hills.

An amazing escapade it was, echoing to his credit
amongst both British and Sikhs.

Yet only the beginning.

Leaving the fort under the command of one of his
Pathans, he went up on the road toward Rawal-Pindi.
Near there a company of Sepoys was marching to join
the rebels. Nicholson met them, riding ahead alone;
ordered the troopers on parade at once; identified the
ring-leaders and placed them under arrest . . . and
the soldiers obeyed, cheered loudly, followed him . . .
and let us not forget that they were Sikhs, brave men,
stubborn. Yet there was this lone, gaunt Irishman.

There was his courage and—possibly—his blarney . . . ?

The next day brought almost a repetition of the event. A Sikh regiment, with two pieces of artillery, was marching from Rawal-Pindi to Hazara to throw in their lot with the rebels. The mutineers advanced. So did John Nicholson with his few troops. He spoke to the malcontents. They hesitated; then, suddenly, salaamed, and returned to the service of John Company, remaining loyal throughout the Second Sikh War.

Already, amongst certain of the Sikhs, an aura of superstitious awe was beginning to form about John Nicholson's head. Already they were associating his name with that amazing prophecy which, almost two hundred years earlier, Gobind Singh, one of their *Gurus* or Saints, pronounced, and in which he foresaw the fall of the Moghul Empire, the rise and fall of the Kabuli wolves, and the coming of the British and their eventual triumph—saying:

"At the end of the Sambar year 1800 (A.D. 1743) the Sikhs shall take possession of many lands. Three years later they shall spring out of every bush, and there shall be terrible warfare between them and the Moslems. A powerful king shall come from Afghanistan and kill countless Sikhs. He shall continue his victorious progress throughout Hindustan as far as Mathura, bringing everywhere destruction and death. None shall be able to withstand him. As prophesied by Guru Arjan, he shall raze the Golden Temple of Amritsar to the ground, but the Sikhs shall plunder his camp on his retreat from India. In the Sambar year 1900 (A.D. 1843) the Moslems who survive shall lose their empire. A Christian army shall come from Calcutta. The Sikhs, fighting amongst each other, shall join them. There shall be more strife, and men and women shall be expelled from their homes. Other Sikhs shall join the Brahmins against the English and suffer greatly. But the real Sikhs shall hold their ground and survive. The English shall possess great power and, by force of arms, take possession of many principalities. The combined armies of the English and the Sikhs shall be very strong and rich as long as they rule with united councils. The empire of the English shall vastly increase, and they shall in every way attain prosperity. Wherever they take their armies they shall conquer, and bestow thrones on those who assist them. Then in every house shall there be wealth and happiness and religion and learning, and in every house a woman. The English shall rule for a long time."

Thus the prophecy; and Nicholson, for one, seemed to exemplify it. His daring tactics might have quelled the whole trouble at the start. But orders from Lahore tied his hands. Sir Frederick Currie, newly attached to Lawrence's staff by the central government, was against making too much of the affair. He was convinced that Chatar Singh was not entirely to blame, that Abbott had probably gone too far in his distrust of the old chief.

But Nicholson did not agree. Either Chatar Singh was innocent, or guilty; must be either entirely exonerated, or submitted to the severest penalties. In the latter event—and Nicholson, personally, was convinced of the man's guilt—a display of force was necessary to keep the population in hand. He suggested that three regiments and guns should be sent against Chatar Singh immediately. But Currie, though he admired and praised Nicholson, hesitated. In the four days it took him to make up his mind, matters went completely out of hand. No troops were despatched; negotiations with Chatar Singh fell through; and, finally, the old chief declared definitely that he was fighting a Holy War.

On the 20th August he marched his entire force toward the south. Abbott brought up his troops to reenforce those of Nicholson, and they agreed on a plan by which the enemy was to be hemmed in and regularly besieged.

But, again, Lahore headquarters held them back. Fake peace overtures were being made by Chatar Singh while he was seeing to his final preparations for the advance on Lahore. Currie, taken in by the chief, instructed Nicholson to parley with him. But scouts informed Nicholson of Chatar Singh's real intentions. There was no time to lose. He decided that the only thing to do was to harry the enemy at all points and keep him nervous and jumpy. Using the fortress of Attock as his base, he marched and counter-marched his men, keeping them on the run about the enemy in a manner which almost led the latter to believe that Nicholson could be in two places at the same time. Nonplussed, the Sikhs stopped their advance, while Nicholson sent urgent messages to Currie for reënforcements.

These apparently minor operations were actually very difficult to carry out. For all Nicholson's men were Moslems, and the time was the month of Ramazan, Islam's Lent. Weakened by the daily fasts between sun-up and sun-down, his men were not in the best of physical condition. But they responded magnificently to Nicholson's orders and did marvels in the way of long marches beneath the rays of the Indian midsummer sun that crackled down like a rain of spears. By September the actual position was that Chatar Singh, still bluffed into not moving, had eight thousand men and sixteen guns, while Nicholson, continuously marching and counter-marching, was holding him in his place with seven hundred foot and horse.

Not only that. Too, it was his task to keep reënforcements from joining the Sikhs.

On the road from Rawal-Pindi to Hasan-Abdal stood the Margalla Tower commanding a pass. Hear-

ing that Chatar Singh's own son was moving up troops
to his father, Nicholson decided to capture this tower
and thus keep the two forces apart. It was held by a
dozen sharp-shooters. Working their way, mostly on
their stomachs, to within assaulting distance, they
rushed forward on Nicholson's signal. He himself led
the way to the foot of the tower where he found that
the only entrance was twelve feet above the ground
and that only four men had followed him, the others,
raked by the sharp-shooters' fire and some of them
wounded, having dropped behind. Finally even these
four ran back to safety; and, furiously trying to tear
stones out of the wall, to climb up hanging on by his
finger nails, he was at last forced to give up his mad,
single-handed attack as some Sikh cavalry approached
at a gallop. Retiring under fire and carrying a
wounded trooper on his shoulders, by some strange
freak of fortune he was not hit.

This fact started a tradition amongst his followers
as well as amongst his opponents that he was immune
to bullets, a legend which, later on, on more than one
occasion, saved his life, when superstitious natives
were unable to bring themselves to lift a rifle at him
or to hold it steady when they did fire.

The attempt to foil reënforcements from joining
the Sikhs failed. The situation was made infinitely
worse by the loss of John Company of Shere Singh,
who passed over to the enemy with all his men. For
the moment further operations in that part of the Punjab seemed hopeless. An entire new campaign had to
be worked out. Nicholson withdrew to Lahore.

Hereafter, for many weeks on end, he had to pursue a maddening and thankless routine of duties; he
was required to keep the rebellion localized; to break
it whenever and wherever active; to rush from spot to
spot with his inadequate forces; to prevent the main

army of the Sikhs from reaching Lahore until fresh British units could be brought up.

Troops were coming out from England, with Sir Charles Napier as Commander-in-Chief. But there was delay after delay; and Nicholson was kept on the jump; as soon as he had attempted, often achieved, one task with the fifth of the men necessary, appeals for assistance came to him from another quarter.

The army of the *khalsa* was getting into its stride. From end to end of the Punjab the war-conches screamed and brayed. Loud and triumphant rose the shout that the *Mlech,* the unbeliever, was being defeated. Chilianwala, though the patriotism of school histories prefers to call it a drawn battle, was in reality a minor catastrophe, since the British lost 2,400 men and officers, four guns, and the colors of three regiments.

But, at last, before Sir Charles Napier's arrival in India, conditions improved. Lord Gough (formerly Sir Hugh Gough) restored his reputation by the crowning victory of Gujrat. Too, Multan had fallen. The Afghan wolves had been chased ignominiously back to their native hills.

So, at last, the tide turned. The Punjab was being conquered. But it was a hard task, a lengthy task, during which Nicholson pursued his duties strenuously and earned further recognition. Whether it was in such a lowly, if important, duty as finding boats for a river crossing, or such a grave duty as bringing over discontented Sikhs to the service of the Company, he invariably managed to achieve his end. The bearded, handsome, lean Irishman was indefatigable. Many official despatches of the time mention him for conspicuous service. Not satisfied with his routine work as political liaison officer between the army and Lahore, he volunteered for all sorts of dare-devil, dangerous tasks.

By March, 1849, the *khalsa* was disintegrating. The old prophecy of *Guru* Gobind Singh was being recalled. Men were coming over to the Company fast. Peace talk with the chiefs began. In this, too, Nicholson played an important part. On the 7th March Shere Singh was in the British camp, discussing terms, and on the following day Nicholson could announce to Lahore and the central government that the war was at an end.

The terms were sweeping. Maharajah Dhulip Singh abdicated and received an allowance of £58,000 a year on which he lived, for many a decade, as an English country gentleman in Norfolk. The Punjab was annexed—a virgin field for the administrative talents of John Nicholson, the two Lawrences, and the Governor-General, the Earl of Dalhousie, advanced to a Marquessate. The rule of the *khalsa* was over. Yet, ultimately, thanks mostly to John Nicholson, the Sikhs became passionately loyal to the Union Jack—proving this loyalty over and over again; instrumental in saving the Empire during the Indian Mutiny of 1857; standing by the British on countless occasions since; pouring out their blood at the time of the World War.

In the rearrangement of government which followed peace, Nicholson found himself deputy commissioner in the very area over which he had ridden and fought for months. Everywhere the people received him with enthusiasm. He was favorably compared with the late native rulers. He had achieved a sort of local halo, and Abbott reported that "anything great or gallant accomplished by our arms is ascribed to Nicholson."

For good measure a Hindu holy man identified in him the reincarnation of a Brahmanic deity; several other religious teachers followed this metaphysical lead; and the cult of Saint *"Nikalsain"* dates from this period.

Not that the object of worship cared for his elevation. Approached by the high priests of the *"Nikalsain"* sect, he first mocked them; then drove them from headquarters with curses and blows, reminding them that their own Sikh doctrines lay great stress on the unity and omnipotence of God, that "There is but one God, the True" is the constant reiteration of their hymns, that in the *Japji,* the Bible of the Sikhs, it is written:

> "By thinking I cannot obtain a conception of Him,
> Even though I think hundreds of thousands of times.
> He hath no color nor outline.
> He is not old nor is He young.
> He feeleth nor heat nor cold.
> He hath no father and no mother."

Needless to say, the more orthodox among the Sikhs praised Nicholson for this. Yet the cult existed for years, a thankless worship; does still exist; though the *"Nikalsainis"* received no favors from their chosen Irish deity during the latter's lifetime, and though their gatherings, usually held outside his house, at his very door, were frequently broken up by him in person, using his fists or a riding-whip to visit their sins upon these noisy congregations.

For his temper remained the same: sharp, quick on the trigger—and it is interesting that Sir Henry Lawrence, in his official instructions, cautioned his Deputy Commissioner against it. In his replies Nicholson pleaded guilty. Indeed the quality which had been so useful to him in the field had to be curbed in his new rôle as civil administrator. He tried his best—did not always succeed, chiefly when one of his brothers, Wil-

liam, lately out from England, failed to attend parade
and a search resulted in the discovery of his bruised,
dead body in bed.

Everything seemed to point to murder. John
Nicholson insisted upon a thorough investigation and
punishment of the culprits. But, in spite of his furious
protests, the government decided that, just now, it had
enough on its hands and declared that William's death
was due to natural causes.

Otherwise the first few months after peace passed
quietly for him. With his headquarters at Hasan-
Abdal, he rode daily over his domain, administering
justice, attending to the settlement of the land tax,
village by village, at an assessment much below the
rates to which it had been raised by the exactions of
the Sikh chiefs. He was beginning to understand the
country and develop a definite theory as to how to
handle the vast population. Clearing away age-old
governmental practices and malpractices and substitut-
ing a new régime in record time was no easy task. But
he went about it systematically, convinced that he
would have a model district by the time his furlough
fell due.

He was longing for home. But the Company's rules
were against his going. New hands were required to
serve a full ten years before taking a leave. Discussing this matter with some seniors and realizing that his
services were valuable to the Company, he made up his
mind to take a chance.

Packing his few belongings, he notified Sir Henry
Lawrence that he was going home. This action auto-
matically dropped him from the lists. But Sir Henry
was not going to lose his brilliant assistant. He promised that, if he returned to India as soon as was possible, a new post would be awaiting him.

So, in January, 1850, Nicholson sailed from Bombay on the same boat with General Lord Gough and Edwardes. His association with the latter during this voyage was destined to have important results. During the long journey they exchanged ideas on the Indian situation and together gleaned all the instruction they might from Lord Gough, whose knowledge of the land was profound.

At Cairo their paths diverged. Edwardes and Gough continued on to England, while Nicholson wished to see Constantinople where his curiosity and his temper led him into a couple of typical escapades.

The failure of the Hungarian revolt of 1848 had resulted in many of the defeated patriots going to Turkey. The Turks, throughout the centuries, have given asylum to those persecuted by other lands: to the Spanish Jews driven out by King Ferdinand; to hundreds of thousands of Protestants hounded by the Hapsburgs; to the tribes of the Caucasus after Russia stole their hills and commenced to civilize them with steel and graft and vodka, that immortal Slav trinity. Similarly, after 1848, the Osmanlis gave refuge, liberal, sympathetic, unstinted, to the vanquished Hungarians. Amongst them were Louis Kossuth himself and an Englishman, a certain Guyon, late Colonel in the Austrian army and married to a lady of the old Magyar nobility.

Guyon's wife had been unable to leave her country and was incarcerated on the wrong side of the line. With a price on his own head, Guyon could not make any attempt to get in touch with her. He appealed to John Nicholson, who undertook to convey a letter to her. With the message concealed in his top boots, he crossed into Austria. He reached his destination; but Mrs. Guyon was held *incommunicado;* it seemed impossible to get to her . . . a discovery which made

Nicholson more determined to fulfill his mission. He did it—through sheer audacity, not to mention blarney. He approached the guard house, met the officer in charge, got into conversation with him, told him tales about India. There were drinks—and yet more drinks —questions about the Hungarian revolution—the Austrian telling anecdotes, and, presently, mentioning that a lady was back there, in jail, the wife of an Englishman who had served in the Austrian army. Nicholson feigned astonishment. An Englishman's wife—eh? Why—he would like to see her—just because he and her husband were countrymen. The Austrian officer was willing to oblige. Mrs. Guyon was sent for; and, the Austrian having momentarily left the room, Nicholson delivered to her her husband's message which, eventually, led to her being freed.

His other escapade was less successful. Kossuth was living on the Asiatic shore of the Bosphorus, well treated by the Turks, yet under surveillance on which the Austrians insisted. Each day he was permitted to take a carriage ride, and a plan had been formed to kidnap him during one of these rides and to place him aboard an American vessel bound for the United States which, in those far-off, free years, was a haven for men of his stamp. But, thanks to the talkativeness of some American ladies, details of the plan leaked out —and, in consequence, the Turkish authorities who were actually in favor of Kossuth were forced to restrict the latter's movements, and so the business did not come off.

From Constantinople, Nicholson proceeded leisurely to England by way of Athens, Vienna and Berlin, meeting his family in London at the end of April. There he joined half-heartedly in a season which did not impress him. He considered London's vices and filth and misery worse than what he had seen in India,

and polite entertainments frankly bored him. He declared that, both for color and for music, he preferred
the jungle to the Covent Garden Opera. Much of his
time he spent in the company of Edwardes. Together
they were guests of honor at a Mansion House dinner
where, before the Lord Mayor, the Duke of Wellington and other distinguished statesmen and soldiers,
Edwardes, as the senior officer, in a speech of thanks
pointed to Nicholson as "the real author of half the
exploits you have been kind enough to attribute to me."

Presently his vacation palled on Nicholson. He decided to devote the rest of it to a careful inspection of
matters relating to his trade. For war, in those days
before modern psychology began to cure the mental
diseases which, first, it invented and caused to exist,
was still a trade—and an honorable trade; honorable,
too, to love one's country, to hope and wish and labor
for its aggrandizement, its power and wealth and happiness. People may have been less clever; but they
were certainly more decent. They preferred the Union
Jack to Utopia, Magna Charta to Karl Marx, Buc-
caneers to Bolshevists, Polo to Ping-Pong, Wellington
to Wilson; and, curiously, while there was nothing
broad-minded about their nationalism, they were not
narrow-minded enough to be internationalists. That
dismal perversion called pacifism had not yet invaded
Eton and Oxford and surely not Aldershot. Britons
were still ready to light the watch fires of Newark and
Carlisle and to sound the ancient tocsin of the border
—a border grown world-wide since the days of the
Scottish kings—a border, in John Nicholson's high
dreams of Empire, stretching beyond the Punjab, beyond Afghanistan, beyond Kashmir.

So he observed; worked. His first laboratory was
the British home army. Then he proceeded to the
Continent of Europe to make comparisons, carefully

studying the French, Prussian, and Russian military establishments and returning to London in a rather despondent frame of mind, convinced that the fighting force of his own country was far below the Continental standard.

From Berlin he brought back a specimen of the new needle-gun, prophesying that this weapon would have a large part in the making of European history. Too, he preached the German system of education. But the War Office patronized Nicholson and his report. It required the disgrace of the Crimean War to wake up England.

Edwardes, who had married during his furlough, returned to India before Nicholson. The latter steadily refused to consider taking a wife back to his post. He explained to friends that he preferred his profession to any woman; that, furthermore, the conditions in India did not warrant a man putting a wife to the hardships and dangers of residence in that country; that, finally, he travels fastest—and farthest—who travels alone.

In the spring of 1852 he was back in Lahore. He was now a captain and, unless some exception was made, could expect nothing better than being gazetted to a line regiment. But Sir Henry Lawrence kept his promise; and, presently, Nicholson was given an interim appointment as deputy commissioner of Bannu, Reynell Taylor, the incumbent, having applied for furlough.

At once he rode out to his new headquarters at the town of Bannu. Affairs were in a very different state from what they had been when he had gone on leave. The Sikh War over, Henry Lawrence and his lieutenants had performed marvels. Helped by a succession of excellent crops, they had brought an astounding

prosperity to the natives. Taylor, in the border district, the most difficult, had had his hands full. His
greatest trouble had been with the Umarzai Wazir
tribe of frontier Afghans who not only refused to pay
fair and equitable taxes, but went up to the hills whence
they raided the peaceful farmers. In three years Taylor had been unable to bring the raiders to book, though
he had defended the peasants to the best of his ability.

This was the very kind of situation which Nicholson
could handle. The fly in the ointment was neither an
Afghan nor a Sikh, but an Englishman, Taylor's assistant, a certain Richard Pollock. The latter disliked
the new commissioner, comparing him unfavorably to
his former chief who had been an exceedingly quiet
man, willing to work himself to death without attempting spectacular coups or promising wonders.

Nicholson was of a different type. Eight years of
service which had included sensational successes, few
failures, and local deification, had endowed him with
a superb, rather arrogant self-confidence. This man,
who had fought the Afghans and hated them, seemed
to have absorbed some of their characteristics; had,
like so many Britons, become Orientalized in a way.
Told of the marauders in the north and Taylor's in-
ability to dislodge them, he made but one comment:

"I'll have them out of that in a week!"

Pollock resented this; made allusions to cock-sure-
ness; pointed out difficulties. But Nicholson laughed
—and went to it.

To be sure, with hot weather coming on, it took him
more than a week, since he decided to put off operations. But, with the first sign of cool weather, he
marched off at short notice with a force of police;
blockaded the raiders; starved them into submission;
and then treated them in his usual, offhand manner.
He said to them:

"Pay a nominal tribute of a rupee a head and behave well in the future. Or. . . ."

The Umarzai Wazirs knew what the "or" implied. They salaamed with fair grace; declared loudly that *"Nikalsain"* was their father and their mother; promised fealty and kept it . . . kept it, at least, as long as their Afghan blood permitted.

Only one of their chiefs refused to listen to reason. Nicholson gave him short shrift. Hearing that the man was out on a raid, he met him with his troops. There was a sharp skirmish. The chief and several of his clansmen were killed. Nicholson took the bodies back with him; exposed them in public for several days; and had them buried in the same grave with a brace of pigs.

Thus—sired by the bright sword and damed, possibly, by these same pigs—peace was beginning to come to turbulent Bannu, and the Nicholson tradition grew in the fertile valleys.

During this time changes were imminent in the Lahore government. For long Henry and John Lawrence had been unable to agree on questions of policy. Henry believed that the solution of all difficulties lay chiefly in obtaining the sympathy and coöperation of the native rulers, while John considered it more important to gain the affection of the masses of population. Both sent in their resignations. But the Company was unwilling to lose the two brilliant brothers and compromised by announcing that John would be Chief-Commissioner for the Punjab, giving Henry a similar post in quieter Rajputana. Nicholson, devoted to the latter, applied for transfer to Rajputana. But Henry, who knew how well the other was doing in Bannu, persuaded him to remain there.

He continued to work hard. By September, 1854,

he had accumulated all of 185 pounds sterling in savings which he sent home. Decidedly, local idols, Empire dreamers and builders, received less pay in those days than a railway section hand does to-day. But—and nothing else counted with this hard idealist —he was obtaining results, nor always exactly according to the Indian civil and criminal code. He preferred justice to legality; would, by the same token, not have been a success as mayor of Mugby Junction or as chief magistrate of Hugby-in-the-Hole. Knowing that the written law's delays had the effect of punishing criminals long after their crimes had been forgotten by the simple native mind—not that the simple native mind differs from the more complex Anglo-Saxon mind, as proved by the usual miscarriage of justice, in favor of the criminal, under the jury system—he dealt out summary justice on the spot in the most spectacular manner. John Lawrence, whilst personally agreeing, if not with his methods, at least with his results, had to remonstrate with him more than once; wrote to him:

"Don't send up any more men to be hanged direct. Send an abstract of the evidence in English through the Commissioner and allow the regular courts to act."

During a tour of inspection, Lawrence had opportunity to see Nicholson's performances at first hand. As the party was riding out one day, Nicholson, in a high state of fury, was seen dragging with him a *jemadar* of the guard, glorious in his scarlet-and-gold uniform. The man had been making a small percentage off the sale of supplies to the troops in the canteen.

"I am going to flog him," Nicholson said. "You have no objection, have you?"

And, before the startled John Lawrence could answer, the *jemadar* had received a sound thrashing. Nicholson's sense of justice, which tempered his violent passion, knew no rank nor race on the other hand. An

English subaltern, found guilty of an offense, received no better treatment than an Indian. His was the knack of hitting a man in the right place. Thus, when a Moslem priest caused trouble, instead of sending him to jail, he ordered his beard and head shaved.

One could multiply such instances *ad infinitum*. The final result was that, by the end of 1855, in his annual report, he had the unique distinction amongst deputy commissioners of stating that, during the preceding year, in his area not a single murder or highway robbery had been committed. Yet, on taking over the appointment, Bannu had had the worst reputation in the Company territories.

But the period was not without its clouds. When, some time earlier, a new commander of the Punjab Frontier Force was required, Nicholson had hoped for the post which, instead, was given to Neville Chamberlain. He imagined that John Lawrence took exception to him, although, in reality, the latter's dispatches were full of praise for his deputy. When Nicholson asked for a release so that he could join the English in the Crimea, no notice was taken of his request, and, though time and again he was assured that the first good vacancy in the Indian army would go to him, he still remained in Bannu—prosecuting his duties with all his heart and with no consideration of his comfort or convenience, but chafing for action and imagining that he was being deliberately shelved by the authorities.

Pollock, in the meantime, had been completely won over by his forbidding, erratic senior. He wrote:

"He was gifted with a powerful physique . . . of indomitable energy, a very terror to evil-doers. His mind was concentrated on the particular matter in mind, and his devotion to his work never relaxed. He found Bannu a hell upon earth and curbed it. His powers of investigation were great and his

methods severe. People who wanted to kill an obnoxious
cousin learnt that they could only do so by running a considerable chance of being hanged. . . . Nothing seemed to tire him;
a ride of thirty miles before breakfast, to visit a boundary or
scene of a crime, in no way interfered with his working in
court through a long summer day with the thermometer well
above 90. . . . Prompt when quick action was required he
could be very patient when necessary. . . . If he knew when
it was good to be severe in aid of the repression of crime, he
also knew when to pass over an offense lightly. . . . One characteristic should not be overlooked—his generosity. Caring
nothing for ostentation or money, he spent a great deal on
others and little on himself. . . . In society he was never at
his best. Shy and reticent he found it difficult to converse
freely in mixed company. . . . He had a great sense of humor.
. . . I am sure that he had more religion than he was commonly
given credit for, and, with a horror of cant, a great respect for
the scruples and opinions of people whom he had learned to
esteem. . . ."

Before closing this period of Nicholson's life, it
might be worth while to quote one typical example of
his methods.

On one occasion he had established a small camp
near the border in order to parley with some raiding
chiefs. They arrived at his tent where certain formali-
ties were gone through. Despising the British, the
leader of the deputation expressed his contempt by
clearing his throat and spitting on the ground before
Nicholson . . . which, from the local point of view,
was the gravest sort of insult. Disregarding the man's
rank, Nicholson wasted no time in acknowledging the
slur.

He ordered:

"Secure that man . . . hold him down and make
him lick up that spittle . . . now, kick him out of the
camp!"

Down in the Indian valleys such action might not

have signified anything more than arrogance and a touch of the tyrant. But here, in the hills, where Nicholson had only a meager guard and was surrounded by the clansmen of the petty chief, it was a gesture after the hearts of his troublesome audience. He got the terms he wanted; and, thereafter, the offender, through the force of ridicule, lost much of his reputation amongst his own people and was known, from mountain top to mountain top, as "Lickspittle Khan."

With the change of Governor-General came a new appointment for John Nicholson.

In March, 1856, though only forty-four years of age, the Marquess of Dalhousie resigned office, having completed the fabric of British rule in India by filling in the wide spaces covered by Oudh, the Central Provinces, and a number of smaller native States within India, as well as annexing the great outlying territories of the Punjab on the northwestern frontier, and the richest part of Burma beyond the sea to the east.

He was succeeded by his friend Lord Canning who, at the farewell banquet tendered to him in London by the directors of John Company, spoke the prophetic words:

"I wish for a peaceful term of office. But I cannot forget that in the sky of India, serene as it is, a small cloud may arise, no larger than a man's hand, but which, growing larger and larger, may at last threaten to burst and overwhelm us with ruin."

On Canning's arrival, with Bannu now quiet, Nicholson was appointed deputy commissioner at Peshawar, but not for immediate service. With a substitute to hold the position until he was ready, he was sent to Kashmir *ad interim.*

Kashmir had grown to be the holiday resort of worn-out English officials, and, as these visitors increased in numbers, certain problems arose, and a resident officer was necessary to ease the friction between them and the Maharajah's court. To Nicholson went this first appointment. There was no strenuous work of the type he had experienced at Bannu. But here, as ever, he left a decided mark.

Free from restraint, from supervision by the carping graybeards of John Company, in a milder climate and with earnings accumulated in long terms of deadly drill routine at military posts, young officers came to Kashmir to kick up their heels. Not all the sahebs were what sahebs should be. Escapades with native ladies, cases of debt and fraud were continually giving the Kashmir people something to think—and worry— about. Nicholson took matters in hand. He maintained that not to every one was it given to accomplish deeds of derring-do for England; but that the least those lacking the chance could do, was to prove that they were gentlemen and, if they were not, to do the next best thing: to behave as if they were. He maintained, furthermore, that nobody is quite as quick at reading a white man's virtues and failings as a native peasant. He proceeded to punish sportive subalterns quite as severely as he had punished Afghan evildoers; and, inside of a few months, "cleaned up" Kashmir completely.

During this time the Persians had made one of their periodical advances on Herat, and England, recognizing that the Russian Bear was pulling the Central Asian strings, decided to help the Amir of Afghanistan, Dost Mohammed Khan. Nicholson followed events closely. He offered to go over the border in any capacity and gave sound advice to the men in charge. With memories of the last Afghan fiasco, he was all for keeping hands off unless the venture should be undertaken properly—in other words, unless such a large force was sent to the hills that the Afghans should be unable to change their minds suddenly and, as so often in the past, stab their allies in the back. John Company listened to his advice. But his actual services were not required; and, in November, 1856, he was on his way to Peshawar and his deputy commissionership.

His first appearance there must have reminded him of Punjab days. A group of *"Nikalsainis"* were on their knees to greet him and to embrace his knees. He ordered them off; cursed them roundly; and, at once, took up the details of his new work.

Soon after his arrival there was held in his district a *durbar* in honor of Dost Mohammed Khan, Amir of the Afghans. Not only John Lawrence came up from Lahore, but also a great many other bigwigs resplendent in scarlet and gold lace and decorations, and in an open camp an alliance between the English and the Afghans was arranged. Thankful for the help the British had given him in beating off the Persian attack on Herat, Dost Mohammed Khan honestly intended to throw in his lot with them. To Nicholson fell the making of final plans for this occasion. But, at the last moment, he failed to appear at the ceremonies themselves. Making an excuse with reference to some evidence he had to obtain in a murder case, he rode away from the camp not to return until the visitors were on their way home. Challenged by Lawrence to give the true reason, he replied: "I could not have trusted myself there. I would have shot one of them, perhaps the Amir himself." For the details of his captivity beyond the border and the death of his brother were still fresh in his mind.

Lawrence shrugged his shoulders. Such behavior

was typical of Nicholson's attitude to authority. Shown a bundle of official regulations he kicked them across his office, saying:

"This is the way I always treat these things."

He was recognized by his seniors as "a truly great master in the art of ruling a frontier district." Yet, like any line officer who is irked by the impracticability of a far removed and myopic General Headquarters, he continually found his hands tied by that infamous British red tape which always tries to counteract what the red line, the thin, red line, has done. Where instant decision followed by instant action was the only way of handling a sudden situation, he was expected to refer the matter to higher authority and wait weeks for an answer. Henry Lawrence had given him rope. John Lawrence was too conscientious; considered his brilliant assistant at times rather eccentric. The result was that Nicholson, although the border work was so suited to his make-up, longed to get away to another jurisdiction. In this respect he wrote to his friend Herbert Edwardes who, a rising influence with the powers-that-be, pressed the other's claims for preferment with Lord Canning, telling him: "If you should ever have anything of real difficulty to be done in India, I give you my word that John Nicholson is the man to do it." The Governor-General listened sympathetically. He had heard before this of Nicholson's achievements; remembered how, on his first tour through the Punjab, inspecting the battlefield of Gujrat where Nicholson had been merely a liaison and supply officer, an old, bearded Sikh warrior had stepped up to him at one point and, indicating a slight rise in the ground, had announced, pompously, impressively, as though it was the only thing about the battle to matter:

"*Nikalsain* stood just there!"

From other sides, too, the Governor-General heard

flattering evidences of the qualities of this peculiar, self-opinionated young man. Still, through all of this, the latter's one complaint was that, do what he might, he could not establish any personal popularity amongst his brother-officers and civil service employees. Though the people of Bannu said of him that he most closely resembled a Moslem gentleman of the old school in virtues and breeding, though his advice was constantly sought by neighboring British commissioners, he seemed unable to meet his countrymen on their own social ground—with the possible exception of the Edwardes brothers. Something in the man—something deep down in his soul—set him apart. He had many admirers and very few friends, and he felt the gray tragedy of it—considered it unfair and unmerited. Affection for another is, after all, not regulated by a logical formula; and it was least logical—or, perhaps, most logical—that the natives, the Bannuchis, whom he ruled with such a heavy hand, should have the most affection for him—deep, genuine affection—though they feared him, though once a border chief exclaimed:

"There is not one in the hills who does not shiver when he hears his name mentioned! *Nikalsain!* He is a man!"

And, soon, he was going to have a chance to prove this claim to the hilt.

For India was on the verge of the Sepoy mutiny. Edwardes, returned from a three months' trip, brought back word about soldiers in the Bengal stations having refused to obey orders and, in isolated cases, attacking their white officers—a type of intelligence that angered Nicholson who seldom had trouble with native soldiers and was all for blaming the officers, calling them incompetent jackasses, more fit to lead sheep than to

lead men. He wanted to go down to the affected area
and take a hand himself.

On May the 10th, 1857, came more serious reports.
The fat was in the fire beyond a doubt. The Sepoys
at Meerut, not far from Delhi, broke into mutiny,
forced open the jail, swept savagely through the cantonments, and cut down any European whom they
encountered. For themselves, Edwardes and Nicholson awaited results with confidence. But they were
shocked at the behavior of the British in Meerut which,
the largest military station in Northern India, had a
strong garrison of English foot, horse, and artillery,
sufficient to crush the Sepoys long before they reached
Delhi. But, as the latter acted in irresponsible panic,
so did the British behave with irresponsible lack of
decision. On the night of the outbreak they did nothing except to telegraph the news to Delhi; did not
oppose the Sepoys who rushed there, stirred up the
native garrison and the criminal population, and placed
themselves under the authority of the dethroned
Moghul emperor—while the Europeans were content
with blowing up the powder magazine.

In and about Peshawar were three British battalions.
Nicholson went there, convinced that, with Englishmen at his back, he would be able to stop any
incipient rebellion and set an example to the rest of
India. For the trouble was spreading rapidly; action
was necessary. "The matter must be brought without
further delay to the bayonet," Nicholson reported to
Lord Canning and, with Edwardes, made his own independent preparations. One native battalion at
Peshawar (the 64th) had shown occasional signs of
disaffection in the past. Nicholson marched it out of
cantonments and took it to an isolated fort on the
Afghan border. Away from news of the mutiny and
fired with the hope of a brush with invading Afghan

raiders, they were out of the political picture. He then made plans for the organization of a reliable force to be used as a movable column. With this he hoped to move about the Punjab, putting down any outbreak that might start. Each station, he was convinced, would go through a few days of crisis; was convinced, furthermore, that, handled strongly and quickly, each such crisis would peter out in turn.

Between making military preparations he made raids into the mail pouches, learning, from native correspondence, that trouble was brewing all around him. Two more Sepoy battalions were marched to the border and, quietly, the movable column was being gathered and trained.

In the middle of the night of 21st May he was aroused by news from Naushera, a station within thirty miles of Peshawar, that two native units there were in open mutiny. The situation was kept in hand by a young officer who destroyed the bridge of boats leading across the river upon which the camp was sited and kept the mutineers to themselves, unable to scatter to outlying posts and to spread the rebellion. But the report convinced Nicholson that all the native troops about Peshawar must be immediately disarmed. He summoned the colonels commanding the troops and told them his decision. These men, who had served up from the lowest officer grades in their regiments, could not believe the order and begged him to change his mind. But he refused to listen to them; commanded them back to camp to parade their battalions at six the next morning.

When they were drawn up, Nicholson and Edwardes, accompanied by two senior officers, local brigadiers, rode out to the parade ground and issued orders for the piling of arms. There was momentary hesitation on the part of the ranks. But the sight of

"Nikalsain" settled that, and soon the arms they had carried for years were being taken from them and packed onto wagons. Furious that the soldiers whom they had trained should be suspected, the English officers rode up to the carts, tore off their spurs and flung them as well as their swords on top of the pile.

"It was a painful and affecting thing," wrote John Nicholson. "It was impossible not to feel with and for them; but duty must be done, and I know we shall never regret the counsel we gave."

The effect was immediate and tremendous. For the past few days native assistants and clerks in the Commissioner's office had shown signs, unmistakable to those experienced in Indian psychology, of coming trouble. When the small party returned from parade to Peshawar, the atmosphere changed subtly. It was as though a thunder shower had cleared the air. Applications for enlistment in the movable column came in from all sides. A hill tribe was led across the Afghan border, their leader explaining that they had come to throw in their lot "with the manifest masters of Peshawar."

Nicholson was firmly in the saddle; and, had the rest of the British, chiefly the panic-stricken officers at Meerut, behaved as he and Edwardes behaved at Peshawar, the story of the Indian Mutiny need not have been written in blood.

As a staff officer attached to Nicholson at this time was a captain of twenty-four who was to ride through the mutiny, having four horses killed under him and being awarded the Victoria Cross for conspicuous gallantry before Lucknow—a young man later to become world-famous as Lord Roberts. Recording his impressions of this period, he wrote:

"John Nicholson was a name to conjure with in the Punjab. . . . He impressed me more profoundly than any man I have

ever met before or since. . . . His appearance was distinguished
and commanding, with a sense of power about him which, to
my mind, was the result of his having passed so much of his
time amongst lawless tribesmen with whom his authority was
supreme. . . . A man for whom, above all others, I had the
greatest admiration and the most profound respect. . . ."

In the meantime the Naushera mutineers, having
crossed the river, had marched off in the direction of
Mardan, another post at which a sanitarium for
Englishmen was located. Nicholson, immediately, put
two columns in motion to converge on Mardan, one
from Naushera, the other from Peshawar, he traveling with the latter. They could not cut off the
mutineers in time, arriving there after these had attached to themselves what men would join them from
the Mardan garrison and marching off for the hills.
Nicholson rode after them with his Pathans and harried them for twenty hours on end, returning to Peshawar with the regimental colors, 200 rifles, and a large
body of prisoners. As an active force the Naushera
and Mardan mutineers had ceased to exist.

Next he attended to the 64th Native Infantry, scattered in villages along the border. A letter to Edwardes he concluded with: "I have a man who taunted
my police on the line of march with siding with the
infidels in a religious war. May I hang him?" It
was typical of the man; typical of his hate of weak-
spined half-measures in time of trouble.

His reports and letters of this period were full of
praise for his friend and associate, Edwardes. That
his work was so easy—as he insisted it was—was
purely on account of what the other had accomplished,
in the preceding year, with the Afghans. Had their
attitude been hostile, the border posts would have been
swept away in a week. Their refusing to take sides
was worth five divisions of faithful troops to Peshawar.

By now John Lawrence had decided that, with Delhi occupied by the mutineers and promising to be a tough nut to crack, it would be best to fall back from the frontier and to leave Peshawar and the surrounding district to be defended by the Amir of Afghanistan. Immediately Edwardes and Nicholson—who was firmly convinced of the old border proverb: "Trust a Balochi before a snake, and a snake before an Afghan!"—made the air yet more sultry with their protests. Cotton, the military commander of the district and a member of that famous Anglo-Indian family which still thrives from Calcutta to the Moffusil, concurred with their views; and the three wrote to General Headquarters: "We earnestly hope that you will decide that we stand or fall at Peshawar. It must be done somewhere. Let us do it at the front, giving up nothing." Lawrence maintained his position; but, finally, in face of reiterated protests, referred the matter to Lord Canning who agreed with the trio of aggressive juniors by replying: "Hold on to Peshawar to the last. Give up nothing."

Doubtless John Lawrence's attitude increased Nicholson's feeling toward him—a feeling based largely on thin-skinned sensitiveness—and so, when on the 14th June, orders reached him to take command in the field, the manner in which he accepted this position he so longed for was truly Nicholsonian. Leaving Peshawar immediately on receiving his marching orders, he wrote to Sir John Lawrence:

"I thank you for my appointment. I know you recommended it on *public* grounds, but do not feel the least obliged to you."

Succeeding Neville Chamberlain, sent to fill the vacancy caused by the death of the adjutant-general of the small force besieging Delhi, he took charge at Jalandhar on the 22nd June. Neither the mobile

column nor the troops stationed in the vicinity were in
an exactly sweet mood, and Nicholson knew that he
would have a ticklish job handling them. The Rajah
of Kapurthala, who had come out for the English, had
lent some of his personal troops to take over duties
abandoned by some recent mutineers. Major Edward
Lake, Commissioner of the Province and a relative of
the great Lord Lake, conqueror of the Marathas, arranged for a reception at his house when Nicholson
was to meet the officers of his native contingent. Their
senior was Mehtab Singh, a close relation of Kapurthala himself. He arrived at the reception and approached Nicholson with his boots on, a gross insult
according to the local code and comparable to a European keeping on his hat. Nicholson paid no attention until the party broke up. Then, when Mehtab
Singh made for the door ahead of his officers, Nicholson rose and barred the exit. Speaking loudly in
Hindustani, so that all the guests might understand,
he discussed the question with Lake over the native
general's head. It was gross impertinence. Would
Mehtab Singh dare enter the room of the Rajah, his
relative, with his boots on? Was he, Nicholson saheb,
not here in place of the Rajah? A gross impertinence!
he repeated; and, turning direct to Mehtab Singh, he
ordered him to take off his boots, at once, and the other
salaamed and obeyed . . . the story going the gossip
route overnight and echoing to the credit of Nicholson
and his countrymen.

In the meantime the trouble threatening the movable
column was rapidly coming to a point. Chamberlain
had had some men blown from the guns. But it did
not help. It was obvious to Nicholson that two native
regiments, the 33d and 35th, were going to mutiny
at the first convenient moment.

He was no Fabius Cunctator. He jumped first. His disarming of these men, 1,500 Sepoys ready for murder, was a masterpiece of strategy.

Taking a staff officer and the commander of the one white battalion in the column into his confidence, he arranged for a certain bridge to be pulled down. Then he issued orders for the column to proceed toward Delhi. As Delhi was the place where they were expecting to go after their outbreak, the native soldiers fell in and followed the white battalion at the head of the march. Reaching the point where the bridge had been cut the English soldiers, who had marched faster, suddenly left the road and were drawn up with all available guns on the flanks by the time the discontented Sepoys came up. They heard Nicholson's sharp command to pile arms. They obeyed. There was nothing else to do.

So the column—"with the fangs taken out of fifteen hundred cobras," as an old Sikh informed Nicholson —was properly cleaned up and taken to Amritsar the following week.

Straight along John Nicholson was busy making plans for emergencies, listening to and summing up the feeling in his new native levies. On the one hand he needed a force strong enough to put down any local outbreak. On the other hand every armed native was an additional danger to the Raj. Either way the situation was ugly. The more soldiers he had, the graver became the risk. So he had to walk a precarious tightrope, keeping his balance by instinct . . . as he did when, on the 9th July, in spite of their loud protests that they were absolutely loyal, he paraded the 59th Sepoys and ordered them to pile arms.

Within twenty-four hours he was glad of what he had done. For two fugitives rode into camp from Sialkot. There the garrison had mutinied. The com-

manding general had been wounded; the houses had
been looted; English men, women and children had
been murdered right and left; and the mutineers,
their regimental transport heavily laden with plunder,
were marching out of town, in the direction of Gurdaspur, doubtless to murder and loot there and then to
continue through the various intervening stations to
Delhi.

These mutineers were one-half of the 9th (Native)
Cavalry, the other half being under Nicholson. He
was sure his unit would strike the moment the news
arrived in camp. So, at once, he rode over to their
lines and, under the threat of British guns, had them
disarmed. His next move was to deal with the Sialkot
mutineers—to deal with them quickly, before they
reached Gurdaspur. It was July, as hot a month as
red-hot India could show, with the thermometer
above 120 in the shade—and no shade anywhere. But,
commandeering every available vehicle from *gharry*
to bullock-cart, every available beast from pony
to elephant, he announced that the forty-eight
miles to Gurdaspur would be made in a single forced
march.

That night the column started—footing it—slogging
it—carrying on. By daybreak it had covered thirty
miles. Every indication pointed to a roasting day; the
remaining eighteen miles would be more than double
the strain of the distance already covered; and so
Nicholson halted and fed his men, moving forward
about ten in the morning into the torments of a summer sun that was naked, arrogant, enormous—into the
thick, choking, dun walls of Indian dust swirled up by
heavy army boots—footing it—slogging it—carrying
on.

At three in the afternoon Nicholson reached his
objective; placed his artillery; and marched the infan-

try into position. The main body of the enemy was still fifteen miles to the north, plodding forward, toward the guarded city of Gurdaspur in hopes of more loot, more blood. But a good many of the mutineers had scattered; and, with his amazing knowledge of the Indian army, Nicholson, still in the saddle, indefatigable, rode about the campfires, keeping a keen eye open for unattached, suspicious, native hangers-on, surprising every one by the accurate manner in which he identified individuals.

Without a moment's hesitation, having approached a group, he would summon a non-commissioned officer and order:

"Arrest that man. He was of the 46th."

Morning brought news that the rebels had crossed the Ravi river to the north. Immediately, being in back of the Sepoys, he put his force in motion to meet them. The subsequent action, against great odds, lasted about half an hour. Commencing with a rebel advantage, it gradually evolved into a triumph for the loyal troops who, led by Nicholson in person, soon had the enemy running toward the river where there was no bridge. A good many of them fell under musketry fire, while others swam to an island in mid-stream on which they erected defenses.

With his enemy securely bottled up, Nicholson could afford to rest his column for a day. But, toward evening, he completed the task of finishing the Sialkot affair. Sending a small party in boats to the south end of the island, he led the bulk of his forces to the north. When the feint from the south commenced, he disembarked his main body. Resistance was stiff. But the British won. With his sword John Nicholson accounted for the first two of the enemy encountered; then swung his extended line around, sweeping the rebels to the top point of their refuge. Some of them

threw themselves into the torrent. As to the rest . . .
"no quarter!" was Nicholson's order to his soldiers.

By the 22nd July, marching by easy stages, Nicholson had his column back at Amritsar, while he went to
Lahore to confer with Sir John Lawrence who was
generous with him, was glad to forget all the friction
of the past, and freely admitted that events had fully
justified all his subordinate's seeming—more than
seeming—insubordination.

The battle on the banks of the Ravi had kept between three and four thousand mutineers from Delhi.
The next orders the column received was to march,
on the evening of its arrival at Amritsar, to Bias, about
twenty-five miles to the southeast. The meaning of
this was obvious: Delhi was the objective. For
Nicholson, reaching Bias two days later, had convinced
Sir John Lawrence that this was the best plan; that it
was better to weaken the Punjab for a short time and
capture the mutineer stronghold than split the strength
of the British and probably achieve nothing. On the
fall of Delhi he would march his column back and again
patrol the Punjab.

Lawrence, while admitting that Nicholson's activities
to date had been extraordinary, was loath to concede
that this enterprise would be successful and had given
his permission with considerable reluctance. Hearing
that the other during his advance south was attaching
to his column whatever units he encountered, practically denuding the countryside of troops, and making
himself the Commander-in-Chief in all but name, he
grew angry, his final note of protest meeting Nicholson
on his arrival before Delhi and saying:

"You are incorrigible. I must leave you to your fate. Depend upon it, you would get on equally well, and much more
smoothly, if you worked with men rather than against them."

John Lawrence, later on Viceroy of India and raised
to the Peerage as Baron Lawrence of the Punjab and
of Grately, Hants., was destined to become one of
Britain's great proconsuls in the East—the greatest,
with the possible exception of Lord Curzon. Yet he
was wrong, at the time, in his judgment of Nicholson;
admitted that he was wrong, after the latter's death,
when he wrote:

"John Nicholson is now beyond human praise and human
reward. But so long as British rule shall endure in India, his
fame can never perish. Without him Dehli could not have
fallen. . . ."

And, suppose Delhi had not fallen, suppose the dethroned, again enthroned, Moghul emperor had gathered adherents, suppose the rebellion had spread . . .
what then of Britain's fate? Britain—without India
—without its Asiatic dominion! Britain—again a
small, tight, negligible island kingdom, satisfied with
the boiled mutton and thin beer of parochial politics!
Britain—to go the pathetic way of Spain—of Portugal
—of the Netherlands . . . and John Nicholson, that
erratic Irish dreamer, understood . . . he replied to
Lawrence:

"I do not wish to ignore a superior. I dislike offending
any one and, except on principle, would never have a disagreement. You write as if I were in the habit of giving offense.
. . . I can only say that I opposed my opinion to yours with
great reluctance, and had the matter been one of less importance, I might have preserved silence. When in a great
crisis an officer holds a strong opinion in any matter of consequence, I think he fails in his duty if he does not speak it out,
at whatever risk of giving offense. . . ."

Having penned this typically Keltic answer, he
settled down to the business of reconnoitering the

situation before the besieging army which was commanded by General Wilson. He visited every post
and, at first, did not create a favorable impression. A
sapper major whose work had contributed greatly to
the advance of the lines took an instant aversion to
him.

He wrote:

"I told Baird Smith that I could not long stand the man's
haughty demeanor and overbearing style of address. 'That
wears off,' I was told. 'You'll like him better when you see
more of him.' Baird Smith was right. Before many days had
elapsed we became excellent friends."

An infantry captain, likewise, gave his initial impressions of this peculiar captain (acting brigadier-
general) from the Punjab, when he reported:

"A stranger of very striking appearance visited all our
pickets, making most searching inquiries about their strength
and history. His attire gave no clew to his rank; which evidently never cost the owner a thought. This was General
Nicholson. He was a man cast in a giant mold, with massive
chest and powerful limbs, and an expression ardent and commanding, with a touch of roughness; features of stern beauty,
a long black beard, and a deep sonorous voice. There was
something of immense strength, talent and resolution in his
whole frame and manner, and a power of ruling men on high
occasions which no one could escape noticing. His imperial
air never left him, and which would have been thought
arrogance in one of less imposing mien, sometimes gave offense
to the more unbending of his countrymen, but made him worshiped by the pliant Asiatics."

Worshiped, too, by such Britons as youthful
Roberts, later on Lord Roberts of Kandahar, and to
Hodson—famous Captain Hodson of Hodson's Horse
who with his own hands, killed the last of the Moghul

princes and brought to an end the dynasty founded by
Tamerlane and Gengiz Khan.

On his rounds during the morning of the 8th August,
1857, John Nicholson discovered that the Delhi garrison had erected a new battery which raked the besiegers. Returning to Wilson's headquarters, he
asked that the task of reducing Ludlow Castle, the
battery site in question, be entrusted to his column as
soon as it arrived. Permission was granted. But,
when the column marched in, it was met by news that,
in the interval, the Ludlow battery had been stormed
and captured at heavy loss.

Nicholson's officers were furious. They demanded
that they be allotted the next decent bit of work to be
done. But there was nothing immediately on hand,
and it was two weeks before they had a chance to prove
their mettle.

For spies brought word that a body of mutineers
had slipped out of Delhi and had digged in at Najafgarh, to waylay a weakly escorted siege train that was
moving up from Firozpur. This siege machinery was
of the utmost importance to Wilson; and so, within
twelve hours, Nicholson led his men out through a
tropical rainstorm. It was a most difficult march
through successive swamps where men sunk to their
knees, guns to their axles, and horses became completely bogged. Nicholson, as always, rode ahead and
made a rapid, personal reconnaissance. The mutineers
were strongly fortified, facing the Grank Trunk Road
from the north. Their position was particularly
strong in the center. This point he chose for the attack, again himself in the lead.

The charge was savage, heroic—and successful.
With a loss to the British of 2 officers and 23 men

the rout of 6,000 well drilled and well armed Sepoys
had been accomplished.

Nicholson had been given five days to complete his
task and return to the Delhi lines. On the evening of
the third day his force was back under canvas and the
road open for the siege train. It was the most decisive
blow yet struck in the Delhi area. The mutineers were
depressed; General Wilson highly elated, expressing in
his official report his amazement that the leader of this
affair was actually only a captain of thirty-five years.

The immediate result of the Najafgarh action was
that the siege lines were made safe from attack in the
rear and that the entire attention of the British could
be brought on the reduction of the garrison. It convinced the native chiefs that the jig was up, and they
sent an emissary to the British camp to ask for terms.

The emissary was told that there were no such
things as terms. All those who had eaten John Company's salt were required to surrender unconditionally.

The emissary returned with the message. It raised
the Sepoys' resistance to the point of desperation.
But the final outcome was near—and Nicholson, in
many pages of advice to John Lawrence, considered it
detail by detail. Regiments which had actually murdered their officers should be treated without the
slightest consideration. The status and guilt of every
battalion must be thoroughly established. Where men
had held out against the poison for some time, remaining loyal until overwhelmed by the faithless and forced
to throw in their lot with them, it would be best to
show leniency. Here, in these pages, was the deputy
commissioner emerging from the soldier. So protean
was the man's mind that he could think and act as the
swift-striking warrior, and could immediately turn
round and take the long-time view of the civil administrator.

In the meantime Wilson was waiting the arrival of the second siege train from the north. With this the main gate of Delhi could be penetrated. The end was in sight if energy was brought to bear—and John Lawrence found himself in a strange predicament. Nicholson, after all, had been right. The Najafgarh affair had proved it; and Lawrence owned up, writing a short note to the other, congratulating him, and adding: "I wish I had the power to knight you on the spot," and telling the Company chairman in his dispatches that on Nicholson rested the main hope for the taking of Delhi. Naturally the powers realized that Wilson was not equal to the crisis. The latter was beginning to feel this himself; was beginning, furthermore, to be jealous of the junior who had so simplified his task for him.

On the 4th September the second siege train arrived. The sapper officers urged that Nicholson's opinion about the forthcoming operation be consulted. Wilson maintained a chilling silence. He had the siege guns installed—and did nothing else.

Nicholson was furious. For a day or two he actually considered rank insubordination: setting the senior officer aside and taking command of the assault himself. The time was ripe for it. There was no need of further dallying. But Wilson insisted on more artillery work; was eager to put off the moment of battle. Finally, on the 12th September, Nicholson invaded the general's tent. Before going there he had told Roberts he would insist on the attack taking place at once. If Wilson refused, he proposed to call a conference and have Wilson superseded by Colonel Campbell of the 52nd Regiment.

Roberts followed Nicholson. He took up a position near the headquarters' tent. He waited. Suddenly Nicholson emerged and walked toward his own lines with a light step. Wilson had given in. The assault was to take place on the 14th.

The next thirty-six hours were full of activity. Nicholson was here and there and everywhere, supervising the work of the gunners and sappers, planning in detail the lines of the infantry attack, and, at odd intervals, riding across to headquarters to make sure that Wilson had not changed his mind.

On the 13th came the news that he had been appointed Commissioner of Leia by Sir John Lawrence. Nicholson was astonished. Granted that it meant promotion, it seemed peculiar that Canning and Lawrence should deliberately remove their most successful soldier from the field to place him in administrative work. The only possible reason seemed that Wilson, more and more jealous of his junior, had recommended his removal. Too, it was possible that some of the officers of the regular British army looked askance at a captain of John Company's army with the temporary rank of brigadier. Whatever the intrigues in back of it, John Nicholson decided to accept the appointment; and, told by friends that, through staying in the army, he would rise to be a regular general, he pointed toward Wilson's tent and replied:

"Would I be a general? Look at them! Would I be one of those?"

Yes—he would accept the appointment—*after* the attack on Delhi.

Before daylight on the 14th Nicholson had his support troops working into position. He himself would lead the initial attack of the most important column, take general charge after the fury of the first assault had subsided, and finally organize and lead the force to be used in pursuit. It was a complicated command —and, by the same token, the very sort he could handle.

The troops had been divided into four columns. On the right Major Reid with 860 men was to force his way through a suburb of Delhi to the Lahore Gate which he was to penetrate and then to occupy the ramparts above it. Next, on the other side of the famous ridge, Colonel Campbell's 950 men were to enter the Kashmir Gate and push as far as possible into the heart of the city. To the left again, under Nicholson's personal supervision, 1,000 men were given the difficult task of storming the Kashmir bastion and from its height to support the other attacks, while, on the extreme left, with its flank on the river, Brigadier-General Jones' 850 men were directed toward the Water Gate. The whole operation was preceded by artillery fire that continued on the well defended spots, until after sunrise when, at a signal from Nicholson, the guns ceased and the infantry charged. His column was momentarily held up by heavy musketry. So he marched forward alone, sword in hand—a sight that brought the line to its feet again and on toward the breaches.

On the left, Campbell's men soon got through the Kashmir Gate; pushed on; had to be held in check to wait for the other columns. Nicholson's men, too, took their objective, their leader turning to see what had happened to Reid's soldiers at Lahore Gate. He found a lane thick with dead fusileers; found the assault halted in its tracks.

At once, waving his sword, he took the lead. Turning to give instructions, he noticed that no one was following. He called, beckoned, cursed—and was hit in the back by a bullet from the walls. He fell, inclining toward the wall itself, lying half within the protection of a niche. A sergeant ran up; pulled him fully under cover . . . too late . . . it was obvious that the wound was fatal.

Then Colonel Graydon of the assaulting battalion came up. He wanted to remove Nicholson to a place of safety. But the other would have none of it. He wanted to die quietly where he was. His only complaint was that his view of the operations was so poor. Others came. They implored him that he still had a chance . . . they would move him . . . but he refused again and again. He would not allow any one to touch him, much less would he retire from the line.

Finally a Captain Hay with whom he was on notoriously bad terms arrived; and, with characteristic Keltic perversity, Nicholson turned to him and said:

"I will make up my difference with you, Hay. I will let you take me back."

They took him to a field hospital where, by a curious coincidence, he was put on a cot next to his brother Charles. Medical opinion was that neither of them could live through the night. But Charles survived. John did not. But, until the moment of his death, nine days later, days of terrible, agonizing pain, his mind remained as keen as a well-tempered blade. When, on the evening of the 15th, he was told that the infantry line was held up, that the sappers were working under the houses, but that there was a rumor of Wilson's intending to order a retreat, he exclaimed:

"Thank God I still have strength to shoot him, if necessary!"

At last, almost simultaneously with the end, the fall, of Delhi, came John Nicholson's end. He was buried, as he had hoped, opposite the Kashmir Gate—the scene of his share in an attack which, but for him, must have failed.

"*Nikalsain is dead!*"—the news spread from end to end of India.

It reached Peshawar.

There the leader of the *"Nikalsaini"* cult of Sikhs announced that life, after his idol's death, was meaningless and straightway cut his throat.

"Nikalsain is dead!"—you can hear the dirge to this day in the Punjab, from Lahore to Multan and from the Jhelum to the Sutlej. . . .

HENRY MONTGOMERY LAWRENCE

[1806–1857]

who dreamed of justice

HENRY LAWRENCE

HENRY MONTGOMERY LAWRENCE

THERE is the Lahore of high romance which Milton coupled with Asia's fairest towns in his lines:

> *"Samarckand by Oxus, Timur's throne,*
> *To Pekin, of Simoean kings, and then*
> *To Agra and Lahor of Great Mogul*
> *Down to the golden Chersonese."*

There is the Lahore of Anglo-India's modern, social days where Christmas week is to the Punjab's junior civil servants and junior subalterns what the Calcutta race week is to Bengal; where, within a few hours of the city, pig-sticking is at the best and goriest, antelope and deer plentiful, and peafowl and wildfowl shooting along the Sutlej and Ravi rivers the finest "poor man's sport" in the world; where rum-shrubs of almost West African potency are served by dignified, red-turbaned giants at the bars of the Charing Cross Hotel and Nadou's Hotel; where excellent bridge partners can be met any evening at the Punjab Club; and where, according to that nearly forgotten genius by the name of Dhirandra Nat, Babu, in a guidebook printed by Datta Bose of No. 29 Durga Charan Mitter Street, Calcutta:

> " . . . *can be found most elegant and refined entertainment for the visitations paid by the sahebs and the mem-sahebs, though —alack!—there are also temptation here of most proper exterior, yet—alack, alack!—dangerous and leprous at the heart. The women here indeed speak much of love and—alack!—get it. For can anybody help loving the women of Lahore? No! answer I. For—alack, alack!—I have met in Lahore women whose soft lips were thick with paint as well as with ruse. . . ."*

181

There is yet a third Lahore. A Lahore most important to whoever is master of India.

For Lahore squats across the sluice-gates through which, from time immemorial, Hindustan's conquerors have swept, burning, looting, killing. Through Lahore rushed the maelstrom of the first Moslem invaders who, late in the seventh century, almost razed the great Brahminical city to the ground. Three hundred years later, Lahore was plundered by Sultan Mahmoud of Ghazni and his ten thousand ruffianly, hawkish Central Asian horsemen, carrying off hundreds of camel loads of rich spoils and hundreds of women . . . a disgrace which caused Jai Pal, the vanquished Rajput king, to mount the funeral pyre, apply the torch with his own hands, and perish in the flames. Again, in the fourteenth century, it became a prey to the northern Moslems from beyond the Himalayas when Tamerlane—or, as he called himself with theatrical bombast, yet with justification: "I, the Khan Timur Ali Khan of Pure Progeny, the Lion of Allah, the Shadow of Allah upon Earth, the Decreer of Decrees, the Lord of the Fortunate Conjunction, the Master of the Seven Hills and the Seven Steppes—" rode into the Punjab with steel and torch; while, one hundred and forty years later, his descendant, Babar, conquered and sacked the town and, after the victory at Panipat, became the first Moghul Emperor of Hindustan. Here, though Delhi was the capital, the Moghuls held glittering court at intervals for many a century. Here they erected their great palaces and mosques and monuments and pleasure gardens: the Pearl Mosque, the Golden Mosque, the Shish Mahal, the Diwan-i-Khas, the Diwan-i-Am, the Shalimar Gardens, and the Gulabi Gardens. Here, softened by Hindu influence, they built that grand, glittering, ornate city of which we read in "Lalla Rookh." Here, at the disintegration of the Moghul

Empire, the Sikhs—a theistic sect become a warrior race by reason of their faith—centered and consolidated their military confederacy under Ranjit Singh who welded his followers into the strongest native power in India.

It was this third Lahore, the political Lahore, the gate into the north which—after Ranjit Singh had been succeeded by rulers unable to wield the scepter —was incorporated into the British dominions in 1849 and made an integral part of the Empire . . . thanks to John Nicholson; thanks, furthermore, to John Lawrence, afterwards 1st Baron Lawrence of the Punjab, and of Grately, Hants., and Viceroy and Governor-General; but thanks chiefly to his older and less well-known brother, Henry Montgomery Lawrence, the Pacificator—declared, by English as well as by Hindus, to be the noblest, most selfless man that lived and died for the good of India.

Of Keltic stock, like John Nicholson, like Sir Richard Burton, like "Chinese" Gordon, like Sir Henry Havelock, Sir Hector Munro, Sir John Malcolm, Lord Minto, Lord Roberts and so many others of Britain's Dreamers of Empire, he was born in Ceylon on the 28th June, 1806. He was the third of six surviving sons, to say nothing of a bevy of daughters, of Colonel Alexander Lawrence, a veteran of several Indian campaigns, leader of the forlorn hope at the siege of Seringapatam during the Third Mysore War in 1799, and a personal friend of the Duke of Wellington.

Little is known of Henry Lawrence's childhood in Ceylon. It is to be assumed that he made the average boyish nuisance of himself in the dun shadows of Adam's Peak, in the groves of sacred Bo trees, and on the sticky roads of Trinkomalee. He was, however, early slated to follow in his father's martial footsteps,

and, having been appointed to a cadetship at Addiscombe, the Honorable East India Company's military
college, was sent to England where he went through
the proper training of a John Company *protégé*.

Again the passing years have obscured what happened at Addiscombe. Nobody played the Boswell to
Henry Lawrence, since the latter was, after all, only
a cadet amongst dozens of that ilk—due, doubtless, to
die either of fever in the miasmic Sunderbund swamps,
or of a knife thrust in the vicinity of the Khyber Pass,
or of too much curry and brandy within convenient
nearness to Calcutta's cemetery. It is to be supposed
that nothing exceptional happened at Addiscombe.
Just the routine things: squad drill and rifle and bayonet practice, discipline and breaches of discipline,
good marks and bad marks, occasionally a stomach-
ache thanks to too many prawns and too much straw-
berry mess at the local tuck-shop. At all events, he
was gazetted with a fair-to-middling record, was assigned to the Bengal artillery, returned to the East,
and in 1823, seventeen years of age, reported for duty
at Dum Dum.

Hardly an attractive place, Dum Dum. About as
attractive as the soft-nose bullets which bear its name.
Hot, dusty, yellow, and forty-seven different bad smells
striving for mastery. Nor were the natives well-
favored: the women uncomely and slouching with their
dirty cotton *chuddahs,* the men decidedly repulsive with
their flapping draperies of dingy, white muslin looped
into loose drawers, their spindly, brown shanks, and
never a bright-colored turban to relieve the monotony.
Nor were there here the motley flowers of Henry
Lawrence's Ceylon childhood: the gardenias growing
like weeds, the lily-shaped, lily-sweet blossoms of the
tallow-candle tree, the glories of mangosteen and
champac and scarlet hibiscus. Nothing here but tares

—and dust—and heat—and barracks . . . and the whole not a bit like what Macaulay, who must have been drunk when he used such poetic latitude, described as India's "rosy lanes."

His first months in his chosen profession of arms were uneventful. But they were useful, since he applied himself assiduously to two lines of study: his profession itself and the psychology, languages, prejudices, and moods of the natives among whom his lot was cast. A little over a year later, he received recognition by being sent to the front, east, to Burma, the Earl of Amherst, John Company's Governor-General, having declared war on that country.

Burma, whose inhabitants are of mixed Indo-Tibeto-Chinese descent, had for many years been torn by civil strife. Then, late in the eighteenth century, it had been consolidated, with the help of French adventurers, by King Alaungpaya.

His successors were warlike, fearless, hot-blooded, and with a good conceit of themselves. They harried their neighbors right and left. They over-ran Siam, pushed into Assam and Manipur, raided the lands of the chiefs of Cachar, under British protection, finally ventured on an open violation of British territory. Having vanquished all comers, they imagined that the English were their meat. They massed troops; spoke largely about conquering and sacking Calcutta; attacked Sepoys; carried off British subjects; until at last, when to repeated demands for redress no answer had been vouchsafed, John Company commenced preparations for the dispatch of an expeditionary force.

Amongst these preparations orders were sent to young Henry Lawrence to assume command of a six-gun battery—not bad for a boy of eighteen to have an appointment which, nominally, should have gone to a full-fledged major—and to proceed to Chittagong, on the Burmese frontier, where he was to report to General Morrison who headed a division in Sir Archibald Campbell's army.

At once Lawrence found himself confronted with an hundred and one problems of administration. He organized his battery down to the last screw and reported ready to move. But, in the meantime, an event occurred which set him to thinking furiously and which, in later years, at the time of the Indian Mutiny, influenced him tremendously.

Also under orders for Burma, three Sepoy battalions in cantonments at Barrackpore refused service. Informed that they were to make a sea voyage, the soldiers, mostly Brahmins, protested that such a thing would be prejudicial to their caste. Stubbornly—bravely, if you prefer—they would listen to neither threats nor cajoleries. They were then led out on parade, facing a body of English troops, and commanded to pile arms. They did not obey. The situation looked dangerous; and, panic-stricken, the commander of the white soldiers opposite gave orders for a volley. Many of the Sepoys were killed or wounded. The others dropped their weapons and fled.

Henry Lawrence never forgot this affair. For years he brooded over it; maintaining that the slaughter had been brutal as well as avoidable; thinking, in his fine, idealistic young mind, that Empire is not altogether born of Babylonian strength and Egyptian pride, but also of the justice which was Rome.

The authorities, on the other hand, said in the official account that the "matter had been satisfactorily settled" and proceeded with the Burmese campaign. One expedition with gunboats sailed up the Brahmaputra to Assam; another marched overland through

Chittagong into Arakan, so as to avoid further un-
pleasantness with Brahmin Sepoys who thought that a
sea journey sullied their caste; while the third, and
strongest, took ship from Madras to the mouth of the
Irawadi.

The show was on in earnest, Lawrence being attached to the second column, though his particular unit
was to go by water, from Fort William.

At the landing stage he was confronted by trouble.
The pay for his men had not arrived; some of his
teams were commandeered by another battery under
orders from headquarters; and, worse still, the captain
of the transport, for some vague, nautical reasons, refused to take the guns and limbers aboard. It was up
to Lawrence to look after himself and his men. He
did it. Hurrying to Calcutta, he pursued a slippery
Babu paymaster to Dum Dum and all the way back;
buttonholed large, pompous, red-faced *sahebs* of the
civil service who did not wish to be bothered by any
uniformed young jackanapes; made himself a sore trial
and tribulation to every brass-hat staff officer whom he
could reach or waylay; finally, by dint of perseverance
and nagging, winning all along the line—and gaining
the conviction that the entire Indian army needed a
thorough overhauling.

Nor did his troubles stop there.

Before taking his battery into action for the first
time, he had acquired food for additional thought.
The Indian army was as amazingly unready in 1824
as the British home army was in 1914—and will be,
without a doubt, in 1934 or 1944 or whenever the next
war booms along. It took six months to put ten
thousand men in the field; and, once there, the official
remounts camp, from which replacements of all beasts
of burden had to be drawn, was still back in India, one
thousand miles away.

In fact, Anglo-Saxondom was having its typical orgy of sloppy inefficiency.

During the actual campaign, which lasted two years, Lawrence gained a great deal of valuable experience. Moving a battery through unknown and difficult country was generous practice in the leading of men and the handling of odd problems in engineering, while, before the war was over, he had ably participated in fighting. On the march the column was constantly harassed by small bodies of enemy guerillas, and in the final operation there were some pitched battles.

The objective of the expedition was the stronghold of Arakan, perfectly situated for defense. The closer the troops got to the fort, the more stubborn became the resistance of the Burmese and the more difficult the lie of the land. Six successive hill crests required assaulting, and in these engagements Lawrence's battery played a conspicuous part. The final attack was over the summit of the last and steepest hill and through a heavy enfilade fire. Work too hard for beasts—but not too hard for men; and so the artillerymen manhandled the six guns, pushing them up the slopes, rolling them down the slopes, Henry Lawrence in command, encouraging, helping, directing, at last placing the battery where it could cover the storming of the last stockade . . . a triumph for this youngest gunnery officer with John Company's army.

But the campaign and its sequel were almost too much for the rather frail young subaltern acting as major in charge of battery. The war had cost the British over twenty thousand lives, chiefly from the pestilential climate, and an expenditure of £14,000,-000; and the Burmese proved to be as good at bargaining as they had been at fighting. There were innumerable delays in the peace settlement, and it was

not until February of 1826 that terms were finally
signed at Yandabu, ceding to the British Arakan and
Tenasserim and abandoning all claims to Assam, while
the King of Burma retained the whole valley of the
Irawadi, down to the sea at Rangoon.   But in the
meantime fever had attacked the army of occupation,
and Lawrence was amongst those most hardly hit.
He was earmarked for return to England, and against
his name, in John Company's confidential reports, was
tacked the opinion that never again would he be fit
for Eastern service, that the twenty-year-old youth's
career was finished almost before it had begun.

In August he embarked on a sailing ship, armed
with a generous library of whatever contemporary,
professional books he had been able to pick up in Calcutta.   We can make a guess at the titles: *Selections
from the Despatches of the Duke of Wellington,* Walter Hamilton's *East-India Gazetteer,* James Tod's
Rajasthan, Major Hough's *Chronological Exposition
of Military Law,* Henry Prinsep's *History of the Political and Military Transactions in India,* and other
martial textbooks . . . plenty reading matter for the
long, slow trip home which was then regarded as the
greatest rest cure.   Traveling by way of the China
Seas and Cape Horn, it was nine months before he
landed in England; but even in that time he had failed
to regain his health, and there followed another twelve
months of convalescence in the bosom of his family
until, with the aid of walking tours on which he
sketched and studied topography, he felt himself able
to undertake more earnest work.   Never for a moment
had he taken the sentence of the army medical board
seriously.   There was a great deal to be done in India;
he wanted to do his share; if he could not serve again
with John Company's troops, he was at least equal to

attend to other necessary tasks: the interpretation of the native mind to the British and vice versa, and the alleviation of the sufferings of the poor and ignorant.

With these objects in view, he applied for employment in the Irish Ordnance Survey where, for a little over a year, he experimented in the difficult business of analyzing the mentality of a folk with tragic grievances, mixing where he could with the people around their own hearths, probing standards of living and effect of taxation, and, like "Chinese" Gordon years later, formulating a suggestive program for the improvement of conditions. It was considered quite proper and logical that a John Company man should do work in Ireland. For, in those days, the Irish were considered an inferior race—and treated as such—precisely as the Indians in this present year; and, incidentally, there were, in those days, contemporary and quite forgotten Katharine Mayos who wrote about Erin precisely what our up-to-date Katharine Mayos are writing about Hindustan. For it seems to be the duty of the "superior race" to prove its superiority by blackguarding, or paying and causing to be blackguarded, the mentality, worth, and virtues of the "inferior race" which it rules.

It was a happy moment for Henry Lawrence when a London doctor declared him fit once more for service in India. Armed with his recommendation, he interviewed the John Company directors, to be told that he would be posted to a battery on arrival in Calcutta. Early in September, 1829, he embarked for the east, taking with him a sister and a new and valuable recruit for the service in the person of his younger brother, John, just out of Hailebury. This raised the generation of Lawrence in the Company to three, as George was already in the artillery at Karnal.

There, too, went Henry and John; and it was not long before the views of these two, formed by observations on the same ground, began to be expressed in almost daily arguments which foreshadowed more important disagreements between them later. Part of the trouble was that, while Henry had had to be contented with an Addiscombe education, John had passed through an English public school under conservative and insular influences containing none of the traditions of the East India Company.

A comparatively quiet three years followed. Quiet, though far from empty.

For the ideal Company servant of that day was a protean creature equally capable of handling regiments of English or native troops, conducting a survey, supervising an engineering project, occupying a judge's throne or a collectorship. Specialization had not yet been invented and canonized; Admirable Crichtons were in demand; and military lore, political economy, civil law and mathematics were all expected of a John Company man in addition to the tireless study of languages.

During his respite in England, Henry Lawrence had formed very definite views as to the fair and correct method of handling the Indian natives and as to his own future. Like "Chinese" Gordon, like John Nicholson, he believed primarily in justice. Justice was his panacea for all political ills. If justice occasionally had to be dragged up the Via Dolorosa and nailed to the Cross, as during the Indian Mutiny, then it would ultimately rise again.

He devoted his time in Karnal to preparation, supervising his battery, studying his men and guns, laboring over languages and figures, learning to deal directly with the natives, solving problems in minor finance. His one recreation was chess. The few short furloughs that came his way he spent in minor explorations and inspections. One of these took him to the Northwest Frontiers where, attaching himself to a company of sappers, he made a careful study of canal and road building. Early in his service he had come to the conclusion that half the Company problems would be solved with the establishment of good communications. The direction of this work he hoped some day to have in his own hands, and he never lost an opportunity to acquaint himself with the difficulties of his future plans.

The results of his arduous endeavors were highly satisfactory. In September, 1831, he qualified simultaneously for two promotions. In the artillery he earned his jacket, going from the field to the horse guns, and at the same time was placed on the staff as quartermaster of artillery with the additional qualification of interpreter. Since the work was neither onerous nor required a shift of locale, he was able to aim at the next open appointment to which he was gazetted in 1833—an officer in the Revenue Survey.

No post could have been more to his liking. The Revenue Survey was a novelty in India when he joined it; and, like all conceptions of a gifted administrator handled by the ordinary, not at all gifted run of civil servants, it was in a poor state. The idea of the survey was to put the revenue system on a satisfactory basis. Taxes were badly and unevenly divided. Gross injustice was rampant. To correct this, Lawrence decided that, for a time, he must cut himself adrift from all contact with his countrymen, leave camp and cantonment behind him, and mingle with the natives. Hearsay was useless. He must study at first hand before reaching conclusions.

So, for five years, he pitched his tents away from the British and lived among the Indians. He discovered a brand-new theory in Indian administration: that the duties of the dominant race included the protection of the natives, assistance in the development of their agricultural holdings, coöperation to widen their interests; that, furthermore, it was better to under-assess than to exaggerate the wealth of a village; that inquiries carried out on the spot were more useful and met a more welcome reception from the villagers than endless dabbling in duly red-taped documents; and that a network of roads was necessary.

"Push on your roads!" became a tag attached to the end of all his official reports. Unified government was impossible without easy transportation, and by its local conditions could be improved. Famine was a constant dread. Roads alone could create the proper balance and permit distribution of foodstuffs in time of stress.

Meanwhile, due to the thin-skinned sensitiveness of Major Burney, the British resident, and of his successor, Captain Macleod, another war with Burma was in the offing. This war was avoided for the time being; thanks partly to Henry Lawrence who did not believe that Burma was to blame and wrote long memoranda on the subject to the government. That these memoranda from a comparative junior should have been treated seriously speaks for the soundness of their contents and the esteem in which their writer was held by the powers.

Another development of this period was Lawrence's growing aversion to incompetent jacks-in-office. In later years he maintained that he could spot them on sight, could almost smell them out, and said that, in the attitude of an Englishman toward the natives, he could judge his qualifications for the civil service. To assist in the administration of a large, thickly populated area, a man should be in complete sympathy with the governed, even, if vicariously, with their prejudices and superstitions, and should understand the problems

of the humblest laborer and low-caste. The moment
an Englishman disliked the Indians, from either a
racial, religious, or cultural angle, his usefulness was
past and gone and he should be sent home. Nor was his
palling with Rajahs a qualification. To play polo with
His Highness the Jam Saheb of Newanagar, to split
a bottle of extra-dry with His Highness the Maharajah of Bikaneer, to call His Highness the Nizam of
Hyderabad "my dear old trout" was all very jolly—
and all very worthless. The basis for just government,
Lawrence insisted passionately, rested on and in the
minds of the lower classes; he agreed with Akbar, the
Moghul Emperor who, long before the days of Vol-
taire, Robespierre and Rousseau, attempted to found
a land "broad-based upon the people's will" and who
settled land revenue on an equitable basis while the
peasants of Europe were groaning under the heavy
and humiliating burden of serfdom. Indeed, Lawrence's theory of administration was not so brand-new
after all. He simply endeavored to return, though
with more modern methods, to the days when the
Moghuls enforced justice and tolerance, and when
Akbar, a Moslem, endowed Hindu temples and char-
itable institutions, while his European contemporaries
were periodically burning down the synagogues and
mosques and trying to extend the sway of the gentle
Christ with the help of torture and murder.

For five years Lawrence served on the Revenue Survey until, in August, 1838, he received orders to rejoin
his battery of horse artillery and proceed with it into
the northwest, with the possibility of active service beyond the Afghan border. In November the unit
reached Ferozepore to be informed that, the crisis
having passed, it would not be ordered further. So
Lawrence continued for the next two months to serve

in cantonment, bringing his battery up to that high
standard of efficiency which he ever demanded.

January brought different news. The trouble was
not over. From hill to hill, beyond the frontier,
Afghan swords were at the sharpening; the tribesmen
were gathering and strutting about, blustering, thick-
breasted, with big words in their big beards, praising
themselves and their own prowess, and no name too
dirty for those, Sikh or English or Rajput, whom they
were going out to fight, and making fine, bragging
prophecies as is the habit of Afghans in the way of
going to war. In Kabul the men, the women, the very
children, defied the British and roared their war
ballads:

> "*They say:*
> *Dost Mohammed, the Ghazi, makes*
> *ready for war at Kabul.*
> *Loud is the crackle of steel in Kandahar,*
> *the King's town.*
> *They say:*
> *Dost Mohammed, the Amir, has chosen*
> *the path of strife.*
> *He has proclaimed Holy War, He is leading*
> *his young warriors.*
> *Grant them victory, O Allah. . . ."*

The British were less poetic, although every bit as
determined; perhaps too determined, since Lord Auckland, the Governor-General, turned out not to be the
man for the job of cracking the Afghan nut.

Not that, for the sake of *Pax Britannica,* this nut
did not have to be cracked sooner or later, or, at least,
an effort made. For from the day that the Afghans,
upon the confusion which throughout Central Asia followed the death of Nadir Shah the Turkoman conqueror, had, for the first time since the rule of the
Sultans of Ghazni and Gor, obtained a national dy-

nasty founded by Achmed Shah Durani in 1747, they
had helped themselves to a wide Empire, stretching
from Herat to Pashawar and from Kashmir to Sind.
They were not destined to hold all their conquests,
since the Durani lords were prolific in children who
fought to the death with one another on each succession, and since civil strife at Kabul and Kandahar gave
to the Sikhs, their hereditary foes, a chance to turn
the tables. But the Afghans had the topographical
advantage. They retired to their mountain tops.
Then, when the invading storm had spent itself, they
would descend into the Indian plains, raiding, harry-
ing, burning, looting, killing . . . and, wherever the
northern wolves had passed, there would be sacked
towns and villages, like stark carcasses, full of empty
winds wailing among the charred timbers and scarred
walls—there would be the bones of cattle and horses
that they had refused to drive off in their satiety and
glut—there would be a low circling of carrion-fed kites
and hawks—there would be desolation and despair. . . .

Assuredly, the Afghans were unpleasant neighbors;
John Company decided to meet trouble halfway; and
the political staff on the border was considerably enlarged. This staff was under the commissionership
of Sir George Clerk, one of India's ablest administrators, who made Henry Lawrence's acquaintance,
weighed his worth, and appointed him as his assistant
at Ferozepore.

The post was one of peculiar difficulty. Under an
agreement with Ranjit Singh, the founder of the Sikh
kingdom of the Punjab, this territory had come under
British control three years earlier. Naturally weak,
the inhabitants of Ferozepore had for generations been
at the mercy of marauding, predatory neighbors. Since
1835 conditions had somewhat improved. But still
hundreds of lives were sacrificed each year to the sur-

rounding tribesmen; peaceful traders were being plundered; women were carried off; and often there would be farmhouses flaring red against the tall, black night.

Thus the settlement of the State promised to be a long and difficult task. But Lawrence took it eagerly in hand, and, within a year, he had caused his seniors to exclaim in surprise at his accomplishments. Commencing with defense, he created new and restored old forts, garrisoned them with troops, and dealt heavily with all invaders. In the intervals he established, almost in the manner of St. Louis, the custom of arbitrating local disputes on the ground, in the open— wherever the disputants could encounter him. Before he realized it, his fame in this direction spread not only throughout Ferozepore, but out into the adjacent districts. First small landowners crossed the border to seek his arbitration, and, in a few months, powerful and rich native princes were applying to him for judgment in their differences. Furthermore, the Governor-General received frequent requests from independent chiefs for the loan of this quiet Solomon who so understood the native mind that his awards were regarded as law. Already he was becoming The Pacificator.

He had not been long at his new post before trouble in the north broke out in earnest, in Afghanistan as well as the Punjab.

On the 14th November, 1841, tidings reached Ferozepore that Sir Alexander Burnes, the political agent at Kabul, had been murdered. Lawrence acted immediately. Passing on the information to Sir George Clerk at Ludhiana, he enclosed details of his own recommendations which, before waiting for an answer, he commenced to put into effect. His ideas were that all local troops should be concentrated into a brigade under Colonel Wild and moved as quickly as possible to the Sutlej river, with the intention of a rapid advance through the Punjab to Peshawar. The force was collected and marched under his orders. This, in itself, was a minor triumph for his policies and forethought. For, on several previous occasions, permission had been sought from the Sikh court at Lahore for English troops to cross the Punjab. Invariably these requests had been refused. Now, trusting Henry Lawrence as they did, the Sikhs at once granted permission.

Wild's brigade reached the eastern bank of the Sutlej on the 16th December, fully equipped to enter Afghanistan if necessary. There Lawrence joined it, carrying in his pocket Sir George Clerk's unreserved approval of his plans, together with a promise of considerable reënforcements, and, what is more important, his personal appointment as district officer at Peshawar. With this authority he took charge of the expedition and ordered an advance across the river to Peshawar, which city the brigade entered twelve days later, with Lawrence at its head. Peshawar was to be the base for the campaign.

His task was extremely complicated. Firstly, he was responsible for the direction and supply of Wild's brigade; secondly, he had to coöperate with the agent on the frontier, so as to keep the mountain passes open and the hill tribesmen satisfied; and, thirdly, his most important duty, he was expected to maintain cordial relations with the Sikhs by whose permission the troops had been moved up.

Each day brought bad news from the north. The vacillating policy of the British stationed in Kabul resulted as was to be expected. Sir Alexander Burnes' murder was followed by that of Sir William Macnaghten and several juniors. Unable to cope with the situation, Elphinstone had started his soldiers on the disastrous retirement towards the Khyber. These developments worked contrary to Lawrence's plans. The weaker the situation in Afghanistan, the more vital grew the necessity for keeping the friendship of the Sikhs; on the other hand, since the latter hated and despised the Afghans, the fact that the British had been defeated by them meant a loss of prestige to John Company in the Punjab.

This showed in the affair of the guns.

Wild required additional artillery. Lawrence applied to Lahore for the loan of some batteries. Permission was given for guns at Peshawar to be handed over, and, too, a promise was made for a brigade of Sikhs troops. But they refused to fight for the English, while the Sikh artillerymen would not hand over their guns. How—they reasoned—could the British, after their defeat by the Afghans, be trusted with more batteries? There was a threatening atmosphere. The Sepoys were on the verge of mutiny; and, but for Lawrence's understanding of native psychology, but for his superb tact and diplomacy, the whole enterprise might have collapsed then and there.

Operations on a large scale were impossible through the Khyber Pass. But, for the purpose of restoring morale, some sort of immediate action was absolutely necessary.

So a regiment was marched into the pass with the object of capturing Ali Majid, some twelve miles up. It was successful. A few days later, two more regiments, accompanied by several thousand Sikhs, were sent to its support. The Sikhs mutinied, attacked their officers, and headed back to Peshawar, with the result that the Ali Majid garrison was cut off, had to fight its way out, and was forced to return through the pass, to the further lowering of British prestige.

It was obvious to Lawrence that he had to fight against time.

Lord Ellenborough, who had succeeded Lord Auckland as Governor-General in 1842, was as casual and inefficient as his predecessor. He was organizing a force to support Wild's brigade; but it was already several weeks overdue; and Lawrence began to fear that it would not arrive before the Sikhs had definitely turned against him.

That it did not happen was due to the gallant defense which Sale's army was putting up at Jalalabad against the Afghans and which was beginning to impress even the prejudiced Sikhs. Using this as a psychological lever, Lawrence managed to keep the Peshawar situation from actual collapse, until, on the 31st March, the reënforcements were all in, and General Pollock, the new commander, was issuing orders for an immediate advance through the passes.

Under Lawrence's advice, he planned the operations to take place in two sections—the British were sent up one branch, the Sikhs up another, with an arrangement that they should unite beyond the border. It was a great success, chiefly because the Sikhs—again thanks to Lawrence—were kept busy every step of the way. After all, these men whose faith ordered them to wear five articles whose names begin with a K—*Kes,* long hair; *Kangha,* comb; *Kripan,* sword; *Kachh,* short drawers; and *Kara,* steel bracelet—placed their chief reliance on the third, the sword. A warrior race, they cared little whom they were fighting, as long as they were fighting somebody, though the fact that they were battling their ancient enemies, the Afghans, gave zest to their blows.

Sir George Clerk was unsparing of praise for Henry Lawrence who had saved the campaign at its darkest time. But for the blind folly of the central government, vital results might have been obtained. Lawrence, knowing his Sikhs, advised that they be kept going as long and hard as possible to keep them out of mischief. But, with the relief of Jalalabad by Pollock, Lord Ellenborough called a halt, explaining that supplies would have to be arranged for the columns and their communications with Peshawar reëstablished. It was typical of the man. He was a Fabius Cunctator without the Roman's chilly wisdom. Two months, he informed Pollock, were necessary before another advance. But by the time this period had elapsed, the soldiers were weary of the inactivity and openly showed their disaffection.

Under the continued pressure of Lawrence, who had to face the music alone, Ellenborough was forced to give one of his usual exhibitions of opportunism. He declared publicly and officially that the Afghan war was over, and, as a share of the spoils, he offered the Sikhs the territory above and including the passes. This, he imagined, would keep the Sikh soldiery on tap against the time that he actually made up his mind to do something. To a certain extent he was right in his reckoning. The Sikhs, happy once more, settled down to the occupation of the country they were supposed to have won.

But Ellenborough had been premature. The Afghans did not agree with him. Instead of considering the war over, they continued it and pressed back against Jalalabad. So five thousand Sikhs were sent there, under Lawrence, to reënforce Pollock. The latter prepared to advance. But, as usual, he was doomed to disappointment, Ellenborough giving strict orders that there was to be no further forward move . . . and again the Sikhs jeered; they knew that the Afghans held many British prisoners and despised the men who would not rescue their own flesh and blood. Lawrence reported this situation to Ellenborough—who did nothing.

During this time Lawrence's brother George, a captive at Kabul, had been sent down by the Afghans to Jalalabad, on parole, with terms. Henry requested permission to take the other's place and return to Kabul. But the authorities, perhaps rightly, could only see in this a quixotic idea of saving his brother further suffering and would not let him go.

Finally, on the 4th July, Ellenborough instructed Pollock to move. On the 7th August, with Lawrence in command of the Sikh detachment, the expedition headed for Kabul. Kabul was reached; was evacuated in October; and the Afghan drama closed with a bombastic proclamation by Lord Ellenborough, while the troops returned, Lawrence going to Ferozepore where he was given his liberty.

During several months John Company could find him only odd jobs. But on one of these he again impressed every one concerned with his singular genius for organization.

Seconded for temporary work with the Revenue Survey which was proceeding in Kaithal, in six months he managed to change completely the conditions under which the natives of that district lived—and suffered. Before he left, he had justly redistributed and changed assessments, had doubled the number of plows and improved roads, ultimately causing a large increase in the wealth and well-being of the area.

Then he went to Nepal where, for two years, he experienced no event of great importance, though, with his usual thoroughness, he made an intimate study of this remote land which, to-day a paradise for big-game hunters and almost as easily accessible as Simla and Darjeeling in spite of what romanticizing globe-trotters say, was then a *terra incognita;* had only once come into contact with the British when, several decades earlier, General Ochterlony's army had invaded the great Himalayan range and compelled the Nepalese rulers to sue for peace. Lawrence embodied what he saw and heard and learned in exhaustive government reports which, later on, came to be regarded as small classics of their kind.

During this time, also, he wrote considerably for publication, the chief item of his literary output being a spirited defense of the murdered Sir William Macnaghten in which—allowing the chips to fall where they listed—he brilliantly upheld the reputation of his dead associate at the expense of the whole gang of incompetents in the central government.

From the point of view of this same government, his Nepal days were wasted. He should have been at Ferozepore, since the Sikh situation was going from bad to worse. The Sikhs invaded British territory; war was declared; and Lawrence joined the troops in time to be present at the battles of Aliwal and Sobraon. With the victorious army he marched into Lahore on the 20th February, 1846; took an important part in the discussions which followed; and, at the end, found himself burdened with much of the responsibility caused by the peace treaty.

The Punjab was placed under a regency acting for a minor, Dhulip Singh, which was to govern under the control of Henry Lawrence, who was appointed British agent.

His main problem was the question of how the large Sikh army, suddenly disbanded, could be returned to the countryside without causing undue trouble. This task, thanks to his tact and his uncanny knowledge of native psychology, he carried out with a minimum of friction. The next task confronting him was the supervision of the regency council created under the terms

of peace. Since Ranjit Singh's death, innumerable factions, each with a large ax to grind, had arisen at the
Lahore court.   Most dangerous in this collection of
self-seekers was the Ranee Jindan, the widow of Ranjit
Singh and mother of his successor, who, from the beginning, insisted that she should be the sole regent
during her son's minority.   A third matter which
required settlement was the payment of the indem-
nity.

This money was not forthcoming, and the Governor-
General, Sir Henry (afterwards Lord) Hardinge,
agreed to accept the territory of Kashmir instead.
Lawrence considered it a mistake.   England, he insisted, owned more land in India than she could handle;
was about to become top-heavy; and so he persuaded
John Company to sell Kashmir to Gulab Singh, the
Rajah of Jammu, who had commanded the Sikh troops
under him in Afghanistan.

This settled one difficulty, but created another.
Ranee Jindan, through her minister Lal Singh, set to
work to keep Gulab Singh from occupying the throne
which he had purchased.   Kashmir was governed by
Emmam-ud-din, a cultured and refined Moslem, who
acted for the Lahore court. Approached by Lal Singh,
he threw in his lot with the Ranee's party and defied
Gulab Singh to take his new kingdom by force.   But
he had counted without Lawrence who, by some
miraculous means, persuaded the regency council to
furnish him with Sikh troops and marched them into
Kashmir to settle with Emmam-ud-din, who surrendered.

In November, 1846, Gulab Singh was installed as
Maharajah of Kashmir, and, during the *durbar,* Emmam-ud-din gave Lawrence information which created
fresh sensations at the Lahore court. Sparing nothing
in the way of damning detail, Emmam-ud-din presented

complete proof of Lal Singh's complicity. The latter, accordingly, was brought to trial and was confronted with the evidence against him in a court thrown open to all the Sikh nobility who, acting as jury, pronounced him guilty of treason and sentenced him to be deposed. The ministry portfolio he held was declared abolished, and the Ranee was left hereafter without her most powerful ally.

In December Lawrence was faced by a new problem, since the end of the year saw the expiration of the clause in the peace treaty which provided for the occupation and policing of the district by British troops. The British had no more intention of leaving the district than, years later, they had of leaving Egypt. In both cases the withdrawal of troops would have been followed by the same old disorder. But, whereas in Egypt a majority wanted the British to clear out bag and baggage, the majority of the Sikh regency council asked Lawrence to continue maintaining his force of occupation until such time as Dhulip Singh reached his majority. There were negotiations resulting in the treaty of Bhairowal which was to remain in force until Dhulip Singh became of age. Lawrence insisted on clauses which would strengthen his position in future encounters or misunderstandings. The Ranee, he insisted, must have no vote in any matter, while the British resident should be at liberty to handle all local problems that might arise as he saw fit, and while the administrative expenses should be guaranteed by the regency council. Fifty-two Sikhs chiefs voted on the acceptance of these terms and adopted them unanimously. The central government ratified the treaty of Bhairowal, reappointing Henry Lawrence as resident.

Thus, at the head of a council of eight, he became virtual ruler of the Punjab.

Though his administration was not destined to last long, he performed one of the finest pieces of executive work that India has ever seen. He completed his revenue survey of the country, revised the entire taxation of the area, abolished strangling government monopolies, and built a network of roads. Besides, he analyzed, simplified and codified the laws of the Punjab in such a manner that, from this time, it was impossible for cases to be tried on anything but a just basis.

Not that the period was entirely peaceful. For there were still threats of trouble from disbanded soldiers who, if they happened to be unemployed, were easily influenced by agents of the dissatisfied court party; and the Ranee was busy making all the mischief she could. Failing in her attempt to have Tej Singh, leading member of the council, assassinated, she turned her attention to endeavoring to corrupt the Sepoy soldiers in the British army of occupation. But Lawrence, whose secret service agents interrupted her treasonable correspondence with the governor of Multan, acted quickly and decisively, banishing her from Lahore to Benares.

The hot weather of 1847 broke his health. He had to go to the hills to recuperate. At this time, summing up his work with the Sikhs, he wrote:

"They have come to terms, and have settled down, because they have been well treated by us, and protected from their own army and chiefs by us; and because the rights and even prejudices of all classes have been respected."

It was a modest statement. Too modest. Instead of saying "by us" he might have truthfully said "by me," possibly adding "and by John Nicholson." For time and again his opinions, which he enforced, were contrary to those of the central government. This central government was inclined to rattle the sword on all occasions; had not too much love for the man whom, with a slight sneer, they dubbed The Pacificator. Only Hardinge, the Governor-General, appreciated him at his full worth and, on medical advice, the vacation in the hills not having improved his health, issued permission for a trip to England, stating in his recommendations:

"A real peace, to which it has long been a stranger, is reigning in the Punjab. This is mainly due to Henry Lawrence's efforts."

En route to Calcutta, Lawrence handed over his charge to his brother John who was given a temporary appointment pending the arrival of Sir Frederick Currie, and, on the 18th January, 1848, embarked on the same ship with Hardinge who was being replaced by Lord Dalhousie in the viceregal office.

He was perturbed as to the future. He believed that the change had been too recent to be lasting. He wrote:

"Our position at Lahore will always be a delicate one; benefits are soon forgotten and little gratitude is to be expected. . . . It was but the other day reclaimed from a state of the most ignorant barbarism, and has been but little subjected to the wholesome restraints of a regular government. . . ."

Hardinge, on the other hand, was enthusiastic about what had been accomplished and, before the close of his administration, had actually reduced the strength of the Sepoy army within convenient march of Lahore by over fifty thousand men.

On arriving in England, Lawrence was surprised at his reception. Not that the masses cared for this, or any other man, who made their Empire. The masses' Empire was limited by Surbiton and Battersea. The

masses' isles of adventure and romance were Guernsey
and the Isle of Man.   The masses' heroes were such
gladiators of the prize ring as the Nippy Milkman
and Bendigo the Pride of Nottingham.   But Government and Throne did the decent thing.   They patted
Henry Lawrence on the shoulder; invested him with
the K.C.B.; and told him to rest at home until he felt
himself equal to resuming his Indian task.

Back in the Punjab, it did not take the people long
to realize that they were without The Pacificator's
understanding mind.   At once there was trouble.   The
governor of Multan made representations to the effect
that he was both unable and unwilling to live up to the
financial terms of the treaty which, it will be remembered, had been approved unanimously by the Sikh
leaders.   Under advice from the natives, Henry's
brother John, awaiting Currie's arrival, demanded payment.   The governor of Multan resigned, and, when
Currie reached Lahore, he appointed Khan Singh in
succession.

Two British officers accompanied the latter to Multan.   There, in a sudden brawl with the adherents of
the resigning governor, both were killed.   Immediately Currie prepared a punitive expedition.   But the
central government refused its sanction.   Bazaar gossip had it that the central government did not wish to
quell such minor outbreaks, but was waiting for, and
encouraging, a major sedition so as to be able to step
in with full strength and force war on the Punjab.

This war was rapidly coming.   There were skirmishes right and left; isolated border actions; attacks
on British officers; more trouble at Multan; until,
finally, British troops and the whole of the government
machinery became involved.

So the sword-rattlers had their way . . . a way
which was not that of Henry Lawrence who at once

left England, reached Bombay during the last week of 1848, and hurried to Multan where a siege was already in progress. But Lord Dalhousie ordered him away from the front and back to Lahore, since he wished for none of Lawrence's spectacular, if effective, bits of reconciliation; wished rather for war and intended seeing it through at all costs. It was Dalhousie's method. He did not approve of festering sores; preferred amputation to lingering illness; and, in the eight years of his proconsulship, achieved more brilliant results than any Governor-General since Lord Wellesley, perhaps since Clive, acquiring the Punjab, large territories in Burma, as well as Nagpur, Oudh, and a number of minor States . . . nor should he be blamed altogether for the Mutiny which followed his policy of annexation.

The Punjab campaign ended with the overwhelming British victory at Gujrat. Dalhousie now turned again to Henry Lawrence and appointed him president of the council of three which was to administer the new John Company province.

Sir Henry Lawrence's particular departments were those of politics, military affairs, and reconciliations of the natives. His brother John joined as member in charge of all revenue, and the trio was completed by the addition of Mr. Mansel in charge of judicial affairs. The terms of the annexation were duly approved by the Sikh leaders who, in consultation with Sir Henry alone, agreed to give every assistance to the new régime.

This new régime began auspiciously, based on Sir Henry's instructions to his colleagues:

"Promptness, accessibility, brevity and kindness are the best engines of government here. Be considerate and kind, not expecting too much from ignorant people. Make no changes unless certain of decided improvement."

Ably supported by his brother and Mr. Mansel, Sir Henry Lawrence was instrumental in instituting, throughout the Punjab, a system of government which led to unparalleled peace and contentment. With the other two confining themselves to their rather limited spheres, he attended to all general matters, including defense, where he inaugurated the type of native force later to be so well known as "The Guides," and, as usual, occupied himself with the everlasting construction of roads and canals and the perpetual, vital business of creating good will between the governed and governing races.

That the work was successful is a matter of history; is, indeed, one of the most glorious pages in the annals of Britain in India; and it is impossible to calculate how much further it might have progressed had it not been for the fact that, the longer the two brothers worked together, the wider grew the breach between them which had started years earlier, at Karnal, where both had been juniors.

It is difficult to say to whom the blame should be attached, or even to establish that there was any blame due. They held divergent theories on government, with right and wrong on either side. Both were honest, conscientious, intelligent. Both were handicapped by the policies of Lord Dalhousie who, dreaming grand dreams of his own, was more concerned with the future than with the present, and who often, in furtherance of his gigantic schemes, overruled the opinions and recommendations of the best local officers. Finally, John was forced to see matters from the point of view of the financial member of the council, while Henry, having more direct experience with the Sikhs, was inclined to look at things from the psychological, even occasionally the sentimental, angle.

In judging the eventual results of his methods, he declared:

"Money is saved by keeping men contented, preserving the peace, and getting expeditiously through work. Money is gained and revenue increased by expenditure on roads and canals."

John, on the other hand, could not get away from his theory—frequently upheld by a cash shortage—that roads and canals did not appear on the ledgers, that peace and content could not be classified in official rubrics.

They disagreed on another matter. Henry believed that it was more important to reconcile, and make friends with, the native aristocrats. John preferred reconciling, and making friends with, the masses. Henry countered that the masses were influenced by the aristocrats, were under their thumb, that, therefore, his way was a short-cut. But John could not see it. Nor could Dalhousie who suspected Henry of intriguing against him.

Ultimately Henry was proved right. For, during the Mutiny, the natives remained loyal wherever the sympathy of the local Rajahs had been won by inviting their coöperation.

But, at the time, neither John nor Lord Dalhousie understood this. John even went so far as to confiscate, for non-payment of taxes, the property of several prominent land owners, descendants of beneficiaries of Ranjit Singh, who had inherited their property under rent and tax-free conditions. Thereupon Sir Henry, feeling that, as time passed, the loyal Sikhs would only come to regard him as the author of their decline, decided that his position was equivocal, that his further participation in the government of the Punjab would be embarrassing to all concerned, and, in the early weeks of 1853, handed in his resignation. John did likewise; and Dalhousie solved the problem by keeping John at Lahore and transferring Henry to the residency of Rajputana at the same salary.

This decision caused sorrow to the natives as well as to the British subordinate officers. Many suspected that Dalhousie had erred and that Sir Henry, that gaunt, keen-eyed man with the typically Anglo-Indian temper, was the man for the Punjab job. Again and again he had proclaimed:

"We must keep free from the guilt of robbery—of taking property from those who had an unquestionable right to it in order to bestow it on those who have no real claims . . . our remedy for gross mismanagement is to take over management only, temporarily or permanently."

Naturally this policy was popular with the natives who were embittered at Dalhousie's avowed intention of annexing territory at the slightest excuse; and a British district officer expressed himself concisely when he wrote:

"Lord Dalhousie, in removing Lawrence to Rajputana, struck out the keystone from the arch of Punjab administration."

Two high officials in the central government expressed themselves quite as freely.
One declared:

"The powers of mind of Sir Henry—the watchful benevolence, the wisdom, far seeing, provident and sound, which calculated every contingency, combined the whole machinery of the administration into one of the greatest triumphs of modern polity. His was the spirit which inspired every act of the local government, which touched the hearts of his subordinates."

The other opined:

"Henry Lawrence, the friend of every one who is down, the generous, the loved, who got a little more for every one, who fought every losing battle for the old chiefs, with entire disregard of his own interests, left the Punjab amid an outburst of universal lamentation."

Nor was this an exaggeration. The Punjab was grief-stricken; and when Sir Henry set out from Lahore for his new headquarters, he was accompanied by an army of Sikh chiefs who cheered him, salaamed to him, did their best to make his progress a thing of high honor.

He found Rajputana different from the Punjab. The Sikhs had maintained all the virtues as well as vices of a war-like race. Opposing British inroads had kept them constantly on the alert and had preserved their morale. The Rajputs, on the other hand, had, from an early time, been friendly to the British and had lived in comparative peace. Thus—though, according to another, more recent Lawrence, Sir Walter Roper Lawrence, they were and are "the finest gentlemen in the world"—their strength had become sapped, and their courts had grown to be centers of effete ease and luxury.

In the Punjab, beyond his official duties, he had done a great deal of valuable, voluntary work. Thus he had made the first suggestions and recommendations for the establishment of the quartermaster general's department and the Indian staff corps and, government funds not being forthcoming, had built up a permanent memorial to himself in the foundation of the Lawrence Asylum where children of British soldiers might receive an education during the period of their father's service. Similarly, his four years in Rajputana were

remarkable in the direction of improving the wretched
conditions existing in native prisons, the suppression
of *suttee* or the suicide of widows on their husbands'
funeral pyres, and forbidding the killing off the surplus
of female infants.   Instead of making a theatrical to-
do, which would have resulted in the usual prejudice
against a reformer, he went into the matter personally
with each native chief and brought him round to the
right point of view.   That a quiet, mild-voiced foreigner, naturally mistrusted on account of his position,
could thus convince a proud Rajput nobleman that the
age-old customs of his race were nothing short of murder and, consequently, had to be discontinued, was another tribute to his character, intelligence, and understanding of native psychology.

The greatest difficulty with which he was confronted
was not caused by the Rajputs, but by Lord Dalhousie
who, an Imperialist, used all means, fair and foul, to
increase British territory.   One way of doing this was
by the system of reversion: by claiming that, where a
chief died without issue, his lands reverted to the British.   The Rajputs, of course, objected to this.   They
preferred their ancient custom of adopting an heir in
default of issue.   So feeling ran high; had not been
improved by the fact that, during the residency of Sir
John Low, Lawrence's predecessor in office, over sixteen proposed adoptions had been refused recognition
by the Governor-General and the lands in question swallowed by the Company.

Lawrence refused to follow Sir John Low's lead.
He went counter to Lord Dalhousie's wishes; frequently, by dint of insisting, wore down the latter's
opposition and earned as high a reputation among the
Rajputs as he had among the Sikhs.   Official recognition came to him when, early in 1857, he was sent to
Lucknow, as Chief-Commissioner of Oudh . . . sent

there to bring order where disorder reigned . . . sent there too late to avert the coming storm, the Mutiny.

Oudh, once the garden of India, was then a hell upon earth. For years its Moslem rulers, debauchees of the worst sort, had sucked the country dry. There were oppression, anarchy, bands of brigands roaming the countryside, desolation, despair. Finally Lord Dalhousie, influenced this time not by Imperialistic kleptomania but by decency and pity, in the last few weeks of his Viceroyalty, had decided on annexation, writing in a private letter:

"In humble reliance on the blessing of the Almighty (for millions of His creatures will draw freedom and happiness from the change), I approach the execution of this duty gravely and not without solicitude, but calmly and altogether without doubt."

Accordingly, a year before Lawrence's advent, General (afterwards Sir James) Outram, had been ordered to annex Oudh for John Company; the reigning King, Wajid Ali, had bowed to fate, settling down in Calcutta's charming suburb of Garden Reach, there to enjoy a yearly pension of £120,000; and Oudh became British . . . a necessary measure, one of Lord Dalhousie's finest achievements, yet—by the irony of destiny—the one that most alarmed Hindu public opinion and was one of the contributing causes to the Mutiny, spreading far and wide the fear that Great Britain would stop at nothing to increase her Empire.

Dalhousie's administration closed in 1856. He was succeeded by Lord Canning who, loving peace, saw the land plunged into the red maze of war.

It is hard to analyze, for the European mind, the precise motives for the Sepoy Mutiny. Perhaps the real explanation is contained in the one word: Panic . . . panic which acts on an Eastern mob as drink does on a Western.

This panic, too, was based upon a variety of causes.

One cause was the conviction of the Sepoys that their prowess in battle had conquered the Punjab for John Company; another cause was the bazaar rumor that the Russians had vanquished the British in the Crimean campaign; that the many deposed Rajahs, living on munificent British pensions, had nothing to do except to make trouble and foster intrigues; a cantonment rumor that the cartridges served out to Indian soldiers were greased with the fat of pigs—animals unclean alike to Hindus and to Moslems; that John Company had not opened a sufficient number of higher government posts to natives of tested education, talent, and loyalty . . . this last a state of affairs which Sir Henry Lawrence pointed out to his superiors, insisting that even the army supplied no proper career to native gentlemen since the latter could not rise above a certain rank.

But his warning went unheeded; and it was only after the Mutiny and with Sir Henry dead and buried, that Queen Victoria affirmed the principle which he had so unceasingly urged:

"And it is our further will that, so far as may be, our subjects, of whatever race or creed, be freely and impartially admitted to offices in our service, the duties of which they may be qualified by their education, ability, and integrity duly to discharge."

But this came later. Too late. . . .

Things were happening, quickly, dramatically.

The first open trouble occurred on the 27th February when a newly arrived Sepoy detachment mutinied at Berhampore. The affair was followed by other significant details.   Native chiefs, usually so scrupulous in matters of etiquette, exhibited signs of growing arrogance.

The old-timers felt a new, disturbing tenseness in the atmosphere.

Particularly Sir Henry.

Immediately on his arrival at Lucknow he proceeded to make preparations against any possible disaffection.   A defensive position based on the residency and the old fort of Mattchibhown was laid out.   Military stores were piled in both places.   At the same time he went carefully into the matter of redistributing the troops in the neighborhood, quartering all available British soldiers within the city limits and placing the most doubtful Sepoy regiments in cantonments across the river.   At the same time he himself applied to Lord Canning for a high military rank which, in case of trouble, would permit him to act in the capacity of soldier as well as civil administrator.   Lord Canning complied.   John Company went a step further, nominating him provisional Governor-General in event of any accident happening to Canning.

As the heat increased, so did signs of trouble.   On the first of May, Captain Carnegie of the 7th Oudh Infantry reported to Lawrence that his regiment had mutinied and seized their quartermaster's stores with all arms and ammunition.   Sir Henry acted promptly. Leaving word for the nearest British troops to follow to the cantonment drill ground, he hurried in advance of them and, by the time they arrived, had himself gathered the Sepoys in some semblance of order.   They were immediately disarmed; and, on the spot, he held a court-martial, tried the ringleaders, found them guilty, and passed sentence—though, in no case, sentence of death.

Discovery of seditious letters and literature in bar-

racks warned him of more serious outbreaks in the near
future.   He redoubled his efforts to keep things in
hand.   Daily thereafter he made inspection trips
through the lines, conversing freely with the men and
making full reports to Lord Canning.   It was evident
that the trouble was deeply rooted.   The general
opinion among the disaffected Sepoys was that the time
had come to boot the British out of India for good and
all.   The latter—it was claimed—had been yoking
India to their Imperial chariot; had altered the entire
Hindu mode of living, were trying to alter the mode
of thinking, and aiming at undermining caste system
and religion.   It could not be tolerated.

On the 10th May came the explosion: the mutiny
at Meerut, followed by the march on Delhi, and the
proclamation that the ancient Moghul Empire had
once more been established.

A less stubborn race than the British might have
caved in.   Their situation seemed hopeless.

Here were they, so few, so isolated.   Here, all about
them, were millions of warlike Hindus . . . and India herself, a dark land with a bright edge, like an
abyss licked by a flame of fire . . . and there was the
wrath of this India; the wrath of this gigantic, tragic,
sweating peninsula which was often exhausted, thus
dormant, but never appeased. . . .

Never appeased—though Henry Lawrence, going
his daily rounds—never appeased . . . and yet he
had done his best, as John Nicholson, Hardinge and so
many others had done their best!   And here the Sepoys
were marching, marching, marching beneath the Grand
Moghul's green banner. . . . Brahmins marching beneath Islam's banner, the banner they had once hated
and feared—because, even more, they hated and feared
the English.   And they would sweep on—thought
Henry Lawrence—these thousands; and they were

only the advance guard of millions to come . . . and they would destroy what he, with his puny strength, had helped to build up—British civilization, British peace, British progress—agricultural, industrial, commercial, administrative.

North, east, south, west they would march—and kill—and tear down.

Men of broad vision had clouted and worked here. They had opened up agricultural and mineral wealth; had constructed roads and canals; had improved living conditions; had stopped foul and beastly customs; had brought, as they saw it, justice, decency, the things worth while . . . and this huge torrent would surge over it all, crushing it like so many greedy locusts, out to eat away the face of the land, to set the clock back a thousand years. . . .

Thus, if not the opinion of the Hindus, then at least the opinion of Sir Henry Lawrence and many other decent Britons. A divergence of opinion which had to be settled with blood . . . and even Sir Henry, the Pacificator, who hated blood, despised armed strife, saw this—and prepared.

Sepoys beyond the river were confined to their own side and the residency and the fort of Mattchibhown prepared for a siege. Officers were ordered to use patience and firmness with their men, while playing a game against time. Supplies were brought in as quickly as possible. Lawrence supervised and directed every last detail.

On the 29th news came that the rebellion had spread, that Islam's green banner was everywhere, defiant, flouting. On the following day all but one regiment of native troops stationed at Lucknow mutinied. The fact made little difference in the activities which Sir Henry was pushing forward. Every one was set to work preparing for defense and narrowing the line of resistance about the residency itself. Lawrence was working twenty-two hours a day. His health broke down. On the 9th June, under medical orders, he retired to his quarters, leaving his task temporarily in the hands of a council under the presidency of a civil service officer.

At its one meeting this council passed resolutions directly contrary to those of Lawrence. Immediately, in disregard of the doctor's advice, he returned and again assumed control, going his daily rounds about the entrenchments, looking personally after every detail. In the meantime he had sent out cavalry patrols through the province to feel the temper of the people and act as outposts for the supply of information as to any hostile movement in the direction of Lucknow. They were away on this mission when, on the 30th May, the last regular native troops across the river mutinied, killed their officers, and moved into the city and toward the residency. With the defense preparations that had been made and using the one loyal regiment, the Thirteenth Native Infantry, the mutineers were chased back over the river and, a day or two later, all discontents in town were sent after them.

In the month that followed Sir Henry Lawrence was the defense of Lucknow himself. Despite his ill health and the terrific heat, he was indefatigable in his labors. Realizing that the position held was too great for the available troops, he made plans toward concentrating everything within the limits of the residency, at the same time keeping up regular communication with the outside and with his far-flung cavalry patrols. To add to his difficulties, severe cholera broke out in the garrison . . . and there were few doctors, no nurses, a scarcity of medical supplies.

So things went on until, on the 27th June, happened the tragedy of Cawnpore.

There Nana Sahib, the last of the Peshwa dynasty which had built up the Maratha confederacy and whose name, for all time to come, will be infamous in the annals of India, had been at first profuse in his professions of loyalty.   But, when the Sepoys in garrison at Cawnpore had mutinied, he had put himself at their head; had granted a safe-conduct to the few Europeans, more women and children than fighting men, who had carried on a heroic defense in a hastily constructed entrenchment; had then exposed them to a murderous fire, only four men, who swam across the river to the protection of a friendly Rajah, surviving to tell the black tale.

Cawnpore's fall released an army of Sepoys; and Lawrence, not the one to allow himself to be caught in a trap, gathered what he could spare of his few troops and moved along the Faizabad road to meet the mutineers in the open.   His soldiers fought gallantly at Chinhat, but were defeated and driven back to Lucknow.

The siege began.   All stores, the single weak British regiment, and all European residents were moved into the residency.   Mattchibhown was mined and blown up.   Sir Henry's preparations were so well made that, in spite of unparalleled hardships and against overwhelming odds, the little garrison held out until, on the 16th November, 1857, Sir Colin Campbell (afterwards Lord Clyde), preceded by Generals Havelock and Outram, came to the relief.

But Sir Henry did not survive to see it.

On the morning of the 2nd July, after a particularly busy night, he retired to his room for a short rest.   He was very much satisfied with the work which had been done and was outlining more plans for the future, while talking, seated on his bed, to Wilson and George Lawrence, his nephew.

As they were conversing, an eight-inch howitzer shell came through the wall, hissed for a minute on the floor, and exploded. His companions were knocked over, but unhurt. They picked themselves up. They found Sir Henry under a pile of masonry. His leg had been blown off, high up towards the hip.

For the next forty-eight hours, in intense, unspeakable agony, he attended to his duties: handing over the defense, appointing successors to himself in the military and civil departments, disposing of what possessions he had, dictating long reports on the conditions of affairs to the central government.

Then, on the 4th of the month, he died. On the same day they buried him. He sleeps there, under a monument upon which the epitaph reads:

"Henry Lawrence, who tried to do his duty."

WILLIAM WALKER

[1824–1860]

*who, braggingly, dreamed
of adventures*

GENERAL WALKER

WILLIAM WALKER

THE name of William Walker—or of John Smith or Jack Robinson—is not exactly reminiscent of forgotten knight-errantry, of spurred and booted deeds. It is a good, plain, home-spun English, thence a good, plain, home-spun American name.

Yet, is there anything more romantic in the wide world than a typical American; a man—let us say—whose great-grandfather, rifle in arm and knife in boot, came out of Virginia into Kentucky, in the days when Kentucky was the farthest frontier, to see what was going on beyond the ranges, to listen to the pipe calls of the wilderness gods; whose grandfather, following the shifting frontier, drifted into Kansas, when it was "Bloody Kansas," and thence, via Panama, to California, to the tune of *"Oh, My Darling Clementine"*; and whose father mined and ranched and played poker and drank his red liquor straight from Alaska to the Sierras?

Here, in such a man, is real, full-blooded romance, before which the crusaders of Europe's Middle Ages can hang their heads in impotent shame.

Brian Boru? Richard Lion Heart? Geoffroy de Bouillon? Tamerlane? Roland of Blaives? Amadis and Palmerin?

Let them take a back seat. Let real romance move to the front: Smith—and Robinson—and Walker. . . . William Walker who sought gold, sought power, but, primarily, sought adventure, sought an Empire of his own, in Central America . . . might have achieved it, but for that peculiar spirit of bragging rodomontade which tainted his character.

225

He had his first innings with—or against—fate in the fourth decade of the nineteenth century when the gold fever struck America, breaking up families, re-orienting careers.

One would have guessed that young William Walker, then a journalist in the city of New Orleans, would have been effectively inoculated against this fever. The man, at the time, seemed so prosy—though his short career had been varied enough. But in his boyhood, spent largely in reading for long hours to an invalid mother and professing religion to the usual extent of electing the church as a vocation, he had been considered none too adventurous—"As refined in his feelings as a girl"—and certainly hardly equal to the long hike across the Continent and the rigors of a mining camp. Besides, he was satisfied with his writing job, penning an occasional article denouncing the filibusters operating in Cuba, and, in his twenty-sixth year, was considering marriage.

The process of settling down to the responsibilities of life had not been rapid and had taken him onto the threshold of two other professions, in addition to the casting of eyes towards the ministry, before newspaper work had occupied him in the capital of Louisiana.

Born in Nashville, Tenn., on the 8th May, 1824, after graduation from the local university, at 14, he had taken his M.D. at the University of Pennsylvania. He had topped that off with a year of study in Paris during which he had found time to visit most of the European capitals. After a reasonable test on his return, Nashville dubbed him "the most accomplished surgeon that ever visited the city," praise to which must have been as ashes in the mouth of the young man who was just in the process of deciding that the law, not the operating table, was his field.

It required a couple of years in New Orleans, where

he nailed up his first legal shingle, to convince him further, that recognition at the bar lay at the end of too long, dull and crooked a path. But these years were not wasted. For they landed him in what he seemed to like more than anything else—an associate editorship on the *Crescent,* where he made sufficient mark to earn a position on the *Picayune* when the first paper changed hands.

In addition to congenial work, there was Miss Helen Martin to keep him settled. She was stone-deaf. He was forced to master the sign language of mutes to tell her that she was his one and only little woman. A handicap to a man, like Walker, inclined to express himself, in and out of season, in stately rounded, Bryanesque phrases. But it only increased his affection. For the man, after all, was middle-class; was without practical, aristocratic brutality. The slogan of *Service* had not yet been invented. Had it been, he would have been one of the original sub-scribers . . . would have believed in it, even later on, when, most decidedly, he spoiled the Egyptians . . . would have declared that he spoiled them by token of that same *Service.*

At the time the "gold rush" was at its height. Si-multaneously, New Orleans was struck by one of its periodic yellow fever epidemics. The object of Wil-liam Walker's attentions was amongst the first victims. And, being a sentimentalist, he decided that he hated New Orleans, that New Orleans had murdered his best beloved—and he set out for California and whatever he might find there.

San Francisco offered him a chance to show what was in him. As an editor of the *Daily Herald* he at-tacked the authorities for their incapacity in handling the lawlessness then rampant, and, when a judge de-

nounced the press from the bench, he replied in such
stinging terms that he was found guilty of contempt
and fined $500. He was almost in a position to head
a popular party. Refusing to disburse, he was incarcerated, only to be released when the papers of San
Franciso raised the public to a protest meeting.

Despite this publicity, he was a retiring individual.
He left San Francisco to enter into a law partnership
with one Henry Watkins in the new town of Marysville during which uneventful period he kept very much
to himself, but began to learn something of certain
schemes which were afoot to colonize Mexico and
Central America. At last his real calling beckoned,
and it did not take him long to find his way to the
head of a rather limited profession—that of filibustering.

In the days preceding the Civil War, filibustering
was a sport as well as a vocation for certain hardy
American adventurers. Many decent people in the
United States condemned the practice. Others—with
an unconsciously Gilbertian humor—declared that the
filibusters were noble crusaders, invading Central
America to bring to the Popish black-and-tan republics
the blessings of Protestant Christianity, to save these
benighted lands through the miracle of Nordic culture
. . . an explanation tragic in some, comic in other re-
spects . . an explanation which might have elicited
a reply similar to that of a great Afghan Amir who
remarked he did not mind England usually having an
ace up her sleeve, but he did object to England's claim
that Jesus put it there.

The fact is that each and every raid into Central
America had its own particular origin and found its
roots in the ideas of a single adventurer, occasionally
of a clique. Filibustering was never a "cultural" and
not even a political movement. It was, always, the

result of either greed or lust for adventure or lust for
power. And Walker was neither the first nor the last
filibuster, but just an outstanding one—*the* outstanding
one.

At its birth the scheme resulting in Walker's first
attempt to establish an independent republic on Mexican soil was lacking in any of the sensational elements
which it later developed. Some Californians, quiet
men as Californians then went, decided to settle in the
State of Sonora. The idea came to them at a most
inopportune moment. Two French expeditions,
manned by exiled aristocrats who had found the gold
rush too strenuous for them, were already creating
trouble for the Mexican authorities; and when the
would-be American colonists sent two of their number
to negotiate for a grant of land near Arispe, the attitude towards them was not encouraging.

A year or so later, with the current French nuisances
out of the way—the Marquis Charles de Pindray mys-
teriously shot and Count Raoul de Raousset outlawed
by the government and back in San Francisco—the
question was again mooted. Walker and his partner,
Watkins, were engaged to undertake the preliminaries
with the Mexican government. They failed in their
mission. Far from giving any concession, the authorities at Guaymas refused to recognize Walker's passport, while the Governor of Sonora would not grant
an interview until after the two agents had reëmbarked
for San Francisco.

But Walker had caught the fever. To settle an
American colony in Mexico! Such was his ambition.
Almost he persuaded himself that it was his cultural
duty, his God-decreed mission. And, like many another missionary, he decided that, if his duty, his mission paid one hundred per cent profit, so much the

better. The man might have been a Christian Scientist, happily blending the spirit with the cash. He maintained—without the slightest irony, for the man was singularly ingenuous at heart—that the people in Sonora were simple folk who needed him, needed his superior American brain; that, without him to protect them, they were entirely unable to cope with the depredations of the Indians; that it was up to him to be their Moses.

His optimism was infectious. The other colonists, or, rather, would-be colonists, followed his lead. They were a bit like certain Y.W.C.A. and Y.M.C.A. workers who, after the recent war, caused gigantic laughter on Olympus by declaring it was their duty to remain in France and teach the benighted Frenchmen the beatitudes of Anglo-Saxon home life.

A brig, the *Arrow,* was purchased and loaded with provisions, arms and ammunition. Suspecting that illegal plans were afoot, General Hitchcock, commanding the military district, had the brig seized and handed over to the Federal authorities.

At once Walker shifted operations to another vessel, the *Caroline,* and, loading her before the U. S. authorities could devise means of getting round the local courts, sailed for a destination unknown. Grandiosely he called his forty-five men the "First Independence Battalion." As grandiosely he appointed himself colonel and dictator, intent on achieving by armed invasion what, in its heathen blindness, the Mexican government had refused to permit peacefully.

On the high seas and definitely committed to his venture, Colonel Walker set about reconsidering the details of his invasion. His predecessors, quick on the trigger, quick at the looting, had done little to advertise the blessings of Anglo-Saxon civilization as interpreted by armed filibusters. Nor did his own memories of Guaymas increase his eagerness to land at that port. Besides, the Mexican authorities were watching the spot, and even the gallant, self-appointed colonel realized that forty odd men were rather few to wage war against a well-drilled national army.

Therefore he determined to prosecute his campaign by degrees. He would begin by occupying the Lower California peninsula. Using it as a base, he would invade Sonora.

Inspection of conditions at Cape San Lucas proving them to be far from ideal, he wasted little time there and proceeded to La Paz where he landed his Independent Battalion on the 3rd of November.

Then, for a boisterous hour or two, a heroic opera— or, perhaps, a comic opera?—was played to a meager audience of sardonic Mexican Indians. The local governor was arrested. The standard of Walker's brand-new Republic was unfurled on the flag pole of the executive mansion, replacing the Mexican colors. And a proclamation, short, containing only twenty words, but bombastic enough to please even Walker, declared that Lower California on this day of the Lord had for all time to come renounced its allegiance to Mexico and taken its place amongst the Sovereign States of the World.

Then loud hurrahs!

The firing of a salute which, happily, killed only an inquisitive cow!

And Colonel William Walker, drawing his sword, appointed himself President of the Independent Republic of Lower California!

For nearly a week the new Government functioned smoothly. The guard changing outside the President's office attracted an approving crowd, while from within issued two declarations that (*a*) fixed the law of the land as being similar to that of Louisiana and (*b*) established freedom of trade with the world. Also, the new President decided that La Paz was not a suitable capital. So, intercepting a new Mexican governor arriving to relieve the one held prisoner, adding him to the bag and fighting a rearguard action with the local troops who took heart when the invaders commenced to embark, he made a second unsatisfactory reconnaissance at the Cape and sailed north to fix his seat of government at Ensenada, about a hundred miles from the California border.

It had not been much of a battle. Half a dozen filibusters armed with rifles against a dozen Mexicans armed with machetes. But both sides claimed a decisive victory. Walker, indeed, wrote about it in thrilling, Homeric prose; and Watkins, using this account of the "Great Battle of La Paz," as he called it, to rouse American enthusiasm, opened a recruiting station in San Francisco.

There he did a rushing business. Within a month he joined his chief at Ensenada with two hundred recruits, willing to do or die—willing, too, to help themselves to the loot.

In the meantime, the Independence Battalion had a trying time, though work had progressed. For Walker—then as always—took himself seriously. He formed a cabinet and gazetted a number of officers. His party consisted of forty-five people. Of these he seconded three for political work, appointing them respectively Secretaries of State, War, and the Navy, and commissioned eight men in the Land and Sea Forces of the Republic.

George Cohan, in his most rollicking comic opera, could not have done better. But, unlike George Cohan, William Walker did not consider it funny.

In justification of the warlike majority of his cabinet Walker's troops had early smelled more powder.

Surrounded by the Mexicans in a house on the outskirts of the town, the Independence Battalion, less a
couple of navy men left on the *Caroline* who put to
sea with all the provisions as soon as the sounds of
fighting reached their ears, defended itself for three
or four days until, in a sally costing the life of one
officer, they drove off the besiegers.

The arrival of Watkins, who did not stay long after
finding how things stood, brought numerical strength
to the new Republic. But, as they had omitted to bring
provisions with them, the gain was somewhat of an
embarrassment. Yet it permitted offensive operations,
and immediately a raid for supplies was launched
southwards in the direction of the village of San
Thomas. To justify this, the Mexican bandit, Melendrez, who had his headquarters there, was elaborately
declared a menace to the peace and outlawed by President Walker who then despatched a detachment to
confiscate the property thus declared forfeit.

The San Thomas raid brought in horses and cattle,
but did little to relieve the hardships under which the
men lived or lighten the boredom of their existence.
But the Colonel-President did his best to turn his soldiers' thoughts away from themselves by submitting
them to intensive training. Far from a rabble the
Army of the Republic was overdisciplined. Between
military etiquette, drills under the burning sun and insufficient rations, there were frequent desertions; and,
once a fugitive was out of gunshot of the lines, there
was no agency to bring him back. The returned Watkins was still recruiting, however, and the balance between deserters and reënforcements was about equal.

Having maintained his position in Ensenada for two
months, Walker began to feel secure and prepared for
his next step. By a proclamation of 18th January,
1854, the states of Lower California and Sonora were

united in the Republic of Sonora. Thus was effected
the liberty of a Mexican state without its brave saviors
setting foot on its soil.

It was about time they did. For camp life at the
capital was not improving the morale of the troops,
and the martinet in command was not helping his own
cause. With the details of the march over the mountains complete, he made a reapportionment of mounts,
changing his original battalion from a cavalry unit to
infantry of the guard. As the battalion had only been
mounted since its members had managed to appropriate
horses for themselves, they failed to appreciate the
empty honor accorded to them and fell out to hold a
protest meeting. Walker's riding into this with a demand that all present should register on the spot,
an oath of allegiance to their President, though it
proved further his unquestionable courage, only pre-
cipitated matters, with the result that he not only lost
about fifty men, who started on a desperate hike to
the California border, but also, more valuable at the
moment, fifty firearms.

Undaunted by the mutiny, on the 13th February,
Walker paraded his remaining one hundred and thirty
men, turned his back on his temporary capital, and set
out to find a new headquarters geographically better
suited to the needs of his extended dominion.

Throughout his expedition the California press,
then, as to-day, jealous of the fame of its sons, native-
born or adopted, putting them almost on a par with
its climate and its grapefruits, had been filled with
gorgeously colored accounts from the Walker front.
By the farce of San Vincente Walker's fame spread
across the California border; gave to the world at
large something worth reading. Rounding up sixty-
two half-naked, flea-bitten natives outside the town, he
declared the meeting a political convention of repre-

sentative Lower Californian citizens; ran the mystified Indians, whom he insisted on calling delegates, through the hoops; silver-tongued them in Spanish as superbly as any W. J. Bryan; and, with his own hands, penned a petition for them to sign and submit to their paternal President—himself.

By this delightful document, on behalf of the delegates, who had sworn allegiance and marched through an arch of flags of the Republic, he prayed his excellent self to assume the reins of government, place the land under martial law until such time as order might be restored, and requisition his loyal subjects for all necessary supplies.

Three weeks later, leaving a garrison "for the protection of the loyal citizens," the army moved northeastward toward the Sonoran border. The enthusiasm of the rank and file was not greatly increased from the start by the shooting of two and the public flogging of another couple of delinquents on the farewell parade. In fact, by this time the expedition was beginning to get irritated with their leader. His exaggerated idea of his own importance, his arbitrary commands and his insistence on being treated with punctilious ceremony hardly endeared him to adventurers who had come to escape the tedium of civilization.

In the meantime things had been happening back in San Francisco. Hitchcock had been superseded by Major Wool who arrived with instructions to maintain the neutrality laws of the United States and do all possible to put a stop to the activities of the filibusters. Within two weeks of taking up his duties the new area commander had arrested Watkins and closed his recruiting bureau. A few days later he apprehended the Secretary of State of the Independent Republic of Sonora, visiting San Francisco in the interests of President Walker. Thus, simultaneously, the sources of finance and reënforcements were cut off, and the success of the invasion became a matter of doubt. The two were subsequently tried, found guilty and fined $1,500, a fact which seems to show, in the light of later events, that comedy in high places was not confined to the area south of the Mexican border.

At last, the Colorado, dividing the two states of his republic, was forded and the Walker headquarters were in Sonora. In crossing the river the army lost all its horses and cattle; the men were wet to the skin; conditions which suggested to a second batch of fifty men that they had prosecuted the matter far enough and sent them wandering northward in search of the United States.

Three days in Sonora, with grumbling adventurers on his hands, were enough for the President to realize that he had made a miscalculation. The time was not quite ripe for the establishment of freedom in Sonora, and it was meet that he return to the friendly locality of San Vincente, where the national convention had endorsed his government, to conduct a preliminary campaign of education to prepare the Sonorans for their natural rights. So he trailed back across the mountains to find that Melendrez had killed off his San Vincente garrison and was waiting to do the same for the main body.

It was then he seemed to lose heart. These Mexicans! How blind!

But he would do better by them next time and for now wash his hands of the business and return to the practice of law in California.

Again he formed his pitiful column and headed north. But Melendrez was on his trail and harassed his retreat at every point, finally placing his bandits between the retired President's army and the friendly

Californian border. Melendrez gave notice to the commander at San Diego of his intention to capture Walker and his men, and was told that the United States were not interested and would not interfere. News spread through Southern California that a battle was promising on the Mexican border, and the hills along the line were lined with picnicking spectators.

Melendrez laid out his line conveniently close to the border and demanded Walker's surrender. The Ex-President, a mere colonel once more, knew his Mexican too well and pushed an advance guard forward with orders to charge when they had made contact with the enemy. It was the 8th of May, Walker's birthday, and though he was worn out he joined with the enemy in a confident state of mind. The Mexicans stood threateningly firm, until the assault neared home when they came to the conclusion that the others were in earnest and scattered in confusion. Elated over his success, the victorious leader pressed forward to the head of his troops, crossed the border and surrendered himself and his army to Major McKinstry, commander at San Diego, who had taken a front seat for the entertainment, and undertook to report as soon as circumstances permitted to the Area Commander at San Francisco.

At liberty under indictment, Walker was placed under bond after his arraignment, on June 2nd. At his trial, which did not open until October, the "Ex-President of Sonora" insisted that the belligerent nature of his jaunt was purely an accident brought on by unforeseen circumstances arising after it had left the United States on a peaceful colonizing scheme. After eight minutes' conference, the jury acquitted the prisoner—the principal, whose agent and subordinate had previously been found guilty on the same charge and fined.

Awaiting his trial, Walker had returned to Marysville and his legal practice which he now used for political purposes, serving, thanks to the publicity he was getting, as a Committeeman of the Broderick Anti-Slavery wing of the local Democrats during a turbulent convention and election. He also drifted back to journalism, holding editorial positions on a Sacramento paper and the San Francisco *Commercial Advertiser*.

South of his first hunting ground, however, affairs were afoot which were shortly to take him once more afield. The Republic of Nicaragua was a breeding ground for things more irritating than its mosquitoes.

Geographically the turbulent country offered the most convenient link, at the time, between the Atlantic and Pacific. The proposal to join Lake Nicaragua with the sea to east and west and establish a transoceanic canal was under consideration. Already Cornelius Vanderbilt's Accessory Transit Company, carrying east and west bound freight and passengers, was competing with the Panama Railroad and had cut the time of the latter, from New York to San Francisco, by two days.

Since securing their independence from Spain, the Nicaraguans had divided into two parties, the aristocratic Legitimists and the Liberals. These two parties disagreed violently on all points, including graft. So sharp were their quarrels that, as elections shifted power from one party to the other, the successful clique found it necessary to shift the national capital. With the Legitimists in the saddle, as they were in 1854, the country was governed from Granada; while the Liberals issued their orders from Leon.

The Legitimist ascendancy, used beyond its limit, had resulted in their opponents breaking into open revolt and laying siege to Granada.

One of the proprietors of the San Francisco *Com-*

mercial Advertiser, on which Walker was working during and after his trial, was a certain Byron Cole. In the late summer of 1854 this man made a trip to Nicaragua in connection with a mining concession in which he was interested.

Cole found his mining property worthless. But he was introduced to another, more promising, form of enterprise shortly after his arrival.

Francisco Castellon, a lately defeated presidential candidate, had just been forced to raise the siege of his opponent's capital. Where—he wondered—could he discover brave lads who would help him to reverse the result of the ridiculous and evidently crooked election? Cole thought he might be interested in answering the question. On certain terms. The terms were talked over, signed. Cole agreed to supply three hundred armed men. Castellon agreed to pay—through his handsome, beaked Castilian nose. And Cole returned to San Francisco to consult that rising authority on such matters—Lawyer-Editor-Ex-President-Ex-Colonel-Once-Doctor William Walker.

Walker studied the Cole-Castellon document. He told Cole that, if the latter could procure another document, promising to three hundred American colonists rights to settle in Nicaragua together with the privilege of carrying arms, it would be good enough for him. Cole, after another visit to Nicaragua, produced the exact paper to satisfy the other who, at once, undertook the task.

It was in February, 1855, that Walker agreed to undertake the task of delivering the men to Castellon. But he was not able to sail from San Francisco with the first installment of fifty-eight before the 4th May. After the Sonoran affair, the arrests in connection with which had been made at the instigation of the military, Major Wool had received instructions amounting to orders to mind his own business in future, from Jefferson Davis, Secretary for War at Washington. So, as local feeling was all with the adventurers, the new expedition had nothing to fear from the authorities—barring, always, the sheriff in his capacity of executor of writs of attachment for debt, and it was upon the financial rocks that Walker came near foundering this time.

Finances accumulating slowly, the impatient leader had to be content with a disreputable vessel, the *Vesta*, which had not improved after having been laid up for several months at the ostensible end of a career of thirty years. On this, as seaworthy as funds would allow her to be made, Walker embarked his men and loaded her with provisions and equipment bought with stock in his venture. The creditors of the *Vesta's* owner rubbed their eyes when they saw her preparing for a voyage and remembered their interests. Getting no satisfaction, they had the brig attached. This only served to set the ship chandlers thinking. What was the Nicaraguan scrip worth? Perhaps it would be better to have lawful currency for their goods. At their instigation the sheriff boarded the *Vesta* again and removed the sails to a neighboring place of safety.

Walker, at his wit's end, limped from place to place endeavoring to settle difficulties and put to sea. For his various activities had lately involved him in a controversy ending in a pistol duel at eight paces, in which he had received a painful wound in the foot. This did not assist him in his investigations. Nevertheless he found that his obstacles were in the nature of a vicious circle. The men he had enlisted were longing for a change of scenery or a little money to ease the boredom of dock loafing. As long as they received none, their presence was a standing menace to the community. Hence the dunning of the owner of the *Vesta*,

who in turn vented his annoyance by influencing the
provision suppliers to libel the vessel so as to recover
from Walker.

By having a friend persuade the owner's creditors to
grant a release of the vessel, Walker finally broke
down the chain of opposition and, entertaining the
deputy on duty whilst the revenue men replaced the
sails, put quietly to sea, returning the intoxicated
deputy from a point outside his jurisdiction. "The
Fifty-Six Immortals," as, by some arithmetical error,
the fifty-eight filibusters on the *Vesta* had christened
themselves, were thus outward bound to the freedom
of Nicaragua on the 4th May, 1855.

It was the 16th June before they anchored at
Realejo, in northern Nicaragua, and disembarked.
With little delay Walker marched his men inland to
Leon and reported in person to Castellon who was
delighted with even this small assistance. At a pathetic ceremonial welcome Castellon bestowed authority on his new allies. First the entire band were
naturalized, and the regiment was rechristened "The
American Phalanx." Walker received a commission
as colonel in the Nicaraguan Army and the addition
of one hundred and ten natives to his command.

Slight difficulties then arose as to the use to which
the Phalanx would be put. How employ it to the
greater glory of the Democratic cause? Castellon had
his ideas, that it should form part of his army preparing for the renewal of the attack on Granada. But
Walker differed and, after several conferences, had his
way. His scheme was simple. Reëmbarking at Realejo,
he proposed to land near San Juan del Sur, the western
terminal of the Accessory Transit Company's trans-
Nicaraguan line, throw his force across Vanderbilt's
trail and recruit as best he could from the fitful stream

of California-bound passengers. Castellon wanted action; Walker was content to build up a purely American force.

In the execution of his program the latter discovered his left flank to be threatened from the Legitimist stronghold of Rivas. To give himself freedom of action, and incidentally to score an easy victory to the enhancement of his own local prestige, he decided to remove the menace. The Phalanx and native attachments concentrated and marched to the assault. In the early afternoon of the 29th June the attack was launched.

"The First Battle of Rivas," as Walker always called the engagement, proved an ill omen. Rivas was defended by about 500 Legitimist troops. With their first volley these put Walker's native allies to rout and then proceeded to bottle up the American Phalanx in a group of outhouses. For nearly five hours the siege was maintained. Finally, in a desperate dash the surviving filibusters made good their escape and then pursued their dejected way to San Juan del Sur. Not only had Walker sustained a defeat; but the Phalanx had suffered serious losses in the killing of its lieutenant-colonel, major and ten men, and the wounding of three officers and seven men.

On reaching the coast, the disheartened party found their brig, as had happened to Walker before, had put to sea without orders. But their colonel's forcible language found them a Costa Rican schooner and two recruits from the beach. Getting away from San Juan del Sur as soon as possible, they overhauled the crazy *Vesta,* and in her the filibusters returned to their original port of disembarkation where they landed on the 1st July, 1855.

At Realejo Walker penned a scathing report of The First Battle of Rivas to Castellon. The failure of the

undertaking had been the fault of Castellon's commander-in-chief who had opposed the venture from the
beginning and had supplied troops, whose loyalty was
under suspicion, to support the gallant Phalanx. The
colonel of the Phalanx ended with a threat to return
with his men to San Francisco unless an inquiry was
immediately instituted, and, after despatching the message, remained in haughty retirement whilst his
wounded were recovering.

Ultimatum as well as reticence were a bluff designed
to gain a respite for his gallant Phalanx which, just
then, did not feel so gallant, was, indeed, whining and
complaining. The double bluff worked. An American
resident of Leon, acting for Castellon, approached
Walker with offers of transport for his men to the
Democratic capital and care for his sick and wounded.
For at the moment the Legitimist forces held the initiative, and Castellon was expecting their arrival before
Leon at any hour. His whole behavior being with
just such an advance in view, Walker climbed down
from his high horse and proceeded to Leon to confer
with the Democratic leaders.

By this time the situation was plain to all concerned.
Walker was undoubtedly an indefatigable worker and
a born leader of forlorn hopes—in his own interests.
Freedom and minority rights were appealing slogans,
but secondary matters to the colonel of the American
Phalanx.

Leon having recovered from the scare caused by a
threatened siege, Walker proposed that he be sent on
a second expedition to the Vanderbilt Trail. Castellon, backed by Munoz, the general, whom Walker
blamed for his recent defeat, had no idea of using the
contract men so far afield. Walker was to join the
general staff, while the Phalanx would be disbanded
and its members divided into four or five groups for

attachment to various units throughout the Democrat army. From an independent force they were to be made into small bodies of shock troops under native generals.

Walker was furious at the suggestion. He stormed out of the council swearing that he would march his command away from Leon. From his camp he sent a requisition to Munoz for the necessary military transport, the reply to which was the surrounding of the American camp by native troops. Walker immediately issued an ultimatum to the effect that any Democrats under arms in the neighborhood of his lines after an hour had elapsed would be regarded as enemies. This caused Castellon to back down and, on condition that Walker would remove himself from Leon, filled his transport requisition. With all except permission to pursue his pet plan, Walker marched the Phalanx to Chinandega and prepared to set off on a second venture up the Vanderbilt trail.

In the meantime his loss of officers at "The First Battle of Rivas" had been somewhat made up. Byron Cole had turned up to act as Walker's attaché at Democratic headquarters. With him had arrived Bruno von Natzmer, a Prussian officer, long a resident in Nicaragua, who understood the psychology of the people and knew the country. He was a valuable addition to the Phalanx.

At Castellon's headquarters Byron Cole worked hard as agent of the man he had himself employed. He acted with a great deal of tact. In consideration of renewing the original contract, he obtained a commission for Walker to deal with the Accessory Transit Company on behalf of the Democrats. This, he assured the council at Leon, would result in their obtaining the sympathy of the board of the largest financial organization in the country. Thus, satisfying Castel-

lon for the nonce, he obtained permission for Walker
to do exactly as he pleased. Now that the filibusters
were on Nicaraguan soil, the clauses in the first agreement which Walker had recognized to be contrary to
the United States' Neutrality Law were of no consequence.

Castellon later protested that his appointment of
Walker was not intended as permission for the Phalanx
to proceed to San Juan del Sur. But it was then too
late to alter the intention of the obstreperous colonel.
In fact Walker was still concealing his plans. Honduras was at war with Guatemala and had asked the
Nicaraguan Democrats for assistance. Declaring that
such allies could not be left in the lurch, Walker proceeded to Realejo, ostensibly en route to Honduras.
With the Phalanx marched a force of natives brought
by a native Indian, Valle, who had taken a fancy to
the methods of the filibuster colonel.

At San Juan del Sur, Walker received a message
from an old Californian associate, Parker French, one
of the most slippery rascals on the Pacific Slope, in
those days a kaleidoscope of all America's and half
Europe's gaudy and reckless rascals. Their latter-
day descendants, indeed, have reformed. They have
joined the Elks and Rotary; have voted for prohibi-
tion; have flung about their shoulders the rather self-
conscious mantle of all the civic virtues. Not so their
Argonaut ancestors. And Parker French was one of
them.

In his letter to Walker, the other intimated that he
had been to Granada to confer with the Legitimists.
Therefore—less for reasons of honor than for reasons
of safety—he could not approach a Democrat officer.
But there was a way out. He suggested that he be
arrested and taken aboard the *Vesta*. There he explained that his sympathies were entirely with the

Liberal element and received a commission to recruit
seventy-five men in San Francisco.

The Phalanx was then disembarked and marched up
the Vanderbilt Trail to the point where the Accessory
Transit Company's trans-Nicaraguan passengers
changed from the Lake Nicaragua boats to carriages
bound for San Juan del Sur. The idea was to camp
here, recruiting from the next few parties of westbound Argonauts, the latter, men not exactly picky and
choosy as to what they did or whom they did as long
as proper pay, or improper loot, was forthcoming.
But Walker's calculations miscarried. For the garrison at Rivas, hearing of his advance, marched towards
the trail to engage the filibusters. Finding that the
latter had already passed, they followed them to the
shores of the lake.

There, in the morning of the 3rd September, the
Phalanx discovered its predicament. With its back to
the lake so that the Nicaraguan contingent could not
escape, it turned to defend itself. The victory they
gained over six hundred Legitimists, without losing a
man killed, was a triumph for Walker. Having driven
off the enemy, the Phalanx advanced to find over sixty
dead before them and picked up more than a hundred
and fifty guns.

After the victory, the Phalanx returned to San Juan
del Sur to rest on its laurels until the second week in
October. An opportunist always, Walker saw that
none of the chances presented by the occasion were
lost. Twice hit during the engagement, he had remained at the head of his men to see that his orders,
contrary to the local custom, that there should be no
butchery of the wounded and prisoners, be carried out.
Together with his defeat of the enemy these incidents
enhanced his reputation throughout Central America

with the result that additional native recruits were easy
to find.

From the United States also came reënforcements
of the type he preferred—thirty-five Californians, including two survivors of the Lower Californian fiasco.
To cap his fortune, Castellon succumbed to cholera;
and his successor, Escoto, seemed willing to give the
filibusters a free hand.

In the draft from San Francisco the presence of one
individual gave the colonel new hope. Parker French
sent Charles MacDonald, introducing him as a friend
and intimate associate of Garrison, the San Francisco
agent of the Accessory Transit Company. MacDonald
might be able to enlist the sympathies of the Vanderbilt interests on behalf of the filibusters. Vanderbilt,
after all, was as much of a filibuster as Walker himself.

With his command, including natives, numbering two
hundred and fifty, Walker decided it was time to be up
and doing. From the interior came news deciding him
in the course to pursue. Alarmed at the threat of the
Phalanx, the Legitimists had transferred the Granada
garrison towards Rivas, leaving their capital almost
unprotected. Seeing in this the justification of his
policy, he determined to lay siege to the Legitimist
headquarters and cut the forces of the enemy in two.
The accomplishment of this was easier than he expected.

Taking his soldiers back to the lake he embarked
them on a Transit Company's steamer, commandeered
for the occasion, landed a few miles north of Granada
and, in the early morning of the 13th October, moved
on his objective. There was no trouble from the few
sentries on duty, and Walker had his breakfast in the
town. To identify himself with the Democrats, he
then released all political prisoners, and to curry favor

with the opposition made stringent rules against anything in the way of looting.

With his entry into Granada, Walker's status in Nicaragua underwent a complete change. From the happy-go-lucky existence of a free-lance rover he now moved into the tricky, incalculable atmosphere of Central American politics where heads are at a discount in keeping time with the irregular pulse-beat of the Latin—and Indian—heart. And Walker's mentality was never exactly overwhelming. Shrewd he was—but short-sightedly shrewd. His dreams of Empire were always petty; always revolving around cheap loot and the adventures themselves.

He had found it easy to keep together and discipline his own filibusters and even native troops. But the handling of rival political factions and families was a different matter. From now on he was unable to make one friend without creating a dozen enemies to offset the gain. Every time he opened his mouth—and he did so often, loudly, braggingly—he made mischief, for himself as well as for Nicaragua.

In the customary manner of the country, the local government approached Walker the day after his arrival with the offer of the Presidency of Nicaragua. He refused the honor with a flourish calculated to gain him the confidence of the stronger party and suggesting that the high office be wished upon the Legitimist leader—Corral. A commission, accompanied by John Wheeler, U. S. minister at Granada, waited upon Corral with the news of his appointment. But the haughty aristocrat refused to consider even the termination of hostilities with any one save Walker himself. As the filibuster was beginning to see the workings of the Nicaraguan mind he, in his turn, rejected this suggestion, preferring to keep his power behind the throne.

With this matter in the balance, the stormy petrel of Walker's career again appeared on the scene. Parker French landed with sixty men, on the 17th October, at San Juan del Sur and proceeded to create a situation. Commandeering a steamer, he saw fit to try to obtain control of the eastern entrance of the lake. This so roused the native garrison at San Carlos that they retaliated on the next Transit Company's westbound vessel and killed a woman and her child. Walker was unable to remonstrate with the bringer of recruits. So he overlooked the provocation and accused the Legitimists of bad faith. To show his earnestness in this regard, he picked on one of the late Cabinet ministers residing in Granada and had him shot.

Then he declared martial law and held the foremost Legitimist families as hostages, announcing—without the slightest humor—that this was necessary to "guard American interests against any further breaches of faith."

A burglar demanding that his stolen property be watched by the police!

A League of Nations mutually insuring each other's ill-gotten gains!

But it worked. Corral's officers, anxious about their relatives kept as hostages, forced him to open negotiations. The outcome of the Granada convention, on the 23d October, was that peace was signed between Legitimists and Democrats, and the outline drawn for a plan of government by a cabinet chosen equally from both factions under the provisional presidency of Patricio Rivas, a sound old Legitimist with slight Liberal tendencies. Corral was made Minister of War, and Walker—no longer a mere colonel, but a full-fledged general—commander-in-chief. Finally blue, regarded, for some obscure reason, as a combina-

tion of the factional hues, red and white, was adopted
as the color of the new nation.

Before the treaty agreed upon at the first meeting
was formally signed, Walker was losing Corral's favor.
It had been agreed that on the 29th Corral should
enter Granada in state, accompanied by his Legitimist
soldiery, to inaugurate the new régime. Coming into
the square, he was pained beyond words to discover
that Walker had a company of Democrat troopers
drawn up in the receiving line. What a breach of
faith! In spite of what had been "formally" agreed,
could the fat-head filibuster believe that the Legitimists
would put up with the presence of Democrat soldiers?
However, with the latter as well as filibusters about,
nothing could be done just then. Walker was duly
embraced and kissed in view of the cheering assembly,
and the two mounted the steps of the cathedral to
swear on the Gospels anent their good faith with regard to the new treaty—and to think their own, not
at all Gospel-like thoughts—while a *Te Deum* ascended
to the skies.

With the arrival from Leon of Jerez with the
Democrats' ratification of the Walker-Corral treaty,
the commander-in-chief, with an eye to the balance of
parties, proposed him for the portfolio of Minister of
Relations, and, the suggestion being accepted by Rivas,
the appointment followed. This was enough for Corral. He despatched letters, couched in unmistakable
terms, calling for assistance in changing the existing
state of affairs. Nicaragua for the Nicaraguans, Nicaraguan Legitimists he meant. If this foreigner was
permitted to control affairs any longer, the end was
inevitable. His letters fell into Walker's hands, and
Corral was immediately arrested. Professing a profound faith in the American sense of justice, he was
tried by a court drawn from the Phalanx which found

him guilty, though recommending him for mercy. But
Walker, always the martinet when power was on his
side, denied this mercy. In the afternoon of the 8th
November, during the siesta hour, Corral was stood
up against a white wall and shot by a squad of alien
adventurers.

The martyrdom of their leader might have been
almost forgotten by the Legitimists had not Walker
pressed, and obtained, the appointment of Selva, an
active Democrat, to the vacant Secretaryship of War.
With the announcement of this the aristocratic party
decided that the filibuster colonel was a menace to the
well-being of their country, a sentiment he himself did
not help to allay when he disbanded all native troops
of both factions, maintaining only the Phalanx to keep
order in Granada.

Whatever effect all this had upon the native mind,
there was one man it impressed. Two days after the
shooting of Corral, John Wheeler, United States Minister to Nicaragua, recognized the Rivas Government.
His action seemed to strengthen Walker's hand considerably. But the feeling of security it gave was
short-lived. On the State Department in Washington
hearing of Wheeler's premature and entirely unauthor-
ized declaration, a repudiation was immediately issued,
and only friends at court saved Wheeler for Walker's
cause.

Before hearing this news, whilst still confident of
support from the United States, Walker received more
solid earnest of good will. All along he had suffered
qualms as to the finances of the government he had
virtually created. Suddenly these were allayed. Mc-
Donald, in the interests of Garrison, Accessory Transit Company Agent at San Francisco, not only offered
to advance Walker funds but actually removed $20,000

in gold from one of the company's trans-Nicaraguan shipments and handed it over. As Walker accepted this advance in the name of the government of Nicaragua and, further, as he gave as security for the loan the royalties due the government on Transit Company traffic across the Isthmus, everybody was satisfied—for the time being.

To this time the effects of Walker's lack of tact had been limited to native Nicaraguans. The Democrats, his original employers, mistrusted him for having countenanced a single one of their opponents in the government he had created. The Legitimists remembered the two heroes he had martyred and pointed at the inclusion of Democrats in the Cabinet. Now Walker was about to build up some feeling against himself with his own countrymen.

During the hectic days in which he had been engaged in frenzied finance with the creditors of the owner of the *Vesta* and the provision merchants of San Francisco, another Nicaraguan expedition had been preparing to start for the same country from New York. Its leader, Colonel Henry Kinney, had set as his sailing date the 7th of May, three days after the *Vesta* actually left from California. But Kinney, too, had difficulties to face and had only been able to clear, by means of a ruse, on June 6th. With respect to Kinney's intentions towards Nicaragua there could be little doubt. A letter published in a Texan paper, emanating from him, contained the following:

"It requires but a few hundred Americans to take control of all that country. . . . I intend to make a suitable government, and the rest will follow."

After more than his decent share of trouble, Kinney reached his objective, the Mosquito Coast, where he held certain concessions from the colored ruler set up by British naval officers and traders. Penniless on his arrival and under the ban of both the United States government and the Accessory Transit Company, Kinney nevertheless gathered a few beachcombers about him and in September, 1855, had himself elected civil and military governor of some undefined area on the east coast of Nicaragua. Walker's successes, however, were too much for Kinney's establishment. His officers deserted to enlist in the Phalanx at Granada, and finally Kinney sent two of his few remaining officers to Walker with proposals of pooling their interests. It was a bold bluff, but was sent to a bolder man. Walker pondered the question for almost a minute before replying:

"Tell Governor Kinney, or Colonel Kinney, or Mr. Kinney, or whatever he chooses to call himself that if I ever lay hands on him on Nicaraguan soil I shall surely hang him."

As one successful filibuster to the minions of a failure this sounded impressive. Rather than return to Kinney the embassy joined the Phalanx, and Walker gained two recruits.

Unfortunately, however, Kinney had many friends. Some of the recruits to the Phalanx from the Transit Company's human shipments had been advance agents of the other expedition. They resented Walker's refusal to coöperate with the man who had interested them in Nicaragua. Further, Kinney had many political connections in the United States, and when he was practically deported, on February 14, 1856, on an order signed by William Walker, general-in-chief of the Army of Nicaragua, the occurrence only served to bring the name of the signer to the notice of men who were in a position to do him harm in the United States.

Two years later Kinney again landed in Nicaragua as advance agent of a proposed invasion by English

Mormons. He was deported again—Walker was not involved—and was finally shot campaigning for the governorship of Texas.

Amongst Walker's activities as commander-in-chief was the establishment of a newspaper in Granada. *El Nicaraguense* appeared within a week of the capture of Granada and was published every Saturday. Through its columns the late journalist missed no opportunity of helping his cause. In the third person he hailed himself as coming "as a friend of the oppressed and a protector of the helpless and unoffending." Seizing on an Indian tradition to the effect that the Spanish yoke would finally be thrown off through the efforts of a man with his own variety of eyes, gray, he christened himself "The Gray-Eyed Man of Destiny" and saw to it that his paper kept alive the title and tradition upon which it rested. Whatever the trouble brewing for him in Spanish and part-Spanish circles, the Indian population could not be turned from his service.

Walker's successes had been largely due to the assistance rendered him by the Transit Company. In one of its lake boats he had moved to the taking of Granada; he had received funds from its shipments; and, once established in the Nicaraguan capital, recruits to the Phalanx had been transported free from San Francisco. In December, 1855, the reason for these acts of charity became apparent. During that month three men arrived from San Francisco and wasted no time in putting up to Walker a proposal. The trio consisted of McDonald, who had negotiated the "loan" from the Company, W. R. Garrison, son of the San Francisco agent of the Transit Company, and Edmund Randolph, who had practiced law in New Orleans with Walker, had defended him after the Mexican affair and had since acted on his behalf in California. To sweeten their dealings with Walker they brought on the same ship with them a hundred excellent recruits for the army.

The internal affairs of the Transit Company were at that time reaching a crisis. During the absence of Vanderbilt in Europe, Garrison, Sr., and Morgan, the New York agent, had played the stock to their advantage, causing the absent one considerable loss. On his return he had accepted the state of affairs with one eye on the future. With a threatening: "I shall not sue you, I shall ruin you," Vanderbilt had set to work on a slow but sure campaign to obtain complete control of the corporation. With the resources at his command there was no doubt about the outcome. Garrison and Morgan realized that their time was approaching.

The proposal made by Garrison's emissaries, therefore, was simple. Part of the Nicaraguan charter of the Company depended on the payment of royalties based on their business across the country. These had not been forthcoming, and during 1855 the Legitimist government had sent representatives to New York to endeavor to obtain a settlement. An offer of $30,000 had been refused and settlement by arbitration was pending. According to Garrison, the Transit Company, by failing to pay these royalties, had forfeited their charter. Under Walker's influence Rivas could be made to cancel the agreement and grant a new charter to Garrison and Morgan. If Walker could not see his way to effecting this little deal, reënforcements, supplies and finance would immediately stop.

For how long could he maintain himself on his own resources? How long would it take him to come to an understanding with the Vanderbilt interests?

Walker—and Vanderbilt! A small adventurer and

expert in loot—trusting a big adventurer and expert in loot!

But it was obvious upon which side of his political bread the butter lay. Digging up his dormant, legal lore, Walker found old scraps of precedent with which to salve his conscience and proceeded to agree to Garrison's demands.

The four men then secretly prepared a new charter, and on completion of the work young Garrison left for New York with a copy for Morgan's approval, while McDonald carried a similar draft to Garrison, Sr., in San Francisco.

The interval until the return of these two was a busy one. Though Walker's residence in Granada was comparatively uneventful, elsewhere affairs were moving in a manner which was later to affect his destiny tremendously. In San Francisco the Federal authorities had long since ceased worrying filibusters who embarked for doubtful parts. The officials in New York, however, waged a constant war on the waterfront; and though, with the public against them, they did little to dam the stream of reënforcements to Nicaragua, they did succeed in keeping the whole business before the Washington politicians.

Then, too, certain negotiations were being carried on with the Transit Company proper in New York. Being suspicious of Mr. Parker French, for excellent reasons, and, besides, being personally in that unscrupulous gentleman's debt, Walker was only too glad to accede to his request that he be appointed Nicaraguan Minister to the United States. On leaving for his post, French received instructions to approach the Transit Company on the subject of the royalties owing the Nicaraguan government. He was authorized to settle with it on terms which amounted to the company carrying Nicaraguan recruits for $20 per head chargeable on the books against whatever sum was finally fixed as the total of accrued royalties.

At the time of French's arrival, Vanderbilt had just found himself in a position to carry out his late threat and ruin Morgan and Garrison. Unaware of Garrison, Jr.'s, presence in New York or of what was afoot, Vanderbilt agreed to French's proposals and, to prepare for his coming control of the Transit Company, commenced drumming up a brisk trade in filibusters calculated to put the Granada government in a happy frame of mind. Protests to the Secretary of State from the Ministers from Central American countries adjoining Nicaragua caused him to laugh. Every man sailing by his boats carried a through ticket to San Francisco. It was a perfectly legal business, and, if they dallied by the way, could he be blamed?

In the first half of February, 1855, events moved fast. With Morgan's approval of the draft charter in his bag, young Garrison left New York for Nicaragua. McDonald, with Garrison, Sr.'s ratification, was already back in Granada. At a meeting of the Transit Company in New York Vanderbilt was elected to the presidency of the corporation and celebrated the event by ousting Morgan from his job. On Garrison, Jr.'s, return to Granada there was an immediate conference with Walker. On the following day President Rivas signed the revocation of the Transit Company's charter. The joy of Rivas, on being approached by Walker with the paper purporting to free his unhappy country from the domination of a foreign company which had lately done little but bring dangerous-looking adventurers to his capital, was touching. This Walker was obviously a man in whom confidence might be placed.

But the next day, the 19th February, all things were

altered. Again the high-minded commander-in-chief
asked for an audience, this time to present for signa-
ture a new charter made out in favor of Garrison
and Morgan.

That the terms of his second Charter were less favorable to the government increased Rivas' suspicion
and drove him to rebel. Thereupon Walker, with a
superb sweep of his hand, reminded him that he,
Walker, commanded the only armed force in the capital. But the other was not the sort to knuckle under so
easily. He, too, was capable of a *beau geste.* He
thought of Corral who had died like a gallant gentleman. He remembered how, to pay for Parker French's
raid, Mayorga, the Legitimist cabinet minister, had
gone to his own particular white wall. Rivas was getting on in years. He would die soon enough. Thus,
why not finish his life in a fearless protest which might
save his country? He made this protest; declared that
the old Charter was null and void.

Walker stormed, threatened. He even granted a
point here and there. On the other hand, Rivas'
heroic resistance did not stand the gaff. So, after a
few faint outbursts the Morgan-Garrison Charter was
granted, signed, and delivered.

So, with the first cargo of filibusters organized on
the Vanderbilt scale on the sea from New Orleans,
the news from New York and Granada crossed. Vanderbilt was assisting the man who had acted against
him, Walker's protégés had been driven out of the
company upon which he placed his reliance for support. With Granada practically under his thumb,
Walker, the astute lawyer, had staked his all upon the
wrong horse, and, in doing so, had, as was always
somehow managed for him when he did anything,
made a new enemy. On this occasion, though, his cre-

ation was no tin-pan politician or political clique. In
playing with the Transit Charter Walker earned the
undying enmity of one of the most powerful figures
of the day.

During the development of the Transit Company
affair Walker had an internal question heavy on his
hands. Here fate did not seem to be on his side any
more than in his dealings with Vanderbilt. When the
Walker-Corral Treaty had been signed, a notification
of its purport had been sent to all Central American
governments. Politics in these states ran on precisely
the same lines as in Nicaragua. In Guatemala, where
the Legitimists were in the saddle, they were celebrat-
ing a recent victory over Honduras where they had
succeeded in ousting the Democratic President Cabanas
who had fled to the friendly state of San Salvador. In
the meantime the bulk of Nicaraguan Legitimists had
sought a haven to the south, in Costa Rica where they
were met with sympathy. So it was not surprising that
the announcement from Granada was ignored by all
but San Salvador.

In acknowledging the Walker-created Rivas government, the President of San Salvador coupled his con-
gratulations with a request that the American troops
should be sent to assist his visitor, Cabanas, to regain
his Honduran capital. Walker had captured Granada
in the sacred name of the cause of the Democrats, but
had no intention of spreading the light beyond the
borders of Nicaragua. He refused Cabanas' appeal
and in so doing caused more trouble in the Rivas Cabinet. Jerez, Minister of Relations and a Democrat
from Leon, handed in his resignation. In quitting
Granada, he assured Walker that he would leave no
stone unturned to teach the members of his party that
the American had no regard for their interests. Jerez
was replaced immediately by a Legitimist—an attempt

to keep the party balance—which appointment only resulted in the immediate resignation of Selva, Democrat and Secretary of War in succession to Corral, executed.

Cabanas now took up his residence in San Salvador, devoting his life to stirring up opposition to the Walker régime in the one Central American state under Democrat control. Meantime Walker, tired of making Cabinet officers fast enough to keep pace with the resignations his every act brought, appointed the sole remaining minister, Ferrer, Minister-General and tried to leave domestic affairs, so far as he dared, in the hands of Rivas.

On the arrival of Parker French, Rivas'—Walker's —Ambassador to Washington, at the American capital, with a representative of the abolished Legitimate government still on deck, he was not received with any enthusiasm. The State Department refused to accept his credentials. But this only caused him to move on to New York to arrange for the shipment of recruits to the Isthmus. Finding that recognition of his post would aid him in this, however, he made another attempt, during February, 1856, to be accepted by the Federal government, and, on hearing of the second refusal, Walker persuaded Rivas to suspend diplomatic relations with Wheeler, United States Minister at Granada.

It may have given General William Walker a feeling of importance to cross swords over a few thousand miles with the Secretary of State in Washington. But he was not doing his own interests any good. Noting the progress of the Ambassador affair, the disgruntled Nicaraguans took heart, and the governments of the neighboring States felt secure in planning for the eventual downfall of the filibuster control of Nicaragua.

When the Charter news reached Vanderbilt he was not slow to act. There were two channels open to him, and he used both. His protest to the State Department in Washington bordered on the absurd. With the Presidency of his company in sight, he had actively encouraged recruiting for the last shipment of filibusters before the revocation of the Charter. With the boot hurting on the other foot, he urged the United States government to hurry to the aid of American property in Nicaragua. He was told to refer the matter to the local authorities.

But he could stop supplies reaching Walker and lost no time in doing so. Boats sailing from New York cleared for Panama, and an agent was despatched to head off the San Francisco vessels before they reached San Juan del Sur. For six weeks nothing reached Nicaragua, and Walker began to feel the pinch of lack of supplies.

Not until the 8th April did Morgan manage to have the first ship of the new Chartered Company ready to sail from New York. After a considerable amount of trouble, caused by Vanderbilt, it left. But, at the other end, it encountered great difficulty in discharging freight and passengers. Vanderbilt, with the golden, hard advantage of wealth, was doing everything he could to hamper Walker; and, to make the situation yet more acute, he sent out a special agent to Granada to sow the seeds of discord between Rivas and his American adviser.

But Walker never considered yielding an inch. Rather he proceeded to fight back and entrench himself against an enemy with whom, as the press of the interested world lost no time in announcing, he had no possible chance. By August the amateur commission he had appointed made its final report on the indebtedness of the old Transit Company to the Nicaraguan government. In this it was announced that the State was creditor to the extent of $412,589.16. This settled, the existing property of the company in Nicaragua was confiscated and handed over to Morgan and Garrison in consideration of their returning to Walker the bonds they had received in payment of their services in supplying the Rivas Government with arms, ammunition, food and recruits. Thus was the position of Walker's régime made secure. Or so he thought.

In addition to frenzied finance, there had also been war to handle. The move of the Legitimists over the Costa Rican border settled a feud of long standing. Nicaragua had never been on too friendly terms with the country to its south. But the leaders of the two soon found common ground in their attitude towards Walker. Mora, President of Costa Rica, saw in the presence of the filibusters a threat to his own country. As they treated Nicaragua, so might they some day do to Costa Rica.

Walker regarded the protests made by Mora's Minister in Washington as a mere matter of form; but, wishing naturally to put himself on the best terms with Costa Rica, when he accredited a Minister across the border and the man was immediately sent back to Granada, he realized that after all blood was thicker than water. With the cancellation of the Transit Company franchise Mora was pleased. But, like Rivas, on the granting of the Morgan-Garrison charter he came to the conclusion that things had gone too far. Regarding Walker as a bandit, he called a special session of his legislature and extracted from it authority to take up arms on behalf of the Republic of Nicaragua and a grant of one hundred thousand pesos with which to do it. On the 4th March the vanguard of his invasion set out, and Walker had a war on his hands.

To fight this campaign he had less than six hundred men upon whom he could rely, and in this small command cholera was already beginning to gain way. The Americans had been comparatively immune until this time. But several months in the country told its tale. To hearten him, though, the news of the Costa Rican activity brought back most of the Democrats to his fold; a movement he rewarded by announcing that the national colors would immediately be changed back to the Liberal red and the seat of government transferred to Leon. This latter concession was a dangerous move, making, as it did, virtually two capitals, as it was necessary to leave some of the Cabinet behind to clear up business.

The arrival, on March 9th, of the last batch of recruits carried by the Transit Company seemed a good omen for the "Gray-Eyed Man of Destiny," and immediately thereafter he despatched a force to invade Costa Rica.

This battalion, a hastily put together collection of Germans, French and Spanish, without any discipline, left for the border on the 12th March under the command of the man recently rejected by Costa Rica as Walker's minister. The animosity born of the treatment he had received when attempting to present his credentials, was calculated to give him ardor; but it could hardly be expected to endow him with military lore. His men, loosely organized in four companies, straggled along in the heat more or less as they pleased. There was no advance guard, and the stragglers followed along for miles. At Santa Rosas they walked into the Costa Rican advance guard, stood their ground for a busy five minutes, and then broke in a terrible rout. Having executed wounded and prisoners, the Costa Ricans then closed and proceeded on their invasion.

Fully confident that he would hear of a victory at any moment, Walker was down with fever when the news of Santa Rosas reached him. With it came the information that the advancing army could not possibly number less than four thousand. There was no time to be lost. He paraded his six hundred Americans and, sick as he was, led them from Granada to Rivas. On hearing the news, Granada behaved shockingly. All Americans not under military discipline hastened to pack what they could and get out of the country; and immediately, from Leon, came the information that the northern Central American countries were about to join causes with the victorious Costa Ricans. The dismay spread even to the till then reliable Phalanx, and, in an endeavor to raise their drooping spirits, the officers indulged in a drunken party.

But Walker was not in the mood to permit such behavior. Parading his men he made a threatening, bullying harangue and stood them ready to receive the enemy. Already the fugitives from Santa Rosas were passing through; and these were stopped and to some extent reorganized.

As he waited, two scraps of information reached him at the same time. The first, which was true, was to the effect that the Costa Ricans were over the border and halting before coming on. The second, born of panic and treachery, told of the invasion of Nicaragua by San Salvador and Honduras. Nonplussed, Walker decided to return to Granada and embarked his men for the capital by way of the lake. Asked by one of his subordinate officers to leave a small party at Rivas to get information of and to harass the enemy, he burst into one of his celebrated tantrums and told the volunteer to mind his own business. The move he made and his behavior whilst making it show that at this time the Colonel was badly rattled.

On the lake, however, he tried a ruse. Sailing in the opposite direction from Granada, he hoped that the Costa Ricans would be led to think he was about to invade their country. But the enemy completely misread the move and decided that the hated foreigners were making an exit from Nicaragua by way of the Caribbean. Glad to see the last of them they made no attempt at attack, and Walker sailed round the lake to Granada.

At the old capital news was received to the effect that the invasion had reached Rivas and the other war had not developed. He lost no time in getting his men on the road again and with six hundred under arms marched on Rivas. At a little after eight in the morning of April 11th the Americans attacked the sleeping Costa Ricans with everything but numbers in their favor. The Second Battle of Rivas did little for William Walker's military reputation. Brushing aside the sleepy sentries, the Americans reached the center of the town just as the garrison was beginning to wake up. They climbed the roofs and surrounded Walker's men. Later, unable to do as much damage as they expected, the Costa Ricans set fire to the buildings about the plaza, and the Americans were in a desperate situation. With nightfall, after losing one hundred and twenty casualties, Walker found a way into the open, and his command crept out, leaving the wounded to be butchered next morning by the enemy.

But what Walker had failed to do, cholera achieved most effectively. It is a debatable point whether Walker accepted the cholera as a Jehovah-sent ally come to the rescue of Nordic supremacy. At all events, the Costa Ricans lost approximately six hundred men at Rivas from American rifle fire; and, immediately afterwards, pestilence broke out in town, due to the fact that no effort was made to clean up the streets after

the battle, and men died fast. Deserted by their nominal leader, brother of the President of Costa Rica, the
terrified remainder started out for home, and by the
middle of May, spreading the disease through every
town they passed and taking it back to their own country, the few survivors scattered to their homes. Twelve
thousand people in Costa Rica perished in the succeeding epidemic, and once more the superstitious natives
of Nicaragua could point to the "Gray-Eyed Man of
Destiny" who could not even throw away his chances
by shocking generalship.

Nor could he, apparently, be assailed from within.
Legitimist uprisings behind his back during the Costa
Rican War were easily put down by his native allies.
For all that, things were not entirely easy with him.
Cholera he dodged rather effectively by moving his
own immediate force to the old Transit Company's
landing place in the lake. But friends brought news
from Leon, where Vanderbilt's agents were stirring up
President Rivas against his commander-in-chief, and
intercepted mail showed beyond doubt that Costa
Rican orders for arms and ammunition were being
filled in England.

On the 4th June, 1856, Walker entered Leon. The
people gave him a tremendous reception, hailing him as
deliverer of their country from invasion. But this
proved to be only half the interest they had in him.
For several weeks Leon had been enduring the false
labor pains of a typical Nicaraguan election. With
that section laid waste by the war not voting, three
Democrats, Rivas, Jerez and Selva, had each been striving to obtain the necessary number of votes to put him
in the Presidency. Each Sunday the polls were open;
but nothing like a proper result had been obtained.
Thinking that Walker would bring the capital back to

Granada, the inhabitants of that part of the country now nominated him as head of the government. He came to Leon as a conqueror and a presidential candidate. On arrival, after the celebrations, songs and dances, Walker insisted that Rivas order a completely new election started. Rivas acceded, as usual, and, having got what he wanted, Walker marched his men back to Granada on the 11th June, leaving behind a company of rifles, as a presidential guard, under Von Natzmer.

Walker's exit from Leon was as great an event, and more official, than his entrance. Glad to see him off, the Cabinet marched out of the city with him and, to the disgust of a chronicler who noticed Walker wipe the spot, Rivas gave the General a boisterous farewell kiss.

But Jerez had been at work, and before Walker was a day's march from Leon a courier from Von Natzmer brought him ill tidings. Jerez had said that Walker was planning to shift the capital back to Granada, and the result had been a sudden change in the atmosphere. Later in the day Jerez had issued an order to Von Natzmer about certain sentries he had posted, and, on the latter refusing to obey, an open breach had resulted. Immediately a rumor spread that Walker had left instructions for the arrest of Rivas and Jerez; and Von Natzmer, becoming alarmed, had seized the local arsenal where he and his small detachment were soon besieged by a howling mob calling for the extermination of all Americans in the country. In the excitement Jerez and Rivas vanished to turn up a few days later in Chinandega. There, in high-flown language worthy of Walker himself, they issued declarations to the governments of San Salvador and Guatemala to the effect that poor Nicaragua was again ripe for saving by its friends.

Walker, however, was not interested in Leon. He pushed on to Granada, leaving Von Natzmer to whatever fate might overtake him, and from there issued a proclamation defining Rivas as a Provisional President created by himself under the treaty of October 23, 1855, but now no longer capable of holding office since leaving his capital. The presidency, so Walker maintained, had returned to his own pocket. By the same declaration, all acts of Rivas since the proclamation of a new election were voided and all men obeying or helping him were outlawed. In Rivas' place Fermin Ferrer was appointed Provisional President pending the election.

There followed the usual Latin bombardment and counter-bombardment with proclamations. Away to the north Rivas denounced Walker and all Americans, and a new candidate, Estrada, entered the lists to throw mud at every one already there. Rivas' last proclamation had set the date of the election on June 29th. With a week to go, Walker threw his hat into the ring and commenced to prepare for his own election. Booths were erected hurriedly in Rivas, Granada and some smaller towns; and the naturalized soldiery were requested to express their choice. All through the long Sunday the returns came in to Walker who was busy with a map upon which the populations of the provinces from which he could not hear were divided amongst the candidates as he estimated they might vote. The result was an overwhelming success. Out of 32,000 odd votes Walker was elected to the Presidency of the Republic of Nicaragua with over 11,000 more votes than his nearest rival, the faithful Fermin Ferrer.

With the announcement of the ballot, the Provisional President fixed July 12th for the inauguration of his successor. On that morning the army was pa-

raded and escorted General William Walker to the
prepared platform where, under the flags of Cuba,
France, the United States and Nicaragua, he swore on
bended knee to perform the duties of his high office in
the way they deserved and then congratulated the elec-
tors in a cut and dried speech. The evening was given
up to a banquet which included over fifty toasts, drunk
by fifty guests, first and last of which were "The President" and "Uncle Billy."

The problems confronting the new executive were
not many. The matter of a Cabinet was settled at
once. Ferrer became Secretary of State, and other
loyal Nicaraguans filled remaining offices with Americans under them as sub-secretaries. Apart from this
question there only remained the business of raising
enough money to keep the wheels moving and attracting likely looking Americans to the country. There
had been a few arrivals lately; but these had done little
more than keep up the strength, and, with conditions
as they were, the through-passengers had preferred to
go on to where their tales did not do much good to the
recruiting.

In the meantime the opposition was acting. On the
day of Walker's inauguration at Granada, a detachment from San Salvador reached Leon. A week later
a Guatemalan force brought the troops under Rivas,
who had about 500 Nicaraguans under him, to 1,800.
Too, Honduras had notified Leon, on the 7th July,
that she would send assistance. On the 18th, Honduras, Guatemala, and San Salvador formally entered
an alliance, declaring their individual independence
and recognizing Rivas as Provisional President of Nicaragua. But their affairs were not immediately to go
forward easily. With the three bodies of men in Leon,
Rivas appointed the commander of the San Salvador

troops as commander-in-chief. Immediately the Guate-
malans were up in arms, there was a scuffle in the
square, and martial law had to be proclaimed in the
capital.

In the meantime Walker was endeavoring to meet
his own problems: finding funds and importing men.

On July 14th he issued a decree by which all public
documents might be worded either in Spanish or English; and another providing that, in order to bring some
order out of the existing confusion about land titles,
all real property be registered within six months. He
made no bones about the intention behind these pro-
nouncements. Frankly they were "intended to place a
large portion of the land of the country in the hands
of the white race." The natives knew nothing about
titles and registration, and in any case the Americans
could be counted upon, without any barrier of language, to act before the Nicaraguans.

In order to make these provisions more telling and
simplify the task of "the white race," these decrees
were followed, on the 16th of July, by another which
declared the property of all who had acted against the
Republic—Walker's Republic—since October 23rd,
1855, to be forfeit and a commission appointed to deal
with these cases. On condemnation, land was to be
appraised and put up for auction, no bid for less than
two-thirds of the estimated value being accepted, to be
paid for immediately in Walker scrip or cash. This
deal was calculated to bring in money and liquidate
much of the public debt.

Now the new Nicaraguan navy was in action. A
Costa Rican schooner had been seized in the harbor
of San Juan del Sur, equipped with two six-pounders,
christened the *Granada,* and placed under the commander-in-chief, Lieutenant Irvine Fayssoux, a Mis-
sourian who had served in the navy of the Republic

of Texas after which he had participated in various Cuban raids. On July 21st the *Granada* left the harbor of San Juan del Sur on a cruise "being the first vessel that ever went to sea as a governmental vessel," and proceeded to capture a few ships on board one of which was the Costa Rican owner of the Nicaraguan navy. For his ill luck in falling into Walker's hands the mercantile magnate was deemed guilty of treason, tried, sent to Granada, tried again under Walker's auspices and shot in the plaza. To claim damages from the Granadino régime was equivalent to treason.

On the rejection of French by the State Department at Washington, Walker had appointed a new Minister—Father Augustin Vijil, curate of Granada, a renowned orator who had earned for himself the title of "The Bossuet of Nicaragua."

Unfortunately for himself, Vijil had been in favor of much of the early Walker administration and, before things had fully developed, agreed to succeed French. Accepted by Secretary Marcy, the tide of opinion soon turned against the padre, directed by the ministers of other Central American countries, until his post became unbearable to him and he returned to Nicaragua in early July and applied to be allowed to leave the country immediately. Representation in Washington appearing necessary to Walker, he now sent another American, Appleton Oakman, as his minister, arming him with a letter to President Pierce in which the following appeared:

"God grant a continuance of a happy harmony between the two sister republics linked in the same continental cause. God preserve you many years for the happiness of your citizens."

This missive Oakman presented on August 15th, but had to wait a month for any notice to be taken of it, when Secretary Marcy informed him that the political condition of Nicaragua did not justify his recognition.

With revenue in mind, on July 31st, new decrees were issued and went into force. Expenses had been met as they arose by seven per cent scrip which assumed an exchange value of about seven cents on the dollar, giving Walker an excuse for stopping the interest feature in later issues. Against this there was now a Tariff revision which permitted those articles more likely to be used by the Americans to enter the country free, but placing spirituous liquors and tobacco on a twenty per cent basis, and providing three open ports in the country. Together with this decree were also established the sales of licenses to storekeepers.

By this time the Costa Rican government, in reply to an inquiry from the allied Central American countries to the north of Nicaragua and under pressure of Spanish agents, joined the anti-Walker union, promising to render active aid as soon as it had recovered from the cholera epidemic. To show the direction in which the wind was blowing for Walker, about this time a French man-of-war convoyed San Salvadorean reënforcements for Leon to port and protected their transport from a threatened attack by the *Granada,* while, in the first week of August, a thirteen-ship British fleet anchored in the harbor of Greytown. Hearing of these last movements, Walker proclaimed all Central American ports, with cited exceptions, in a state of blockade and ordered his "navy" to see that the order was carried out.

He had spread his force out against an attack from the direction of Leon, occupying Managua and Masaya with small garrisons and sending mobile units as far forward as possible to scour the country for supplies. Toward the end of August he was considerably cheered by the arrival at Granada of the Hon. Pierre Soulé. Before the Rivas-Walker break a half-million dollar loan, on public lands, had been authorized. In this connection Soulé arrived, to be at once taken in hand by the President who ironed out all difficulties, and, on the 28th August, authorized a loan of half a million dollars, at six per cent, secured by public lands, to be handled by a New Orleans house.

But the soldiery of the Republic were no cause for optimism. Summer and inaction had helped the spread of both cholera and typhoid, and these as well as the scarcity of rations since the trouble with the Transit Company caused frequent desertions. These, however, were greater still in the native companies whose members found it easier to live on the land than the filibusters. In an endeavor to stop this trend and also to get the Nicaraguans working on behalf of the government he had installed, Walker, on the 5th September, probably on the advice of Soulé and without doubt with later legislation in view, issued his decree against vagrants by which men without visible means of support who did not seek employment for fifteen days might be put to work on the public account for a period of from one to six months.

The day after this act was promulgated it was followed up by a second legalizing labor by contract, contracts running into terms of years, and providing that workers breaking labor engagements might join the vagrants on the public working force.

These two provisions were obviously made with an eye to attracting American capital to a State notorious for the haphazard nature of its labor. But concluding, on second thought, that something more iron-clad would not harm his case, Walker, on the 22nd September, went a long step further. On this date he proclaimed that all acts and decrees of the Federal Constituent Assembly as well as of the Federal Congress were declared null and void. In declaring this, Walker permitted no mistake made as to his intention. The Anti-Slavery Law of Nicaragua was no longer on the statute books. This was obviously a matter he considered necessary at the time. The statement has been made that Walker's Mexican and Nicaraguan escapades were undertaken only with the view of establishing slave areas. In his pre-filibuster days he was well known to be against slavery. In justice to him this should be pointed out.

On the 18th September the allied army at Leon commenced its march on Granada. By the morning of the 24th they were approaching Managua where a filibuster outpost was stationed. The strength of the Rivas forces appearing to be overwhelming, the officer in command marched his men out, and the first of Walker's strongholds fell without a shot being fired. After a comfortable rest in Managua, the enemy again took to the road, anticipating something rather warmer in their reception at Masaya where four hundred filibusters were strongly entrenched and sending insulting challenges to their opponents. But the fire-eaters were to be disappointed again. As in a previous instance, Walker made an error of judgment and withdrew his entire force to Granada before the enemy had made contact. Then, instead of harassing the advancing army, he left it severely alone with the result that before he realized it Rivas' men were interfering with the rationing of Granada. This was too much.

An attack on Masaya was immediately ordered, and the result of it was again an old story. The entrance to the town was simple; but, once inside, the filibusters were surrounded and had difficulty in fighting their way out of a fruitless position.

While this action was in progress, a split occurred

in the enemy command with the result that two leaders withdrew their men from Rivas' main body, refusing to fire another shot for him. But the insubordinate couple changed their minds when they realized that all Walker's forces were bottled up in Masaya and headed for Granada. There they played havoc with the civilians left behind. Five prominent American citizens of pre-Walker vintage were shot in cold blood, and the town was put to the sack.

But the Masaya expedition had extricated itself. On October 13th, a year from the day he had first entered the Legitimist capital, Walker marched it back to drive the insurgents out and restore order. He had lost few men at Masaya. But the reëntry into Granada was expensive, and he also found that during the short occupation the enemy had cut heavily into his supplies. Not satisfied with the state of affairs as he found it, Walker thickened the atmosphere by ordering the summary execution of two Guatemalan officers, captured at Masaya. These were polished and accomplished gentlemen who had received part of their education in Europe and during their captivity had made a deep impression upon the American officers with whom they came in contact. A protest against the sentence was made by their filibuster friends, and, in refusing to listen to it, Walker only succeeded in impressing upon his own officers that he had committed an unpardonable injustice.

The remainder of October was spent by Walker in strengthening the defenses of Granada and preparing plans for an attack on the waiting allies at Masaya. But on the 1st of November he received bad news. Recovered from their troubles, the Costa Ricans were ready for war again, and an army was moving on San Juan del Sur. This it occupied on the 7th, and the filibusters realized that their communications with San

Francisco were cut. In this condition and with the
Masaya army now in the neighborhood of three thousand men, Walker was driven to desperate means.
For once he adopted a bold plan. He would sail
his troops from Granada to the Transit Landing,
march down the Vanderbilt Trail, attack the Costa
Ricans, return at once, and try his chances with the
allies.

By the 12th he was on the outskirts of San Juan del
Sur, attacked, defeated and demoralized the Costa
Ricans, and the next morning was marching back to
the lake. On the fourteenth he was again in Granada
with orders for the march on Masaya issued. He set
out that night with five hundred and fifty men. But
halfway to his objective he learned that Jerez, commanding a detachment of seven hundred, had left
Masaya two days before with orders to occupy Rivas.
It was essential to success that this body should not
join up with the Costa Ricans and that, in particular,
the Vanderbilt Trail should not be held by them. To
protect against these eventualities, two hundred and
fifty filibusters had to be sent back to the Transit
Landing to look after the situation.

With the remainder he closed on Masaya and
launched his attack during the evening of the 15th.
It took him two days to achieve his invariable siege
result. By midnight of the 17th, with a third of his
men out of action, he was in the central square surrounded by the garrison he had started by attacking.
Worn out and on the verge of giving in, his men insisted on being retired. Before morning they had
dribbled out of the town and were shambling after their
leader back to Granada. Had the allies made the
slightest effort at pursuit, the Walker episode would
have ended there. But it did not. Overjoyed at finding their enemy gone in the morning, they could do

little but celebrate their victory, and the chance slipped
from them.

During the morning of the 18th the defeated force
reëntered Granada, and preparations for abandoning
the capital were immediately set on foot. Rivas was
to be the new capital, and all capable of marching there
were sent off overland. Those unable to reach Rivas,
were taken to the Transit Landing and encamped.
There were other details that had to be looked after.
In the hospitals were over a hundred men suffering
from cholera, typhoid, dysentery, yellow fever and sun-
stroke. These it was decided would have to be evacuated. When all were clear, Granada was to be put to
the torch. For the wounded Walker chose the island
of Omtepe, in the lake, an extinct crater which from
earliest times had been reserved entirely for aboriginal
Indians. There under pouring rain, attacked by the
frightened natives day and night, the bulk of the
invalids died until, under hot protests from the doctors
in charge, Walker removed the few survivors to Rivas.

The burning of Granada proceeded with no signal
success. Seeing they were detailed for destruction,
the party detached for the task considered the sanest
method of going about their work was to start on the
wine shops. More men had to be recalled to continue the job, and while it was going forward, the
Masaya garrison, having learned of the evacuation, attacked the town from three sides. For four days the
siege was carried on before the enemy realized that
the defense was weak. Then, after offering the officer
in command free passports back to the United States
for himself and men if he would surrender, the assault
was pressed furiously. Under terrible conditions the
beleaguered force held out, retiring gradually through
the streets, burning as they went, and leaving behind
them a trail of dead, shot and killed by disease, until a

reënforcement permitted Walker to send a body of men to the relief of Granada. They were successful at the first attempt, and the survivors were led out during the night after their leader had erected a sign reading, "Here was Granada"—nothing was left of the old Legitimist capital. Of the 277 men in Granada when the siege began only 111 accompanied their relief out of the ruins.

The month elapsing between the evacuation of Granada and the relief of the demolition party had been a hard one for Walker. At Granada he had that detachment to consider. Daily he sailed up the lake to study the situation from the water. But, until he had his reënforcements, there was little chance of helping them. His remaining men at the Transit Landing were in no good shape. Cholera and the other pestilences attacked them, food was insufficient, and it rained steadily. On the island of Omtepe his invalids were dying daily. Not only were Walker's medical officers incompetent; but their appliances and stores of drugs were entirely inadequate. To add to the difficulties, the Costa Ricans at San Juan del Sur had received reenforcements and had thereupon joined hands with Jerez at Rivas. Nothing seemed to go right. To add to the gloom, news came that Fayssoux had been defeated at sea and the navy obliterated. This was almost the last straw for many; but it turned out that the eyewitness had seen wrong. The Costa Rican barque had been sunk. The reversal of facts was a tremendous tonic at the Transit Landing, and Fayssoux was granted a brevet-captaincy for the dramatic surprise he had created.

In New York, Vanderbilt's Christmas Card to Wall Street, printed in all papers, had announced that he shortly expected to have the Nicaraguan question set-

tled for all time. Had he known it his interests on
the Isthmus had already started to turn. During November Vanderbilt had sent two representatives to
Costa Rica with offers of coöperation and advice.
"Stop Trans-Isthmian traffic and Walker is finished"
was their song, and on the 22nd of December a party
of men had wiped out Walker's garrison on the river
between Lake Nicaragua and Greytown. This done,
they proceeded to Greytown, took over the boats in
the harbor, steamed up the river and captured, without a shot, the fort which had been established at the
point where the river left the lake. Communications
with New York were now out of Walker's control.

But it was not yet entirely as Vanderbilt wished.
Three separate shipments of Walker recruits were
landed at Greytown and, under men who had already
served with Walker, attempted to regain control of
the river and lake. Their operations were desperate,
but badly handled; and finally the British naval commander in Greytown insisted that the whole body be
removed. This was arranged, and they were embarked for New Orleans on a British man-of-war.
Thus, in April, on receiving the news, Morgan and
Garrison gave orders that their new line suspend
operations with Greytown. The only outside help remaining to Walker was cut off. It was left to see
how long his famishing men could exist between the
several fires about them.

Walker's force lasted out until May 1st when the
filibuster handed himself over to Commander Davis
of the U. S. S. *St. Mary's*. The experiences of the
first four months of 1857 had proved conclusively that
it was impossible to do anything more in the country.
Fighting in all directions, dying of disease, living on
mule flesh was too much for men who had been offered free passport home for handing themselves over

to the enemy.   Henningsen's statistics of Walker's
Nicaraguan escapade give 1,000 died of disease, 700
deserted, 250 discharged as unfit, 80 captured and the
balance of 480 surrendered.   Of these less than 150
were on their feet and able to fight.

The final capitulation of Walker was arranged between him and Davis.   He refused to treat with the
allies and maintained to the end that he was in the
better position when he left the country.   As a climax
to the fiasco Walker did himself no good by riding off
with Davis and returning to the United States alone
on a separate ship from his followers.   Had he had
any interest in his troops, had he had any sympathy
for the men who had maintained him in Nicaragua, he
might have had the grace to say at least a final word.
He left San Juan del Sur as soon as possible and
traveled to New Orleans by way of Panama.   His
men were soon divided into convenient batches and
sent back to the States as well as possible.

At New Orleans Walker was met with enthusiasm.
He was the Lindbergh of his day.   Crowds went down
to the dock and carried him to a carriage.   There were
banquets and public meetings.   Everybody spoke,
orated, thundered.   And Walker the loudest—and
lengthiest—of the lot.   Unblushingly—perhaps he
fooled himself—he told of his high ideals; lashed with
furious tirades the traitors who had frustrated his
superb, unselfish plans.   Similar receptions greeted him
in several other cities which he visited before reaching
Washington.   There he called upon the President,
Buchanan, and lodged a formal protest against the
actions of Commander Davis—calmly forgetting that
the latter had actually saved him and his few surviving
filibusters from a white wall and a firing squad.

But his greatest triumph was reserved, as usual, for

New York. He was met on the Jersey side by an official welcoming party which carried him to the Battery and submitted him to the customary civic indignities, including official theater parties at the Bowery and Wallack's. The New York balloon did not last long. It was most effectually pricked by the unexpected return of a shipload of the men whom he had deserted, consigned to the port on charity, and arriving there starving and penniless. At once, on the publication of their stories, Walker went into an eclipse and appeared a week later in Charleston, S. C., whence he proceeded to Nashville and entered into an arrangement there with a returned member of his original "fifty-six" for the recruiting of a company for another descent on Nicaragua. This completed, he proceeded to Mobile where he had the audacity, in August, to outline for the press the organization of "The Central American League," created for the avowed purpose of returning to Nicaragua with a larger and better equipped party than formerly.

By October, in response to representations by the representatives of the Central American governments, the Federal authorities began to wake up and took note that there appeared evidence of Walker's recruiting activities in three districts. Agents put to watch these reported that they could not be regarded seriously as, though the public seemed in favor of Walker and his men, there was not enough money among them to make their movements have any serious significance.

Actually Walker was in New Orleans with his plans for sailing far advanced. He might have quietly left in a week, had not a scrap of news reached the local papers from New York giving the correct state of affairs. It appeared in the evening papers of 10th November and was followed by a conference of the Federal port authorities who thereupon proceeded to

Walker's lodgings at midnight and arrested him on a
charge of intention to violate the neutrality laws.
Pierre Soulé now appeared on the scene with a bondsman, and Walker was released to appear again on the
19th. The next day, 11th, the filibuster jumped his
bail, gathered his "staff," and embarked on the Mobile
mail boat to join his ship, the *Fashion,* which had
slipped out of New Orleans as soon as Federal action
seemed imminent. Shortly after the *Fashion* was in-
spected by the authorities. But Walker concealed himself in the bilge, and the 270 filibusters aboard had little difficulty in proving that their intention was to sail
as Trans-Isthmian passengers for California.

On the 14th November the boat sailed from Mobile,
and, once on the high seas, organization of the expedition commenced. Fayssoux and Von Natzmer, together with four others of the original "immortals,"
received commissions and, with a new press and mate-
rials, the ex-editor of the defunct *El Nicaraguense* was
preparing to commence another news sheet the moment
President Walker came back into his "rights."

On the 23rd a company was landed to the south of
Greytown, and the next day Walker put his entire
force ashore on the sandspit across the bay from the
town under the nose of the U. S. S. *Saratoga* anchored
in port to prevent that very happening.

In the meantime the U. S. S. *Wabash,* flying the pen-
nant of Commodore Paulding, was lying in the harbor
of Aspinwall. A few days after Walker's landing,
the Commodore received two communications: one by
the mail steamer *Dee,* from Greytown, written by the
commander of the *Saratoga* asking for instructions and
advice as to what to do in regard to the filibusters; the
other per S. S. *Fashion,* from President Walker complaining that the presence of the *Saratoga* in Greytown
was a menace to his rights.

The net result of these communications was that, on December 6th, through Paulding's agency, the U. S. S. *Wabash* and *Fulton* and the H.M.S. *Leopard* and *Brunswick* sailed into Greytown harbor and dropped anchor. The various commanders then proceeded to lunch with the American Commodore on his flagship. Parties of men were sent in boats up the river, and, before Walker realized it, he was cut off from the interior. Paulding treated with him by messenger, received some high-toned replies, but finally insisted on his surrender which Walker conveyed to him in person, breaking down in tears in the Commodore's cabin when he discovered Paulding had no intention of treating him as more than an outlaw.

Matters, however, were soon settled. Walker surrendered to the United States on condition that he would not be shipped back with his men. They were embarked on the *Saratoga* for Norfolk, while their leader went, established in Paulding's cabin and now on excellent terms with his captors, to Aspinwall where he gave his parole to return by the regular mail to the United States and there hand himself over to the first U. S. marshal available.

He complied with these terms, reaching New York on the 27th December and proceeding the next day to the office of Marshal Isaiah Rynders, one of his greatest admirers, who had been the presiding genius at his reception earlier in the year. Rynders was nonplussed for a time, but in the end decided to take Walker to Washington and lay the case before the State Department. There Secretary Cass decided that Walker's arrest was not in order and ordered Rynders to release his prisoner.

The storm following this second return of Walker from Nicaragua developed into what was called the Walker-Paulding Affair. Walker's dismissal was regarded as showing the sympathy of the administration with his projects. He himself lost no opportunity of stating his case in public or to reporters, berating the Commodore for invading the territory of a friendly country and kidnaping the army and President. The only reparation possible was to have Paulding return the entire expedition to the place from which he had taken it, reëquip it at the public expense and, before leaving Greytown, fire an official salute to the Nicaraguan flag. In December Buchanan dropped Walker's hopes a couple of pegs by condemning the filibustering movement and recommending Congress to pass Acts calculated to curb what was nothing less than robbery and murder. The end of this affair was that Paulding was relieved of his command and, while unemployed ashore, subjected to a series of lawsuits brought against him by those who had financed Walker's expedition.

Having caused and helped along the Washington storm-in-a-teapot, Walker left for the south. Grandiosely he announced that he considered it a point of honor to give himself up there to save the bondsman who had gone bail before his embarkation on the *Fashion*.

On arrival at Mobile he was promptly arrested and sent to New Orleans, indicted there for violating the neutrality laws, and released pending trial. This was precisely what he wanted and gave him an opportunity to remain in the city more or less unmolested for several months. He lived quietly in rooms, seeing men interested in his schemes and making no pretense as to his intentions. As soon as possible he would return to Nicaragua. He would have Christmas dinner in Granada—or what he had left of it.

On the last day of May the trial opened, and things looked black for the filibuster. An imposing array of witnesses were produced against him, and the final charge of the judge was not promising for his case. However, Pierre Soulé and Walker both made able defense speeches, and the jury disagreed. Walker insisted on another trial, looking for all the notoriety he could get. But it was not granted him, and he was again a technically free man.

The next few months were spent in quiet preparation by him and by the authorities in absurd chasing of their own tails. Complicated and contradictory instructions were issued to warships in the Caribbean, and the time of Paulding's successor was chiefly spent inquiring from Washington as to how to reconcile such orders as that making him responsible for any hostile landings in Central America and the one insisting that no action must be taken on suspicion, though all interference should take place at more than one nautical league from the final destination of filibusters.

During October Walker notified the port authorities at Mobile that he was about to sail for Nicaragua with three hundred emigrants, and during the next month papers were requested for the ship in question. The ship was detained.

On the 4th December another clearance was applied for, this time for the schooner *Susan,* only so far as Key West. Under forcible pressure it was denied, and the filibusters decided to sail without papers. One hundred and twenty men were embarked about midnight, and the boat put out. She left under sealed orders from Walker. For several days there was a merry game of hide-and-seek with a revenue cutter. But the government boat finally ran ashore, while the *Susan* proceeded.

On opening the orders, they read their task. The men were to be landed in Honduras, where they were to be used in the capture of the fortress of San

Fernando, the proposed base for future operations. Walker considered himself justified in invading Honduras by the fact that this country had allied itself with the Nicaraguan "rebels" against him.

Before finding port, however, the *Susan* imitated the pursuing cutter and piled herself up on a reef. The crew were safely landed, on December 16th, on an island near Belize to be taken off shortly after by the commander of H. M. S. *Basilisk* who cheerfully offered to carry the whole party back to Mobile. He received a great welcome, including a banquet to himself and the filibusters, on his arrival there. But the next day the leaders of the expedition were arrested and placed under bond.

The news of this effort was sufficient to put Central America into one of its periodical "Walker" panics. But actually Walker had only directed the affair from the side lines and had not intended following it up until it was safely established ashore. But the alarm spread and lasted through the year. All sorts of tales were abroad, how Walker was coming through Mexico, how he had been recognized traveling under an assumed name across Panama with a batch of Californian immigrants, obviously out to land on the Pacific Coast of Nicaragua. Actually he was lying quiet and spent most of 1858 and 1859 partially under cover, only emerging to lecture and keep the "cause" before his sympathizers. Some of the time he spent in New Orleans, the rest in Nashville and New York City.

By September, 1859, he had acquired arms and another ship which was sent to New Orleans, but had no luck in an attempt to clear for Aspinwall. The vessel was libeled and the crew, waiting to join her, apprehended.

In the meantime Walker had performed two feats entirely on his own. In early 1860 his book *The War*

in Nicaragua came from the press to an admiring public, and about the same time he entered the Catholic
Church.   Naturally the religious change occasioned
various opinions from friends and enemies, the former
insisting that it was the conscientious act of a devout
man, the latter maintaining that it was merely an
effort to curry a little favor with the Central Americans.

In November, 1859, the Roatan Island incident had,
so far as the politicians counted, been closed.   This
island had been seized by the British as part of British
Honduras in 1841.   In 1859, as the culmination of a
long dispute, it was returned to Honduras.   Foreign
residents on the island protested against this decision
in vain, and finally several of them traveled to New
Orleans in an endeavor to enlist the sympathy of
Walker in their condition.   Meeting them in April, he
saw an excuse for another expedition.   With Roatan as
a base, he would again prosecute his good work on the
mainland.   Towards the end of April, 1860, he
dispatched his advance party to survey the situation
on the island and await his arrival with a larger force.
When this party, living on the hospitality of the is-
landers, was joined by two further shipments of men
in May and early June, the government of Honduras
became thoroughly alarmed.   In self-protection the
President appealed to the British and requested that
the transfer of the island should be postponed.   On
the understanding that it was a temporary measure,
the Union Jack was hoisted again on Roatan and an
ad interim commissioner appointed by the governor of
British Honduras.

About the middle of June, Walker himself sailed for
Honduras on the *John E. Taylor*.   Finding the British
flag flying on Roatan and thinking that the transfer
of the island to Honduras was perhaps a matter of

days, he landed on a smaller island nearby and bided his time. But the fact soon was made known to him that the transfer would not take place while suspicious characters were in the neighborhood, and he decided on an entirely new line of action.

He was ready to put this into effect on the 5th August and that night proceeded with his men to the mainland. Giving up hope of operating from Roatan, his idea was to capture the town and fort of Truxillo and use it as a base for operations. Proceeding above the town under the cover of darkness, he landed and launched his attack at daybreak. There was little resistance, and before noon the town and defenses were completely under his control. He established his governmental headquarters at once and soon had a hospital and a system of supply working. Among his first acts was the usual Walker pronunciamento to the effect that war was being waged on behalf of the people against a government which stood between them and progress. Finally he declared Truxillo to be a free port, abolishing all customs duties.

This last declaration, so harmless in appearance and only promulgated in order to allow him to confiscate the customs funds on hand, immediately caused him trouble. Within two weeks of his arrival H.M.S. *Icarus* put into Truxillo, and Commander Salmon sent a sinister message to the filibuster. The Honduran customs receipts had been mortgaged to the British Government as collateral for an old debt. Walker's action had not only cut this source of income, but had menaced the interests of British traders. Walker would have to leave the port at once, and, though he and his officers might retain their side arms, all other arms, ammunition and supplies would have to be surrendered. In addition the money confiscated from the customs must be returned.

Walker replied in a tone unusual to him. He had not known of the customs mortgage, and, had he been aware of it, his actions would have been different. No funds had been removed. So there was nothing to render up. But he could not forego his usual chant. He was there to fulfill engagements which he was honor bound to carry through. His presence was a guarantee of the freedom of the people. However, in case he found it necessary to surrender to Salmon, and he did not consider it a dishonor to capitulate to a British officer where no warship of his own country was available, upon what terms could this be arranged?

On Salmon's reply to this communication much has been said and written. In view of later events it has importance, though its content is merely hearsay. The British commander expressed his relief that Walker appeared unwilling to make further trouble and ready to surrender to him. There had been many requests from the Honduran government, residents of Truxillo and the neighborhood for protection. The American consul had asked him to act in the matter. He was not entitled to give Walker the protection of the British flag on foreign soil, but *"would take the responsibility of that."* Over three thousand dollars had been taken from the customs house by some one. Walker would be held responsible for this and the passage money of his men back to the States.

Walker told Salmon's messenger to return for a reply the following morning and, with him out of sight, commenced preparations for evacuating the town. Leaving wounded and sick behind, he led his force of eighty men out of the fortress in the early hours of the morning and set off parallel with the coast for the Nicaraguan border. With daylight a Honduran battalion was after him. On the 23rd August Walker stopped

to fight and there was a short action on the banks of
the Roman River in which the filibusters lost a man
killed and several wounded. On arriving at the Rio
Negro, the Americans could not cross, so they turned
their faces to the sea and followed the river almost to
its mouth. There they established themselves at a
trading post and discussed further plans.

During this time the *Icarus* and a Honduran ship
filled with soldiers had sailed along the coast and,
with the filibusters at a halt, anchored in the mouth
of the Rio Negro. On the 3rd September Salmon appeared off the filibuster position with two cutters containing about forty men and demanded Walker's surrender. There was some parleying. Walker wanted
to be assured to whom he was surrendering, and
Salmon, with a gesture, indicated his rank badges. The
soi-disant General-President was not satisfied. Was
he surrendering to a British officer? He was. The
invaders were ordered aboard the *Icarus,* and during
the trip to Truxillo Walker swore that Central America had not seen the last of him. He would be
back.

He landed on its shore once again. At Truxillo
Salmon handed him and his chief lieutenant over to the
Hondurans. The remainder of the expedition, in various states of collapse and a uniform depth of depression, were accorded the protection of Salmon who
threatened to hang any native who attacked them.
Before going ashore under Honduran surveillance,
Walker took the opportunity to air the injustice under
which he was suffering to press representatives and
issued his last statement:

"September 5, 1860.
"I hereby protest before the civilized world that when I
surrendered to the captain of Her Majesty's steamer *Icarus,*

that officer expressly received my sword and pistol, as well as the arms of Colonel Rudler, and the surrender was made in so many words to him, as the representative of Her Britannic Majesty.

"WILLIAM WALKER."

He was in the fortress of Truxillo for six days, incommunicado, except to the priest he summoned as soon as he was placed in his cell, and on the evening of the 11th September was told that he was to be shot in the morning. He showed little emotion, but expressed an unusual request, for him, that his men should be well treated and not be held in any way responsible for the actions of the expedition.

The next morning he was marched to his wall, a distance of about half a mile from his prison, followed by a large crowd who appeared to be in a hilarious mood. The great Walker, with whose name they had frightened their children to sleep for five years, was on his *via dolorosa*. At a corner of the ruins of an old barracks two squads lined up before him and, after the priest had administered the last rites, fired at him in succession. The commander then blew off his face with the *coup de grâce* and formed his men up for the march back. Later in the morning, with subscriptions from American residents, the priest obtained a coffin for the corpse and buried it with the usual ceremony. Still later the city of Nashville endeavored to get possession of it for burial at home. But the Honduran government refused the request.

So ended his career, as a memorial to which in the square of San José, capital of Costa Rica, there stands to this day a statue in which that Liberty he professed to love so well tramples forever upon his recumbent figure.

CHARLES GEORGE GORDON

[1833–1884]

*who, always, in China, the Soudan, the
Crimea, dreamed of the Christ*

"CHINESE" GORDON

CHARLES GEORGE GORDON

CHARLES GEORGE GORDON was primarily a believing Christian; a man without thaumaturgical misgivings, qualms or curiosity, whose God was the essence and principle of love, and not the essence and principle of a rather remote, prosy and colorless cosmic or evolutionary control. Fate, by token of his inheritance, willed that his trade should be the trade of the sword and the drums; that he should fight Russians, Chinese and Arabs and die with his boots on, facing the foe. Yet, deep in his soul and *with* his soul, he never fought for or against a living human being; but—a modern St. Francis or St. Augustine—fought, stanchly, uncompromisingly, emphatically, for the co-eternity of the Divine Son and against the proud, brazen idols of Pharisees and Sadducees.

This war he waged without hatred, without insisting on putting a Calvinistic halo of ire and cruelty and contempt and intolerance around the steeple of the Church of God. The man was, indeed most curiously devoid of bitterness.

One looks for traces of this bitterness in "Chinese" Gordon, as one does in all those to whom destiny has brought unmerited criticism and unmerited failure. And one finds it only in that one remark of his when, coming down to earth and its hard concerns, he suggested that England has not been made by her statesmen, Whig or Tory, but by her gentlemen-adventurers —amongst whom, doubtless, he was a Lancelot, though a Lancelot quite without Tennyson's hero's annoying naïveté. Half to himself he added that these same

295

British statesmen, through short-sightedness, stupidity, jealousy or selfishness, have often undone what the gentlemen-adventurers have done . . . and, on the day of his death, with the Arabs closing in on him, he might have ranked Statesman Gladstone amongst the stupid or selfish undoers; or, his memory winging back across the decades, he might have included Statesmen Lord Aberdeen, Lord John Russell and Lord Clarendon who, listening to the advice of Statesman Lord Stratford de Redcliffe, committed the criminal blunder known to history as the Crimean War and sent British soldiers to the front without the most rudimentary training, almost without equipment, pouring out their blood at the Alma, at Inkerman and Balaclava and Tchernaya, and before Sebastopol.

There, in the gore and mud in front of the Malakoff and the Little Redan, Charles George Gordon, a lieutenant of engineers twenty-two years of age, received his first lesson in that sloppiness and unpreparedness which is the bane, and for some unknown psychological reason the pride and glory, of Anglo-Saxon democracy —be it a democracy flattered and soft-soaped by a king or bullied by a president—when, in his weekly letter to his mother, he described what he had seen and lived through; how, for instance, the Russians, brilliantly commanded by Prince Gortschakoff, sent out two ships from the harbor and bombarded the French lines for several hours and how the British vessels were "not able to move out to attack them, as steam was not up."

The ships were there. The guns were there. The men were there, keen and willing.

But—"steam was not up."

A common British tragedy.

The sort of twisted, grotesque tragedy which de-

feated Edward the Second at Bannockburn and the
Royalists at Marston Moor; which drove Prince
Charles Stuart back to France and wrecked Buckingham's expedition sent to the succor of the Huguenots
at La Rochelle; which forced Burgoyne's surrender at
Saratoga and caused the disgrace of Majuba; which
killed so many brave men—Gordon himself for
one. . . .

Of course there was, will always be, parliamentary
and journalistic white-washing. The Crimean War
was said to have come as a surprise to Ministry and
country; certainly did come as a surprise to Lieutenant
Gordon.

Born in 1833 and growing up in the lull which succeeded the clank and riot of Waterloo, he had, as one
of a notoriously prolific military family of Highland-
Scot ancestry, entered the Royal Military Academy at
Woolwich as a matter of course. He had been born
in the shadow of that establishment, while his father,
a lieutenant-general who had fought his guns excep-
tionally well at Maida, was serving an appointment
there, and gone about with him during the first ten
years of his life on assignments which took the old
warrior to the Pigeon House Fort in Dublin Bay,
Leith Fort, and the Island of Corfu.

The army for him; as naturally—and predestinedly
—as Lombard Street to a Rothschild and India to a
Cotton, a Warburton, or a Lawrence.

Still, he had been a rather timid child, fearing and
hating the noisy artillery practice that frequently
startled his play about the military works in which his
early days were thrown. It was only in Corfu that
he began to realize his shortcomings and understood
that his particular atavistic trinity should be Beef and
Blood and Brawn. So, at Corfu, very much to his

father's joy, to cure himself of his incipient cowardice, he developed a distressing habit of flinging himself into the sea, though he was unable to swim, and depending upon passing strangers to fish him out.

From Corfu he was sent home alone to enter a school at Taunton. There he remained for five years, building up a reputation for a certain mulish stubbornness and an uncanny and uncompromising sense of justice which were the despair of his autocratic headmaster. Thence he followed the traditional family path to Woolwich Academy where he shocked the officers and the one-legged governor as well as his relatives by his utter lack of enthusiasm, freely and tactlessly expressed, for the clan profession of war.

Not that he was afraid. He had overcome his earlier inhibitions. It was simply that he was not interested in the army as a career. On the other hand, he pursued his studies carefully, with a driving Scotch mastery of infinitesimal details, and stood fairly high on the lists.

Here, again, he displayed the same traits noticed at Taunton. On one occasion the cadets were granted leave to London to attend a circus. On the day before the event, Gordon's name was read out as being among those not included in the permission. Inquiring for the season, he discovered that this punishment was on account of suspicion having fallen on him as having been the ringleader of a commotion which had almost broken up a class. Gordon denied the accusation. Authority was adamant. Finally the real ringleader stepped forward and exonerated Gordon, who was summoned by the governor and told he might go with the other cadets. But he refused. Always ready to cut off his nose to spite his face if a principle of abstract ethics was involved, he stoutly maintained that, as long as official permission was controlled by such an unjust system, holding people guilty until they had proved their innocence, such permission was not worth the having.

It was typical of his congenital obstinacy; typical, too, that he never forgave the governor for what he considered a manifest unfairness, nor forgave him for the graver unfairness of postponing the date of his gazette into the army for a minor breach of discipline entirely out of proportion to the six months' additional stay at Woolwich Academy.

This refusal to forgive was not dictated by hate, nor did it breed hate. It was simply the stating, within his own soul, of a spiritual and ethical fact; a queer Gothic hardness going up like a flight of arrows.

The years at Woolwich had not noticeably increased his enthusiasm for the army as a career. He still preferred the study of the Bible to that of the Manual of Arms. But—and perhaps it was the principal weakness in his character—he seemed unable to go his own way, to defy his family, to choose a different profession. So he did his best. Being gazetted a second lieutenant of engineers and sent to Chatham, he applied himself earnestly to learn more of the technique of his craft, waiting until the differences of Turks and Russians, now rapidly coming to a head, should give him the opportunity of putting his learning into practice.

For a while the Turks had more than held their own, winning a succession of actions in Moldavia and Wallachia of which Oltenitza and Tchetati were the most important. But presently the Russians, commanded by that veteran soldier Prince Paskievich, took a vigorous offensive, and the destruction of the Sultan's fleet at Sinope impelled France and Britain to take a more active part in the campaign. Lord Raglan and Marshal Saint Arnaud, the allied commanders, were

given instructions to "concert measures for the siege
of Sebastopol"; and so, in the autumn of 1854, came
the call for more troops—came Gordon's initial chance.

Not a very martial chance in the beginning.

For, luckily for him, he was spared the ghastly experience of the first expeditionary force. Instead,
quickly gazetted to lieutenant, perhaps as much thanks
to his clan's importance in affairs military as because
of personal merit, he was sent to Pembroke Dock
where he assisted in the supervision of dispatching
war material to the front.

He found this occupation singularly tedious and un-
inspiring. Now that, in spite of his inclination, he
had embraced an army career, he wanted to be in the
thick of the fight. He pulled wires right and left
with the result that, in December, he received orders
to load a shipment of huts for the Crimea and to proceed overland to Balaclava to await their arrival.

It was time, and high time, for the huts. Hundreds
of soldiers had succumbed, were succumbing, to the
lack of shelter. Anglo-Saxon democracy was doing its
inefficient, murderous work; and the Czar's trusted old
friends, Generals January and February, were killing
more Britons than died of bullet wounds. Thus huts
were being sent; and—since there were then, as there
will always be, little ha'penny War Office clerks busy
with the winding and unwinding of medieval red tape—
were being sent by the slowest route possible.

Gordon chafed, protested. Not that it did him much
good. So he did the next best thing. He put his huts
aboard in record time; hurried across France; chafed
at another delay which kept him in Marseilles over a
week-end; and reached Balaclava on New Year's Day,
1855 . . . reached it in time to see Generals January
and February perform their macabre Dance of Death.
For, on the night of his arrival, two British officers

were frozen to death while, during the following evening, two others were smothered by the fumes of a
charcoal fire which they had hugged too closely.

Gordon saw—pitied—and acted; before long was
irritating his seniors with his desire to get something
started and done, to make bricks without proper red
tape straw, to build huts—*horribile dictu*—with whatever material was on hand, and without the orthodox
material prescribed in reams of official regulations.

He must have been a nagging, pestering, annoying
youngster. For he succeeded. Within five days he had
put up several huts; had saved a number of men from
freezing to death.

Perhaps—a debatable point—the War Office forgave him his trespasses.

On the 15th January he climbed the heights and got
his first view of besieged Sebastopol—"I do not think
I ever saw a prettier sight," he said in a letter home—
and on the 28th, his twenty-second birthday, he witnessed the affair of the Russian ships and the disgrace
of the English vessels that did not have steam up,
about which he wrote to his mother who was in
Gibraltar with the general.

Later in the month, still itching to do a turn in the
trenches, he was shifted to railway work—which, he
complained in his letters, should have been finished
long before—and contributed to the completion of a
supply line which was in operation by the latter part
of February. In the meantime the allies had been
grubbing about on their advanced positions, mining
and sapping in an amatuerish way, with little serious
plan, while the Russians were pushing out their defenses and establishing those thorns in the enemy's
side, the Mamelon and the Malakoff, which Lieutenant-Colonel Baron de Todleben, their chief engineer

who had begun the work at an early date, was daily
re-creating and rearming and improving, finally con-
necting them with a continuous *enceinte*.

The Russian resistance was heroic—none more
heroic in the history of warfare with the possible exception of Verdun. Still, after many months, they
were forced to evacuate the town and the forts; but
not before Gordon, like the other British officers, had
become thoroughly bored with his mole-like existence,
doing forty successive twenty-hour stretches in the
trenches. He participated actively in the attack of the
18th June and 8th September, and watched, as he returned to camp for the last time, the Russians leaving
Sebastopol, crossing the harbor on their bridge of
boats, while the town went up behind them . . . "the
whole place in flames," Gordon wrote, "and now and
then a terrific explosion."

In his frequent letters home during the siege, he
made no mention of himself or of his actions. They
were strangely impersonal notes; calm records—those
of an expert—of details in his chosen trade. Already
at twenty-two he had an eye for the complete canvas of
war, the grand military ensemble and symphony, treating the operations as a whole from his particular point
of view of an officer of engineers, criticizing his superiors as subalterns have done since the days of Julius
Cæsar, but, unlike the average subaltern, weighing
these criticisms and accusations carefully, judiciously
separating the wheat from the chaff, and suggesting
alternative schemes where he considered they were
better.

The second winter he spent as part of the engineer
corps which blew up the Sebastopol defenses and, in
May, 1856, received marching orders that sent him
to survey the new border between Russia and the young

states of Bessarabia and Moldavia. On this work he
remained almost a year, building up such a reputation
as an observer of military and political conditions and
an appraiser of national, psychological moods that he
was summoned to Constantinople to discuss matters
with the British envoy, Lord Stratford de Redcliffe,
who was busy trying to counteract his earlier mistakes.

To him Gordon reported that conditions were far
from the ideal in the Danubian principalities. His
manner of putting it was curt and undiplomatic:

" . . . the Jews swarm in the towns. The professions are
monopolized by Germans, Greeks, Armenians and Jews. But
the peasant is with the Russians. The territory is in great
disorder."

The Balkans, evidently, were then as they are to-
day. Nor has the Russian changed. Be his emblem
the Imperial eagle or the hammer and fist, be he
Czarist or Bolshevist, the Bear That Walks Like a
Man is still the same, with the same appetite, the
same claws, the same intrigues.

Gordon suspected these intrigues at the time. Later
events proved him right on all points; and Lord Stratford, for one, believed him, and sent him to Erzerum
to a post on the commission verifying the new boundary
separating Russia and Turkey-in-Asia, to play—a peculiar, rather grotesque position for a young man of
twenty-six—the peacemaker between tricky, anarchic
Slav and bovine, obstinate Osmanli.

For six long, dusty months he tramped the border,
camping with the Kurd tribesmen and erecting stone
markers along the line to which he managed to get the
contending commissioner to agree; finding time to
delve into ruined cities that spoke of the glories of
forgotten civilizations with shivered marble plinths
and mutilated statues, to inspect the slave traffic of

Laristan, to climb almost to the summit of Mount Ararat where, according to Moslem tradition, Noah anchored his motley cargoed ark.

Too, he kept his eyes and his mind wide open. In doing so he found out, was doubtless amazed at finding out, that men living in a state bordering on savagery, men who had never seen a wheeled vehicle nor had ever heard of the scientific innovations that in those years were convulsing the Western World—the invention of the telegraph, the discovery of Neptune, the perfecting of the sewing-machine, the laying of the first Atlantic cable, the pronouncing of Charles Darwin's theory of evolution—that such men, for all their ignorance, could be loyal and clean and brave and possess traits and virtues which, he had formerly imagined, were the monopoly and pride of the privileged races nurtured in the lore of Christianity. He began to lose his tight, insular parochialism and—with that marvelous, quick-pouncing sense of justice which was his forte—to understand that the human race was something not necessarily to be docketed by faith or complexion or nationality, that all peoples had to face the same problems and reacted to them in much the same manner, and that morality was not a fixed thing, a dogma, a fact, but largely a matter of climate and geography; what was right in London not always being right in Erzerum, and vice versa. In other words, he was learning the truth of the Pythagorean theory of number or recurrence brought down to human concerns; also the truth of that saying of the great philosopher, St. Thomas Aquinas:

"Every existence, as such, is good."

Yet, while his mind broadened, his faith remained unshaken. He was one of those lucky, serene few who never passed through a *Sturm und Drang* period; who never felt inclined, through a spirit of youthful contariness, to put Pluto above Jupiter and Hades higher than Olympus. He was, innately, the spiritual opposite of Sir Richard Burton.

By November he was back in England to stay until the spring, hoping daily for orders that would take him to India where the Sepoy mutiny was bringing fame to John Nicholson and the Lawrences, and was being suppressed with a ferocity quite equal to the fanaticism it was revenging. But, instead of to India, he was sent back to Asia Minor to go over the ground again, find the traces of markers the natives had carted away, and act as buffer between a new pair of commissioners, Russian and Turk, each confident of coercing this pink-cheeked Englishman into giving him his way —and both failing.

He did not care for this peacemaking job of work. It palled on him; bored him. But it gave him a practical lesson soon to be of incalculable value: the handling of men.

Back once more in England, it was barracks until, the Opium War of 1840 against China having whetted the appetite of the British coast traders who clamored that the door into the rich hinterland was not sufficiently ajar, Captain Gordon, as he had recently become, was sent with a company of his sappers to assist in forcing this same door wide open.

Arriving at the mouth of the Pei-Ho in late August, he missed the reduction of the Taku forts and came in only for the tail-end of the fighting, being set to the obnoxious task of building huts for troops against the biting Chili winter winds; the yet more obnoxious task —one of Europe's blackest disgraces in its long history of disgraces committed on Asian soil—of demolishing the Winter Palace. Demolishing it, not as a savage might have done, glutted with victory and lust, on the red, unthinking spur of the moment; but doing it cold-bloodedly, slowly, systematically . . . a job which Gordon described in a letter, curtly, bitterly, as "wretchedly demoralizing," indeed, if the truth be told, more demoralizing to the French and English who did it, than to the Chinese whom it was supposed to affect and frighten and awe . . . who watched the destruction, rather amazed, and slightly sneering.

After all, they thought, they had the genius, the sense of beauty. They might be able to build another Winter Palace. But would the Europeans, the foreigners, be able to rebuild the spiritual havoc in their own souls.

Perhaps the Chinese, looking on, remembered how wild Mongol nomads, sweeping out of the Central Asian steppes astride their shaggy ponies, had built this town of Pekin, calling it Khan Baligh; how, becoming civilized under the influence of that China which they had conquered, they had embellished their capital city with an utter refinement of all the arts; how, throughout the Middle Kingdom's many civil wars, friend and foe had always respected this great jewel, the Winter Palace . . . a palace in which the whole history of China was written with fretted stone and porcelain and jade and lac: the might of the Mongols, the faith and gentle breeding of the Mings, the magnificent madness of the Manchus . . . a monument which spoke of a nation's inspiration and folly, great successes and great failures, exuberance and weariness, strength and weakness . . . a Mecca—a Grail . . . and leveled to the ground by the Europeans for "political and moral reasons."

And the Chinese sneered, shrugged their shoulders, mumbled: *"Fan-kwai*—coarse-haired barbarians!"— and Captain Gordon called it "wretchedly demoralizing."

So were the succeeding months.

For his company found itself settled down to camp life outside Pekin with little to do beyond the daily routine, and, for the officers, what social life the foreign settlement seven miles away had to offer. But entertainment and, particularly, dinners were anathema to Gordon, as he admits in his journal, writing:

" . . . horrid wearisome dinner parties and miseries. How we can put up with such things passes my imagination. . . . At those dinner parties we are all in masks, saying what we do not believe, eating and drinking things we do not want, and then abusing one another. . . . Why men cannot be friends without bringing the wretched stomachs in is astounding. . . ."

The man, in spite or because of his basic, never-changing Christianity, was already becoming orientalized; was beginning to understand the trite wisdom of the ancient Chinese proverb: *"With plain food to eat, water to drink, and the bended arm as a pillow, happiness may exist"*; and so, cutting out social engagements, he turned to the fascinating study of the native, so soon to prove invaluable, until, after a year and a half, he was granted furlough.

This he enjoyed to the fullest, walking, with pack on his back, northward to the Kalgan Pass, along the Great Wall, which gave him food for thought and consideration of both historical and military lore—food, too, for realizing that this Great Wall, China's monumental Great Folly stretching its 2,550 miles from Chia-yü Kuan to the sea at Shan-hai Kuan, was not so foolish after all, since, in its time, it did what it was supposed to do: acted as a bulwark against the nomad raiders. Then he went west into the province of Shansi—the ancient home of the *"black-haired race"* even before the days of the Hsia and Shang dynasties —and back again to Pekin and his company of sappers.

He was unaware that, during the months of his absence, fate had been clouting a situation most suited
to his capacities and that, by a curious accident, he,
the man who in later life came to be perpetually overlooked, was about to be given the job of taking that
situation in hand, of saving China from a maelstrom
of Moslem fanaticism. For the Moslem, the Taiping,
Rebellion had broken out.

Caused, primarily, not by the disaffection of the mass
of population, but by the failure of one Hung Hsiu-
ch'üan to satisfy the Imperial examiners for appoint-
ments in the government service who were carrying
out a system instituted under the Han dynasty in 29
B.C., this rebellion, which ultimately cost the lives of
twenty million people, was sweeping across the fairest
portion of the land—rolling on—rushing on—across
towns and villages, fields and hills, like a sheet of
smoldering flame, yellow, cruel, inexorable. Supporting its adherents by the pillage gained with each new
success, it reached its most dangerous point when, on
arriving in the valley of the Yangtse-Kiang, it came
into touch with foreign traders, who were eager to
make up their losses of the past year. With up-to-date
arms and ammunition the Taiping hordes occupied the
cities of the Yangtse delta and were becoming a menace
to Shanghai.

There the foreigners were on the verge of panic—
foreigners in China are, indeed, always either on the
verge of panic or at the peak of it. The lobbies of
the few, shabby hotels and the stout counting-houses
were packed with excited, gesticulating aliens of all
nations. Women's faces were white. Women's lips
curled and quivered. Stoop-shouldered young clerks
tried to keep their necks stiff. Hard-faced older men
tried to keep the flint in their eyes. Not very successfully. For fear spread, like powder under spark,

as the unruly elements of Shanghai, showing sympathy with the Taiping rebels, coiled and moiled through the narrow, crooked streets of the city, marching with banners, with a savage symphony of shouts:

"*Pao Ch'ing Mien Yang!*   Death to the foreign oppressors!"

On, on, on—over the cobblestones, splashing through the thick, blue slime, relentless, resistless—a true, brutal segment of Mongol cosmos—shrilling and roaring:

"*Pao Ch'ing Mien Yang!*"

So the Europeans and Americans shivered in their boots, while steadily the rebels closed about the town, and while the Imperial Manchu troops were incapable of doing anything about it.

All this during Gordon's absence.

But a Gideon had arisen, quietly, out of the foreign community, and achieved great deeds.   Later on Ward, the American who organized the "Disciplined Chinese Force," was almost forgotten.   But without him there would not have been a "Chinese" Gordon. After consultation with the local mandarins, Ward undertook the raising, training and use in the field of a native army, recruited wherever possible and officered by available foreigners.

Ward belonged to the class of born strategists; the class which includes Julius Cæsar, Alexander of Macedon, Attila, Tamerlane, Frederick the Great, Nadir Khan, Napoleon, Wellington, Moltke, Hindenburg— and, in a minor degree, the Marshal de Saxe, Prince Savoy, General Skobeleff, U. S. Grant, Robert E. Lee, and Grand Duke Nicholas Nicholaievitch.   In seventy separate engagements against the rebels Ward suffered not a single defeat, marching and counter-marching swiftly.   Success bred success, and his ranks were swelled by the deserters from the enemy eager to get

on the side which was gaining the victories—not to
mention the spoils. By September, 1862, at the time
of his death in a minor action, his force amounted to
two thousand infantry and two batteries of artillery
with which he opposed and vanquished well-armed
troops ten and twenty times the number of his. So
satisfactory had the work of his corps been to the Imperial authorities in Pekin that, a few months before
its organizer's death, in that grandiloquent manner so
dear to the celestial heart, it had been accorded the
title of honor "The Ever-Victorious Army."

With the cessation of hostilities in the north, the
bulk of the Pekin siege force had been moved to the
Shanghai area together with the fleets of various
foreign powers, and these detachments coöperated
effectively with The Ever-Victorious Army. In the
spring of 1863, Gordon moved south to take the position of senior engineer officer with the Shanghai troops,
and immediately set about surveying the creek-cut
hinterland of the city.

Since Ward's death The Ever-Victorious Army had
not been living up to its name. In succession to Ward
another American, Burgevine, had been appointed to
its command. The man had made an excellent subordinate officer. But responsibility went to his head.
He bragged and bullied—and did little else. The
army received a severe set-back. In a foolish attempt
to make up his loss of prestige, Burgevine grossly
insulted a Chinese mandarin and was immediately
dismissed by the local native authorities. An English
naval officer, Holland, was given the command. The
Briton's success was no greater than the American's.
His leadership did not stand the test of battle. Feeling that, after all, they had backed the wrong horse,
the ranks deserted rapidly. The entire disorganiza-
tion of the unit was merely a matter of time.

But, on the 24th March, 1863, it entered a new and most glorious era of its history.

On that day Captain Gordon's appointment, recommended by the British commander, was approved by the War Office, and the engineer officer left his maps to see what he could do with the peculiar hodge-podge of men he was called upon to take in hand. With a staff of officers picked from the British Expeditionary Force, he arrived at the headquarters of The Ever-Victorious Army and proceeded to reorganize it in accordance with his ideas.

He was then a few months past his thirtieth year with no particular service behind him to warrant high expectations. His appointment had been nothing but an accident. Possibly the British commander, bored with China and life in general, had chosen his name at random. Gordon justified the choice—the accident —but not before he had had to face considerable trouble and emerge the winner in several passages with his personnel and the Manchu authorities.

His work with The Ever-Victorious Army was less remarkable from the purely military point of view of leadership in the field, than from the fact that he organized it completely and efficiently and brought it to the practical shape which it lacked. In addition, by dint of mingling suave tact and occasional hard-headedness, he established a better understanding with the Imperial Government and largely enhanced the prestige of foreigners in a land where their position was getting to be decidedly shaky—almost as dangerously shaky as it is to-day, as an aftermath of the contumely for the Occident which the World War spread throughout Asia.

Under Ward and his two successors The Ever-Victorious Army had existed on terms similar to those enjoyed, or not at all enjoyed, by Chinese troops for hundreds of years. For we must not forget that the Chinese, for better or for worse, have chosen to believe in the force of the intellect and the soul and not of the body; that, despising Mars even more than Moloch, they have founded a democracy ruled by an intelligentsia which, until Oxford and Harvard gave to the younger Mongol generation horn-rimmed spectacles, spats, and half-baked ideas, was ruled through public, competitive examinations; that they have always refused to see the romance in strife and have put the warrior on the lowest step of the social ladder, holding him in the same icy contempt in which a Hindu holds an "untouchable."

Thus, too, had been the treatment accorded the soldiers of The Ever-Victorious Army. There was no such thing as a regular pay roll under the old Chinese system. After the taking of a position, the capturing of a town or the clearing of a locality, the commander would present himself to the local mandarins and proceed to bargain. According to the terms he made, his popularity with his men and their future loyalty would depend—*"all the loot and one hundred thousand taels"* being a Chinese soldier's beau ideal.

With such a bait before them, the native troops would lash out and defeat twice their number of Taipings. But, once a triumph achieved, a city conquered, and all the portable loot carted away, the business of war—like any other business—would take a slump. The soldiers would desert and remain away until the plunder had been sold and the proceeds spent. Broke, with aching heads and bleary, opium-reddened eyes, they would then find their way to Sung Kiang or wherever headquarters happened to be, and apply for another job as warriors.

Thus their victories were never followed up, their advantages never consolidated, while the periods of debauch and the fact that they carried weapons made them a menace to the people on their own side of the lines.

To cure this condition was Gordon's first intention. Both parties were against him. The Manchu representatives preferred to pay on delivery—of victory —and frequently managed to withhold the funds so as to have the privilege of dictating, often for personal reasons, the next place to be attacked; while The Ever-Victorious Army itself objected to regularity of pay for a similarly personal and practical cause. Loot was better than pay. *"No lootee, no fightee,"* declared the men in the ranks, and even the European officers threatened to walk out on strike and cross over to the rebels who were offering better terms.

With the authorities Gordon had one club: resignation . . . not a very heavy club, since he was an untried commander as yet. With his officers he had little power. Dismissal was the furthest he might go— though rumor had it that, on occasion, Ward had gone beyond that, had played prosecuting attorney, judge, and firing-squad—and this threat of dismissal, with the Taipings so eager to employ foreigners, amounted to little. With the men in the ranks he was only permitted to fine and beat them, strictly in the Chinese manner.

But he did not give in. He employed tact and persuasion; he nagged; and—since he was that type of man—he found encouragement in the very difficulty of his task; encouragement, too, in the reading of the Bible which he carried in his saddle pouch. The terrible power of the unadorned words of the Book of God awakened in him a like power—like the power of a hammer hitting square and fair, the power of a great mill-stone grinding out the life-giving wheat; and he was helped by his Christianity which, a narrowly dogmatized faith and finding strength as well as weakness in this dogmatization, is, logically, an enemy of that amorphous shapelessness in which, on the other hand, the adherents of Confucius and the Buddha find strength as well as weakness.

So, presently, he gained his point. To be sure, his officers, foreigners of all nationalities, China Coast adventurers, ex-mercantile marine men, the sweepings of Europe's and America's gutters *in partibus infidelium*, put up a strong bluff. He overcame this bluff; overcame, furthermore, the resistance of his troopers; and, after a few desertions, made up by the recruiting of a corresponding number of rebel renegades, the matter was straightened out.

Then he proceeded to his first victory.

Joining forces with the Imperial leaders at Fushan, a fifty-mile march during which, a new experience for the army, he did not lose a single straggler, operations were commenced for the relief of the invested city of Chanzu. The Ever-Victorious Army, on the 5th April, stormed the besiegers' lines and entered the city with the Taipings fleeing in a panic.

He did not yet trust his soldiers. Their looting instincts were too deeply ingrained. So he marched them back to Sung Kiang where he proceeded to drill them mercilessly. Here again he was faced by difficulties. The old system, with the personnel fluctuating continuously, had had little of drill about it. Now Gordon introduced the British form of drill, specializing in certain simple open-order evolutions. To have the men extend at the proper moment, keep touch with one another during the approach, and attack as a cohesive body at the signal, was the best that could be done and was certainly enough against the enemy whom they were fighting. He furthermore started the system of regular pay and regular rations. Officers received up to the equivalent of $375 a month and men in the ranks about $10. As he expected, this had the effect of developing some sort of self-respect in the unit, and the first disagreement was soon forgotten.

His next enterprise was more ambitious.

Holland had endeavored to take the fortified city of Tai-tsang and had failed. Since that time an Imperial force had squatted half-heartedly before the walls, to be besieged in turn by more rebels. On the 30th April The Ever-Victorious Army, marching now in some fair imitation of military formation, about 3,000 strong, approached, deployed, and waited while its commander reconnoitered the objective.

He chose the west side, that furthest from his lines of communication, straddled one of the numerous creeks cutting this country like a chessboard, and opened with his artillery at about six hundred yards. By noon the guns had advanced to within one hundred yards of the defenses, and the infantry was ready for the word of attack. Gordon gave it. Waving his whangee cane, he took his soldiers forward. Under a withering fire they hardly reached the wall; were about to turn on their heels; discovered presently the difference between their former leaders and their new commander who had learned that Chinese were excellent in an unrepulsed charge, but, once held up in their stride, were inclined to forget all about the matter in hand and go somewhere else as quickly as possible. Not so to-day. Gordon rushed up and down the line, rallying and urging on soldiers as well as officers, until, after sharp fighting, late in the afternoon, the town was his, the escaping Taiping garrison having no choice but to flee into the arms of the Imperial soldiery on the far side of their fortress.

During the attack Gordon had noticed several

British deserters from Shanghai among the rebels. It had infuriated him. When one of them, a certain Hargreaves, a private in the 31st Regiment of Foot, was brought to him, a prisoner, and whined: "Mr. Gordon! Mr. Gordon! You won't let me be killed, sir!" he ordered to have the man taken down the river and shot.

The deserter was led off, while Gordon strolled up to one of his officers standing by.

"Follow that man," he told him, "till the escort is out of my sight. Have him put in a boat till the doctor can see his wounds and then send him down to Shanghai . . . And, remember, I don't know anything about it."

Twenty-two years later, pent up in Khartum, Gordon expressed his curiosity as to Hargreaves' whereabouts.

What happened after the victory was a blow to him. His intention had been to turn about, march quickly to Quinsan, and catch the Taipings there before they realized that the enemy was within striking distance. But, right then, The Ever-Victorious Army remembered that it was also The Ever-Looting Army. European officers as well as Chinese soldiers—though Gordon begged, implored, stormed—refused to obey. Instead they plundered to their hearts' content; carried off all they could carry; sold the loot and spent the money; and then, singly and by twos and threes, dribbled to Sung Kiang and reported themselves eager to perform the next prodigy of valor.

A reverse for Gordon. A loss of face.

Yet, in this military operation, the capture of the city, he had established his reputation as a first-rate strategist; the remarkable part of the proceeding being that he had worked out his plan by instinct, carrying it through with little aid from maps, in spite of the complicated maneuvers involved.

Now he gritted his teeth, again he drilled and consolidated his army. By June, was ready for the field.

It would be hard to find a sadder country than the immediate hinterland of Shanghai. Though immensely fertile by reason of age-old deposits of Yangtse silt, it is dead-flat with no distinguishing marks beyond an occasional pagoda and a few scraggly, dusty towns. But, lying as it does between a great river, a series of lakes and the sea, it has been criss-crossed generously by canals, used for transportation between its various communities.

Gordon proposed to use these canals for his advance, starting from Tai-tsang and working his way eventually behind Quinsan and between that town and the larger city of Soochow, both places being occupied by the Taipings. Tseng Kuo-fan, the Chinese Commander-in-Chief and an able general, doubted the feasibility of this plan. So did Li Hung Chang, a prominent local mandarin whose star was presently to rise most brightly on the firmament of the Middle Kingdom and who was destined to be accepted by Europe and America as the typification of statesmanlike Mongol shrewdness. He was the same official who, grossly insulted by Burgevine, Ward's successor, had caused his dismissal. Gordon, taking Li Hung Chang with him, embarked on a small, armored tug, the *Hyson,* cruised through the narrow waterways, well in enemy country, and demonstrated the possibility of his idea.

On the following day he put it into effect. Accompanied by slower junks and sampans containing The Ever-Victorious Ones and as many Imperial soldiers as possible, the *Hyson* took the lead and entered the main canal beside the highroad from Quinsan to Soo-

chow, cutting off the former place from reënforcements
and, better still, splitting a large rebel column that
was moving up from Soochow, officered by the pick
of Chinese and Tartar Moslems. At the point of
intersection the troops were landed to close on Quinsan, while Gordon on his launch, imitating Napoleonic
tactics, turned to the left and harried the remaining
Taipings toward Soochow, treating them to broadside
after broadside, driving them into the creeks and
ponds, killing them in hundreds, advancing until the
Hyson was able to drop a shell into Soochow itself.
By this time the rebels advancing on Quinsan had been
routed; and the tug turned, rejoined the fighting line
and assisted the infantry from the canal, until, with
the arrival of dawn, Quinsan was captured.

The victory had far-reaching results. Li Hung
Chang, skeptical at first, recognized Gordon's genius.
Encouraged, the latter ordered his army out of Quinsan, with the intention of commencing an immediate
attack on Soochow.

But he was no more successful than he had been at
Tai-tsang. Apprehending a loot-laden deserter headed
for a good market, Gordon had him led on parade
and shot before the eyes of his companions. The
audience was impressed—but not as Gordon had calculated. Two thousand marched off the ground, declaring they would not return until it suited their convenience.

When that time came there was no room for them.
For, as soon as the wholesale desertion started, Gordon went to Quinsan and recruited from the captured
rebels, promising them regular pay and—having
learned a hoary Chinese lesson—such loot as time
would permit them to pick up. He drilled them for
two months and admitted that he was more than satisfied with the exchange, saying that, whereas success

had lowered the morale of his old army, defeat had
improved that of the Taipings.

An amusing incident. An incident reminiscent of
Europe's medieval days when ruffianly *Landsknechte*
fought to-day for Guelf and to-morrow for Ghibelline.

Before trying out his fresh force Gordon was to go
through another annoying experience.

Burgevine suddenly appeared in Shanghai with an
Imperial edict reappointing him to the command of
The Ever-Victorious Army and presented it to Li
Hung Chang. The latter was taken aback. Burgevine had trodden on his toes once, and he had dismissed him. Yet here was supreme Manchu authority
reinstating the man. The foreign residents of Shanghai, on the other hand, as well as the foreign commanders there were pleased with Gordon's work.
They decided to ignore the Imperial edict. But
Burgevine was not to be so easily snubbed. Visiting
the camp of The Ever-Victorious Army, he set to work
on his old officers, of whom a good many were still
with the troops, and promised them less discipline and
more loot. They called on Gordon and asked him to
relinquish his post. In case of his refusal they threatened they would resign their commissions.

Gordon's reply was prompt and curt. They were
open to do exactly as they pleased. He, having received his commission directly from his superiors in
the British army, was going to stay.

In consequence more than half of his European and
American officers moved over to the Taipings with
Burgevine whose death came shortly afterwards.
Crossing a river with some rebel soldiers under his
command he fell into the water and was drowned,
though local gossip insisted that he was pushed in.
The man had been too quick at switching allegiance;

had been too embarrassing even for the Taipings to have around.

Gordon, in the meantime, attended to his muttons, gazetting other officers and training his soldiers until they were ready for something big in the way of battles.

On the 25th July he marched them out on a campaign to capture Soochow itself. Here was another hard military problem. Soochow was situated on a lake, making it impossible to take the city in the rear. So, sending the Imperial army to the north, he moved his new troops to Woo Kiang in the south, and then gradually worked in toward his objective, keeping in constant communication with his allies. It took nearly three months to clear the country and invest Soochow. During all this time the Taiping *"wangs"* or princes made advances to Gordon, secretly suggesting to give up the town for a price. He refused to consider anything except a complete surrender to which all the rebel leaders were parties. Finding him obdurate, the *"wangs"* changed their tactics. They approached the commander of the Imperial army and came to an agreement: at a stated time the Imperials were to march in through the great, northern gate and firing was to cease. But the Taipings—as had been their intention straight along—broke their word. When about a third of the Chinese soldiers were within the walls the gate was closed behind them and they were all put to the sword.

That much the *"wangs"* had accomplished—and no more; since the siege was carried on and Li Hung Chang was now thoroughly enraged, swearing vengeance. Again they made overtures to Gordon. He insisted on his first terms. All or none. Finally the *"wangs"* agreed. They arranged the surrender with him, on condition that their lives should be spared.

On the day of the surrender Gordon did a remarkable thing—or not at all remarkable, if you prefer, since it was so intensely British—the same thing which John Nicholson did at Haripur and Cecil Rhodes in the Matoppo Hills: having notified Li Hung Chang of the details which he had arranged, he proceeded into the city, alone, but for a native orderly.   He met the *"wangs"* and was promptly made a prisoner.   For some unknown reason—given their treachery with the Imperial soldiers whom they had butchered—he was not killed at once; and, with the first rays of sun, he managed to effect his escape and returned to camp.

On his way, beside a creek, he discovered the decapitated bodies of six *"wangs"* whose lives he had guaranteed and who had gone out to parley with the Imperial commander.   Li Hung Chang had betrayed them; had, by the same token, betrayed Captain Gordon.   At once the latter's old, cold streak of iron justice came to the top.   The *"wangs"* had been unfaithful—which was no reason why he, or his, should be unfaithful to them.   It was not the way he figured things —this amazing Scottish gentleman who found all the world's lessons in the Athanasian Creed.   Without a moment's hesitation he sent his resignation by letter to Li Hung Chang and left the field.

This happened in November, 1863.   For the next three months the Chinese tried every means to reacquire his services.   But he would not listen; reported to the British authorities and was waiting for an appointment in his own corps of sappers.   In December the Emperor granted him ten thousand taels from the Imperial treasury, only to have the gratuity refused.   "I could not take the money from them in their miserable poverty," was Gordon's explanation.   He was unable as well as unwilling to patch up his

quarrel with Li Hung Chang. Nor did the latter try
very hard. For, though he was fully aware of Gordon's worth, he had heard a story to the effect that the
Scot, on finding the six dead *"wangs,"* had gone from
camp to camp, pistol in hand, intent on wiping out the
dishonor to his name by adding Li Hung Chang to the
slain.

On the 1st January, 1864, a large gold medal arrived from Pekin together with an autographed decree
of conferment from the Emperor of China. Across
the back of the decree the former commander of The
Ever-Victorious Army wrote his regrets and rejection.

"Honor, not Honors!" was the Highland Gordon
slogan . . . the man was as stiff-necked as any Mani-
chean; was more savagely haughty than any McPher-
son who ever danced a reel beneath the gallows, in sign
of fearless contempt, before the Sassenach strung him
up.

But other forces were at work. The foreign community at Shanghai regarded him as their savior;
represented to him that duty, at times, comes before
honor. Besides, the army itself showed signs of not
wanting to serve under another leader. Without
Gordon, the soldiers were likely to become a menace
to the very interests they were supposed to protect.
So, finally, he agreed to assume command once more.
But he stipulated that The Ever-Victorious Army
should be henceforth an independent unit, not in any
way under control of the Manchu authorities.

In February he was back at his post. By June he
had defeated the Taipings so decisively that he was
able to disband his regiments and assure the settlements that their danger was over. During the last
period of his command he had taken two large cities,

Waisso and Chang Chu Fu, and cleared up the entire delta area. In both these major assaults his force was first repulsed. But in both cases he rallied his men and took them forward again to capture their objectives.

That was where he proved himself unique. The average foreign leader of Chinese had never complained of their courage in attack; but under a reverse they were far from reliable. Gordon alone was able to lead them in such a way that they turned defeat into victory.

So this adventure of "Chinese" Gordon came to an end, with all competent, local observers, military and civilian, British and foreign alike, prophesying for him a brilliant future, admitting that as an organizer, administrator and tactician he stood head and shoulders above every one else on the spot. As a farewell gift the Emperor conferred on him a rare distinction. Together with the hat of a mandarin he was granted the yellow jacket, the highest Manchu military rank— Manchu, not Chinese, since the latter do not honor nor respect a fighting man—that placed its recipient on the Emperor's immediate bodyguard and made him brother-in-blood to all the commanders of the Manchu Banner Corps and to the *Nurhachi,* the Iron-Capped Princes.

His intention was to refuse these tokens. But he listened to the advice of the British ambassador, though he wrote:

"I am sorry it is considered that I should take them. The buttons on the mandarin's hat are worth thirty or forty pounds apiece. They cannot afford it overwell."

Here spoke the Scot figuring in pounds and pence; the Scot, too, in his proud rejoicing over what he had done, when he added:

"I think I have given them a new idea of the foreigner.
. . . They trust me more than any foreigner was ever trusted.
I have never cringed or yielded to any of them and they have
respected me all the more."

But if the Chinese appreciated him at his worth, his
own government barely recognized his existence. He
shared in the routine recognition awarded to those
who had served in China; was given the routine medals
and ribbons and clasps. Too, while retaining his sub-
stantive rank of captain, he received two brevet promotions, major and lieutenant-colonel. But with them
came no appointment in any way commensurate with
his proved ability.

Toward the end of 1864 he returned to England.
There the asthmatic Brahmins of the War Office had
some difficulty in finding work for him.

Rather a beastly nuisance—what, what?—this captain person of engineers who, for some assish reason,
had been brevetted a lieutenant-colonel . . . a man
who had done something or other with a pack of
Chinamen—or were they Zulus—or Burmans? . . .
a stiff-necked sort of lad who, so somebody had said,
was a field-marshal—or was it a sergeant-major?—in
the Chinese—or was it the Turkish army—or the
household troops of the Maharajah of Wotyecallhim?

At all events—nuisance. Damned nuisance. What
will we do with the blighter . . . ?

Then a vacancy occurred. A most important vacancy at a most important spot.

Where?

At Gravesend!

To take charge of the engineer barracks down
the Thames.

His appointment coincided with one of those French
scares periodically stirred up by professional politi-

cians to the glory of their party. To divert the attention of the public from some other question, the government, making cryptic allusions to a possible invasion by Louis Napoleon, secured a grant of twelve million pounds to fortify the mouth of the Thames. The Gravesend engineers were assigned to the job, and, for the next two years, Gordon was busily occupied in "actively wasting the taxpayers' money," as he put it. That the nation should allow such a large expenditure on what he considered useless construction at a time when people in the Midlands, their livelihood taken away from them as a result of the American Civil War, were starving and while in fact the whole country was suffering from a severe business depression, struck Gordon as criminal. The land in and about Gravesend was in a particularly bad plight. The areas in the vicinity of great docks are seldom celebrated for the wealth of their residents; and, in the peregrinations necessitated by his work, he saw sights which showed him that China was not unique in the matters of sordid living and abject poverty.

So he set to work to ameliorate conditions, managing to make of these years, during which officially he was occupied in a most uncongenial task, a very happy and successful period in his life, helping the poor and —let us admit it—preaching to them.

He followed no special Christian sect the tenets of which he was trying to thrust on others. He would have considered the modern propaganda methods and campaign of hate of the Protestant Church as harmful, indecent and blasphemous. When, in his lifetime, emotional religionists pointed to him as a model of what their particular cult, and only their particular cult, could produce, he denied it vehemently. He was simply a believing Christian who tried to live up to his faith.

Shortly after his return to England he performed a small, but very typical, action which was not known to any one until after his death. Despite his various refusals the Emperor of China had insisted on sending him a commemorative medal, a large gold plaque fittingly inscribed. He was approached by the canvassers for a subscription to the Coventry Relief Fund. He could not subscribe a shilling because he was poor. But, shortly afterwards, the mayor of Coventry received an anonymous donation in the form of a great gold coin the face of which had been so disfigured that it was impossible to trace its origin. At the time the Scots captain of engineers, recently returned from China, was unknown in his own country. The gift could not be connected with his name in any way.

"Honor, not Honors!"—though he was entirely without both in his native land.

Regretting his lack of means at a time when the country was in such dire straits, he soon found an outlet for his surplus energies—what was left of them after tramping the Gravesend marshes for hours, supervising excavations and poring over maps. To his charities—how he protested at the word!—he brought the sane, elementary principles of British army discipline.

"Break your man, but only to build him up again!" was the slogan of the thin, red line; was his own slogan.

An engineer, a builder, he set to work to build up the lives of the dock rats who had no chance of doing much for themselves, but were generally broken on the wheel of society. It was humble work. It was sordid. But he did it. He asked for no sort of recognition or assistance. He earned nothing except the reputation of being "rather queer."

He visited poor families. He ascertained their

needs. He weighed their demands. He filled them
to the best of his ability and his lean purse. He gave
food and fuel to miserable old women. He taught
reading and writing to dirty little street urchins. He
outfitted boys and sent them to sea. He found positions for young girls and packed them off to a cleaner
atmosphere.

In his study a large map covered one of the walls.
The Gravesend defenses, doubtless?
No!
Such things were reserved for his office. This was
a map of the world upon which colored pins marked
the approximate whereabouts of scores of ships on
which were sailing the boys who had been rescued from
the slums and placed aboard by Gordon. He preferred the merchant marine for his "kings" as he called
the boys, because he considered that ships that sailed
from English ports carried goods produced in the
country and the more of these found a market abroad
the better the condition of the people back home.

With all of which those most closely to Gordon
could make neither head nor tail of him. But he was
popular, interested in all sorts of things and of a
sparkling wit. The man who said that the only book
Gordon ever read was the Bible, did not know what
he was talking about. For Gordon's conversation was
full of similes and quotations, proving the well-stocked
mind. He objected to the professionally pious. He
hated those who carried the Cross on their arms like
a badge. He refused to coöperate with such and
shrank from their praises, preferring a sincere Atheist
to an insincere Christian.

In the meantime the world was moving.
The Civil War had changed things in America, had
almost weaned the obstreperous trans-atlantic infant;

and the Franco-Prussian war was noisily and blatantly ushering in an entirely new state of affairs in Europe. Through the birth of this new world Gordon worked patiently, building his Gravesend fortifications and modestly doing whatever he could to lighten the burdens of the poor which the political developments were increasing.

With the close of the Continental conflict England was frightened into preparations by the rising, bullying Hohenzollern peril and Bismarck's saber-rattling insolence, and went into one of her periodical military reorganizations. New posts were created. The army was strengthened. Great things were achieved —or, at least, promised and paid for.

But on the staffs created for these great things there seemed to be no room for Captain Gordon who instead, toward the end of 1871, was sent again to the Black Sea as one of the commissioners under the terms of the Treaty of Paris to settle matters on the Danube. For one of the results of the Franco-Prussian war had been new activities—and the same old greedy appetite —on the part of Russia. No one, least of all Gordon, doubted that before long the Slav would be once more at the throat of the Turk. Expecting a second Crimean affair, he spent his time studiously, going over the ground, sketching positions, planning a detailed campaign.

He visited Constantinople, and it was there that he made an impression which led to new employment. For he met Nubar Pasha, a Turkish cabinet minister, who recognized in the other the stamp of man he admired and who approached him with an offer. South of Egypt—a Turkish colony in those days—was the Soudan and south of the Soudan trouble was everlastingly brewing. Let Gordon become governor-general of this equatorial province. There was much to do

down there for a man of his caliber. On one side the
Abyssinians were a thorn; on the other Arab slavers
were harassing and raiding the small communities.

Gordon did not belong to the Turcophile British
school. But he accepted, explaining his reason, later
on, in a letter home, when he wrote:

"Why did I come here? you ask. The thing slid on little by
little. I felt too independent to serve, with my views, at
Malta, or in the corps, and perhaps I felt that I had in me
something that might benefit these lands, for He has given
me great energy and health and some little common sense. . . .
There is now not one thing I value in the world. Its honors
are false; its knickknacks perishable and useless. . . ."

So he went, this Christian gentleman, to serve a
Moslem gentleman; yet, somehow, going on Crusade
as much as ever did Don John of Austria—and though
he chanted his *"Domino gloria!"* with a Scots burr.

First he had to see to matters in Cairo, and what
he saw there did not please him. The Khedive—
after all, in spite of his pompous title, the descendant
of Albanian tea merchants and true to his salt—was
a business man, though not a very good one; was thus
always short of cash, and there were close at hand
Jews ready to lend him all he wanted at what worked
out at thirty-six per cent—doubtless in grateful remem-
brance of this Egypt, the land of their captivity.
Much had been borrowed to open up the lower Soudan. Some of the money had actually found its way
down there—but to line the pockets of the officials at
the Equator, and not in any way to do that for which
it was intended. The area was simply a slave hunting
ground, and it was with the idea of stamping out this
trade that Gordon accepted the governorship of the
Equatorial Province.

He selected a staff of nine foreigners, and, without waiting for them, set off from Cairo, raging against the state of affairs existing in the interior.

In March, 1874, by way of the Red Sea, Suakim to Berber, he reached Khartum to be received with grand Oriental pomp and circumstance by Ismail Yacoob Pasha, governor-general of the Soudan, the province next to his own. He remained there for a week. Khartum was interesting enough. Embraced in the acute angle formed by the *Bahr-el-Azrak,* the Blue Nile, and the *Bahr-el-Adiah,* the White Nile, it contained about 30,000 inhabitants and, enriching the local traders, Arabs, Turks, Copts, Greeks and a few Italians, was an important entrepôt for such Central African products as ivory, ebony, ostrich feathers, *dourah* grain, gum and cotton, and garrisoned by the troopers of the Soudanieh Corps, recruited amongst the inky-black Dinka and Chillouk tribes. Provided one sealed one's nostrils against the miasmic, fever-breeding stenches rising from the bad drainage, it was rather a charming place, with its congeries of small, white-washed houses, its alleys of stately palms, its large gardens of citron and orange. But Gordon did not enjoy his stay—nor can it be said that Ismail Yacoob Pasha exactly enjoyed his visitor. The latter's habits of talking to slaves, of asking all sorts of leading and embarrassing questions, his refusal of gifts, and his amazing eccentricity which caused him to give food and money to ragged, wretched old negro women, were too much for the Pasha—who was greatly relieved and murmured a heartfelt *"Ullah bismillah!"* when Gordon went on his way south, on a twenty-six-day boat trip during which the enormity of his task began to dawn on him, going ashore on the 16th April at his capital: Gondokoro.

A terrible place. Nothing but a military encampment enclosed by a high palisade of straw and composed of straw huts. The ruins of a brick *"canissa"* or church pulled down by the Bari tribesmen who had used the bricks to mix with grease so as to besmear their reeking bodies with their favorite red color. A squat warehouse of heavy tin once filled with *suc-suc* beads and similar trumperies for the savages—a relic of Sir Samuel Baker Pasha's administration. A rude stone memorial marking the grave of one of the latter's most energetic aids, Mr. Higginbotham. Two dilapidated forts manned by four hundred Egyptians and Soudanese—the men whom Sir Samuel Baker Pasha had nicknamed his "Forty Thieves." Enormous crimson mounds built by the famous white ants of Gondokoro.

Deadly fever. Dysentery caused by the "guinea worms" infesting the water. A plague spot. "Shaitan laughed," say the Arabs, "when Allah created it."

Briefly, bitterly, in a letter home, Gordon described it and the surrounding country: a territory almost depopulated by slave raids, the few survivors living at the mercy of the soldiers who stole their cattle and indulged in petty slave deals of their own when out of pocket.

He wrote:

" . . . no one can conceive the utter misery of these lands. Extreme heat and mosquitoes all the year round. . . ."

Six days were enough to prove to him that alone he could accomplish nothing. He must return to Khartum for his staff and for supplies. Too, he must give Ismail Yacoob Pasha a piece of his mind. The man, in regard to slave raids and other things, had lied to him. He must be warned against doing so in the future. His one link with Cairo and the outside world must be made secure and reliable. He went north; met his staff at Berber; proceeded to Khartum where he had a talk with the governor. A hard talk . . . "you *must* do this, Pasha—and you *must* do that!" The other did not argue. Why waste his time swapping words with a madman who preached liberty, justice, equality and similar amazing and reckless innovations? So he bowed, smiled—and became Gordon's enemy, making the latter's task back at Gondokoro so much more difficult.

Gordon's program was far from light.
He wrote:
"The only way to exist in this place is to overwork."
To relieve the misery of the wretched people in his domain came first, and his detailed activities were all mapped out with this in view. He set his soldiers to raise crops in order to keep them from their marauding. He established advance posts to bar the slave traders from the south, as the beginning of a system which he intended to push out gradually until he had the whole of his province protected. He punished severely all slavers caught within the lines.

In three months he was working alone. Two of his staff had died. The rest were down with fever, unable to take their share of the burden. So he shouldered the whole of it, though he wrote:
"My temper is very, very short, and it is bad for those that come across me the wrong way."
He decided that the only method to keep the government of the Equatorial Province on its feet was to move the capital and transport everything several miles up the Nile, to the foot of some dangerous rapids, to Rageef. There he carried on. He made more ambitious plans.
A line of posts must be established all the way from

the Great Lakes to Khartum. Above the cataracts
ships must be launched. These he carefully described,
to be built in pieces for transportation up to their
area, and ordered them from Cairo. He believed that
he had solved the problem of his governorship. The
slavers were not the sole cause of the miserable condition of the natives. Another, graver cause was the
land itself, which was almost sterile. There was nothing to trade, no possibility of any commerce. On the
other hand, there was an immensely fertile territory in
the south, near the Great Lakes, Rudolf, Albert and
Victoria Nyanza, capable of maintaining a large and
prosperous population. That district became his
mark. He would put boats on the lakes and teach the
natives to improve their condition.

It took nearly fifteen months to put the first boat
on Lake Albert; months full of heart-breaking
disappointments, herculean labor, pestilence, terrors.
Worry took hold of him. His mind went round in
circles during the lonely, merciless, sardonic days.
The natives did not coöperate. They wished for no
progress. They did not want traders to follow Gordon's small party with their beads and cloth. Nor did
they wish to see "great chiefs from the mouth of the
river."

Gordon was ever against oppression in any form.
Yet he saw that the end justified the means. Only
with boats working on the lake would the people be
able to support themselves, to improve their living
condition, to become strong enough to defend themselves against the raiders. Thus, for their own good,
they must submit; they must be forced to work.

He wrote:

"I am most inconsistent, so I am. We are dead against our
words when it comes to action."

He pushed on this action. Tribesmen who manned the heights and harried the laborers hauling the sections of the lake steamers were punished. When his soldiers became insubordinate he punished them as severely. He confiscated the cattle of marauding and disobedient local chiefs.

By the end of 1875 he had reached the third degree of north latitude, hauling his boats, establishing posts, driving the slavers off his tracks. Then, on the verge of success, having taken new heart, he found himself faced by a bad stretch of rapids. For miles the water ran but a few inches deep over rocks. It was little better than dry land for transportation. It took three months to get the heavy boat sections over the Duffli Cataract and start on the last seventy miles to Albert Nyanza. During that time men died about him daily. He himself, strong as oak, was trembling with ague one day, and, the next, leading a scouting party, rigging hawsers and running blocks with his own hands, sleeping wet to the skin—and ever longing to get out of this country which he was beginning to hate.

It is difficult to figure out what kept him there. Perhaps it was just that simple, trite thing called duty.

His letters to the Khedive were undiplomatic, to say the least. Why did his royal master keep such a lot of precious rascals in his employ? Why did he cater to the Jews and the other damned Levantine leeches? Why did he not keep his promises for a change and have supplies up as arranged?

The Khedive was surrounded by men who persistently advised that this fanatic be relieved of his appointment. They wanted the money which the Scots madman was spending down at the Equator to help a lot of naked, frizzy, odorous blacks. Besides, Gordon was receiving six thousand pounds a year. Preposterous! Why—six thousand pounds a year would buy a good many Abyssinian dancing-girls here in Cairo, a good many French *cocottes,* a good many cases of sweet champagne. So intrigues were rife against Gordon. But, somehow, the Khedive kept his head and encouraged him.

Finally the enterprise was accomplished. The boats were put together and steamed through the dense, tropical vegetation of Albert Nyanza. Gordon began consolidating his base and communications and prepared his survey. Forts were built and strengthened. Native soldiers were recruited, drilled and taught to shoot, while Gordon wondered if he was giving knowledge that eventually would be turned against him. In the silence and ghastly solitude he made maps, coming at last to the conclusion that the work was far enough advanced to be placed on some one else's shoulders. Too, he was no longer able to cope with Ismail Yacoob Pasha who, from Khartum, was putting obstacle after obstacle in his path, and who considered that, by working too much, his British colleague in the south was setting a dangerous precedent, and who tried all in his power, chiefly by the holding up and stealing of necessary supplies, to spike Gordon's guns.

Two years at the Equator had been enough for the latter. In October he returned to Cairo. He resigned. The Khedive would not hear of it. Let Gordon continue his work—at his own terms. He begged, flattered, made rather a scene, until, to calm him, Gordon told him he would think the matter over. By Christmas he was back in England and, except for his family, sorry to be there.

He remained five weeks. He telegraphed the Khedive that he could not see his way to resume his governorship. But the other was insistent. He pleaded with him to "complete the great work you and I have done." At last Gordon gave in; partly because, in spite of the fact that the British Empire was expanding everywhere and the call for capable men was loud throughout the land, the War Office seemed unable to find a suitable position for him.

His success in China had gone for nothing. His success in Central Africa was unknown.

For those were the days before propaganda became a fine art; the days before columnists, writers of advertising copy, "public relations counsels" and similar ballyhoo specialists could make or mar a reputation deserving or undeserving. It is just as good that it was so. For even "Chinese" Gordon's Christian forbearance might not have withstood the strain of being called "Gordy" or "Slim," of being familiarly slapped on the back by interviewers, of having his memoirs, penned by somebody else and profusely illustrated with pictures of nude African women, sell half a million copies in six months through the aid of some Book Club.

No. He could not have stood it. The man, after all, was an officer and a gentleman.

He returned to Cairo where, in his first talk with the Khedive, he was definite as to the conditions under which he would continue his work in the Egyptian service. Chiefly, his province must be enlarged to include the whole of the Soudan. He was to suffer no more hindrances from wily Ismail Yacoob Pasha. All his conditions were granted by the Khedive, and he was off again via the Red Sea to take charge of his private Empire in the heart of Africa.

The work he faced was harder than any that had gone before. Most of the money which had poured into Egypt in connection with the Suez Canal had been spent on an abortive attempt to conquer Abyssinia.

The Khedive's army had been as soundly thrashed by the mountaineers as, years later, the Italian. Word had gone out that Turkish rule was over. With the Abyssinian border in a state of anarchy and the desert tribes on the west in open revolt, Gordon's governorship was bound to be active.

From Khartum, his new capital, he wrote:

"With terrific exertion I may in two or three years' time make a good province, also have suppressed the slave trade. Then I will come home to bed and never get up again until noon every day, and never walk more than a mile."

Installed with formal pomp on the 5th May, arrayed in the flashing uniform of a Turkish field-marshal, he announced that "the reign of the whip is over," turned the same day to improving the water supply, and in two weeks had set every one in the town to wondering, and a good many to worrying and cursing. He stopped, wherever discovered, all petty thievery and bribery by government underlings. Those who objected were promptly sent back to Cairo. He placed a petition box at the gate of his palace. There piled in suggestions and accusations from the humbler townfolk, all of which he examined and treated according to their value. He was here and there and everywhere, a whirlwind of energy and efficiency.

Then, having surprised and shocked the capital, he left it to surprise and shock the provinces, to take a look at the desert, the rebels, and the Turkish administrators. Presently, having studied conditions and the ground, he launched the Darfur campaign against the slavers; a campaign without precedent in that part of the world. "Traveling like the wind," as the natives maintained, he marched and counter-marched, left one body of troops to catch up and operate with another, struck the rebels always in their weakest spots, herded them about until they did not know where next to turn. Early he realized that the army which, fighting in a desert, could keep its opponent away from water, was bound to win in the end. Thus the backbone of his strategy was:

"Hold the wells!"

A bitter merciless war it was, in a bitter, merciless land—a land of aridity, vacancy, solitude—a sneering land, yellow, denuded, shivered, sterile—with often a harsh, red-hot wind booming out of the south, blowing away the sand, till the supporting granite and schist were bare to the bone. And ever Gordon's battalions marching and counter-marching until, at last, the slavers began to show signs of weakness. He did not wait for more. He knew the Arab mind. He opened secret negotiations with individual sheiks, playing one against the other. Together they outnumbered his men ten to one, and he had not much trust in the half-trained soldiers whom he led.

He wrote:

"Three hundred of the enemy, if they showed any 'go,' would send my men rushing to my house. I have no faith in them and less in their officers."

But diplomacy and his trick of squatting on top of the water holes were at work; and finally word came to him that the slavers were waiting at Shakka to submit to him formally. With one Bedouin guide, astride a fast racing dromedary, he set out to the center of the slave trade and, crossing one hundred and eighty miles of desert in six days, reached his goal on the 9th September. There were long hours of parley. But the slavers signed on the dotted line. They promised to break up and leave the Soudan.

The most difficult to handle had been a youth by the name of Zubair, whose father had controlled the entire trade. In later years Gordon was destined to remember this man.

A victory.

Yet, back in Khartum, he soon understood that all his work in the blinding desert had been wasted. Behind him, as he returned from Darfur, the forces he had divided and destroyed closed in again—exactly as they would close in after each future war he cared to wage against them and, always, to win. The experience was heartbreaking; but it proved to him that he had been right straight along. He must help the poor natives so that, better fed, more plucky, they would be able to defend themselves. This he did, preaching and doing, as he had preached and done about the Gravesend docks.

Men suggested, or were suggested by others, to come out and assist him in his work. He replied:

"Give me the man who utterly despises money, name, glory, honors; one who never wishes to see his home again; one who looks to God as the source of good and the controller of evil; one who has a healthy body and an energetic spirit and looks at death as a release from misery—and I will take him as a help. If you cannot find him leave me alone."

At the same time, when his family proposed that he might find better employment in England, his answer was equally in the spirit of John Knox:

"I can only feel that I would not desert this government for anything that could be offered to me, for it would indeed be cowardly. I would use my very life to aid the Khedive."

The months in the desert had not improved affairs closer to his capital. There news of an Abyssinian invasion reached him. Hot-foot then to the border to discover that the cry of "wolf" was entirely unjustified.

In November came a call from Khedive Ismail for

help. He was annoyed—he had so much to do—but dropped a hundred odd tasks to go to his employer's rescue. The creditors were after the Khedive demanding settlement, with eyes on the Suez Canal and the rich Nile valley. All the Jews, Greeks, Armenians and other Levantines declared loudly that they were British or French or American subjects; yelled for warships and soldiers; declared that it was Europe's duty to collect their little bills, including one hundred per cent compound interest.

Gordon had foreseen this, but was practically helpless. He did what little he could. He volunteered a cut in his salary, wiring to Cairo, on his way up via the Red Sea, his offer.

No action of his could have been less welcome to the usurers. Jews, Greeks, Armenians, Levantines, and, too, Frenchmen and Englishmen were furious. They were all ready and eager to scrape the Egyptian carcass clean. That one of their own side should of his own volition let the Khedive off payment of a single penny lawfully owed was well-nigh high-treason.

They complained, whined, wept, while Gordon arrived in Cairo and, without waiting to change from his dusty traveling uniform, hurried to the palace and had a private conference with the Khedive. The latter had trust in two men: Gordon himself and DeLesseps. They were to be his representatives on a commission to solve the financial crisis. This work was to start at once . . . an arrangement decidedly unpopular with the European Levantine jackals.

A cursory survey proved that immediate action was necessary. The commission, Gordon estimated, would require several months to complete its findings. In the meantime one or two emergency measures must be taken. The government employees' salaries were in arrears. Funds were not available for this because of the enormous interest running out of the country on the foreign debt. These payments must be suspended until internal accounts were leveled; and the alien leeches must submit to the obvious: the reduction of interest to a point at which it could be met.

At once Levy, Papakopoulos, Gulabian, Smith and Durand rose and roared. They banded against Gordon. They yelled as they had never yelled before.

A brevet-colonel in the British army dictating to men with the rank of ambassador! Impossible! Impudent! What if he *was* a field-marshal in the Turkish army? Was he not merely a loan from his own army? What if he *had* done this and that and the other silly thing in China and the Soudan? Brave—was he? Perhaps! But—to lower the rate of interest . . . ? A crime! The man was a Judas, a renegade!

Snubbed and insulted socially and officially, Gordon soon recognized that he was fighting a losing battle and saw that, if he was not careful, he would sacrifice the interests for which he had been laboring in the Soudan. He was warned that if he remained in Cairo, a thorn in the side of the debt commissioners, the British War Office would recall him and post him to garrison employment. He might resign, of course; but it would hopelessly affect his prestige with the Egyptians. His British army rank was more valuable in his work than the higher rank given him by the Khedive.

So, bowing his head to the inevitable, he returned to Khartum in May, 1878, to plunge into office routine, tussles with an insufficient treasury, squabbles with Cairo officials, and raids against the slave trade. Fever attacked him. He was alone for days and nights in the great palace, wandering from room to room, his poor, tired brain tortured with imaginary problems. But he recuperated his former strength. He labored as he had never labored before. He helped. He obeyed the Christ's words:

"Feed my lambs."

Soon, once more, it was active service for him, since the slavers' depredations in the south had become too flagrant to be overlooked. An army under Gessi was sent against them towards the end of 1878, and in March of the next year Gordon moved his own head-quarters—consisting of a camel and the case containing his official uniform which so impressed the natives—to Darfur.

In twenty-one broiling summer days he covered six hundred and thirty miles on camel back between his garrisons, feeling out the position of the enemy. The slavers had found a method of meeting his plan of squatting on the water holes; a scheme guaranteed to strike straight at his heart. When water ran out, they would herd the less favored of their captured slaves into bands, tie them together, and leave them to die in the arid desert. Gordon was hoist with his own petard. He moved through an avenue of skulls; writing:

"All the skulls of slaves. Am I to blame? Why should I at every mile be stared at by the grinning skulls of those who are at rest?"

Gathering a small force from outlying garrisons he brought in, in three days, four hundred slaves, abandoned in the desert. "A drop in the ocean," he called it. Besides, they had to be fed, and Cairo was demanding taxes.

Then, when Gessi was beginning to show results with his expedition, news reached Gordon that the Khedive had been deposed. The creditors had been too much for him. His successor, Tewfik, promised to be more

amenable to reason.   Gordon knew exactly what he
was to do.   He hurried to Khartum, thence to Cairo,
resignation in hand.

What a reception!

English, French, Levantines were scrambling and
scrapping for whatever Egypt could give them in the
way of loot.   Bankers and financiers were at each
other's throats.   But they stopped their row when they
saw the common enemy: Gordon.

But—Gordon was to go?   The usurers were allowed
in the temple?

Hosanna!

Gordon was not to go yet, though.   With his departure, the Abyssinians had taken heart and had
crossed the border.   Tewfik begged his assistance, and
he returned the way he had come, on another adventure
of his governorship, trekking straight to the root of
the matter, five days of fast travel and tortuous climbing, until he was at Gura, in the camp of the Abyssinian
commander, Ras Aloula.   In the open, under a pouring
rain, he put on his field-marshal's uniform and approached the enemy leader who, having heard of the
state of affairs in Cairo, treated him with studied insolence.   For three days Gordon parleyed.   He could
achieve nothing. Threats were met by laughter. Abyssinia—he was told—was not to be bound by any agreement.   Let the Egyptians fight if they felt like it.
Gordon asked for a delay.   Ras Aloula suggested that
he himself was powerless; that the king should be
visited.   Gordon agreed and soon discovered the reason for the proposal.   It required nearly a month to
reach the royal palace, over three weeks of travel up
and down precipices and along impossible roads.   The
journey had been arranged to prove to this soldier,
whose desert reputation had preceded him, the impossibility of attacking Abyssinia.

Gordon swallowed his lesson. He visited King Johannes who demanded more than Gordon was authorized to grant. So he left, carrying a letter from King Johannes to Tewfik. Gordon opened it. It spoke of a "secret" treaty between the two rulers. It was evident that Tewfik had sent him on this mission to Abyssinia simply as a bluff, to impress his insistent creditors. Now Gordon decided that his resignation would be final.

On his way to the coast news came from Gessi that young Zubair and ten slave-raiding chiefs had surrendered and had been shot. Here was the *"wang"* situation again. But this time Gordon did not waste time or words, declaring:

> "It was the only thing Gessi could do—in this country. I told Sulieman Zubair that he would be shot if he opposed the government again. Gessi carried out my threat of two years back. I declare if I could stop this traffic I would be shot this night myself. Think as I may I cannot see any end to this business or any use in my staying here."

In Cairo he was received precisely as he had expected. His countrymen disowned him. His messages to Ismail, the former Khedive, were garbled and changed to suit ends and handed to the press. He was accused of being insubordinate, treacherous, and mad. Tewfik did not dare protest his resignation, and, by the end of 1880, he was back in England.

He planned to rest. He needed rest so. But soon he received an offer of employment. The Basutos had been annoying the government of the Cape of Good Hope. Having worked in the diamond fields, they had taken their pay in firearms. Suddenly the Cape authorities—after the Basutos had spent good cash for the weapons—discovered that it was illegal for a

native to own a rifle. Confiscation was attempted, but
failed. Would Gordon lead a punitive expedition,
take the guns away from their irresponsible owners,
burn a kraal or two, and do his little bit for the
Empire?

Gordon would not. He suggested that the gentlemen at the Cape hire somebody else, less squeamish in
such matters.

A few weeks later he accepted another offer. Lord
Ripon had just been appointed Viceroy of India and
had asked him to accompany him as his private secretary. "In a moment of madness"—as Gordon put it—
he accepted; and repented before his journey to Bombay was over. Conversations on the boat—"There
will never be another rebellion in India. The people
are too weak from want of food to fight!" "To hell
with the whole lot!" "Knock 'em down when they
complain!" indicated very surely that he would not fit
in with the Government House crowd. Famine, war
and debt seemed to be regarded by these gilded incompetents as the correct state of affairs, and their
chatter ran to society, hunting, and sports in general.
If there was famine, had not the same famine been
there before the British occupation? Had there not
always been misery and pest in India? Why bother?
Gordon tried to argue with them. He quoted Cromwell's blunt words: "That which maketh the one rich
and the many poor suiteth not a commonwealth." But
the Official Mind was not interested. The Official
Mind considered Cromwell a dangerous radical who,
luckily, had been dead and buried these many centuries. The Official Mind preferred Warren Hastings
to Cromwell and the London *Times* to the Gospels.
The Official Mind was, after all, only Upper Tooting
masquerading in ermine and velvet. So Charles George
Gordon did a typically Gordonesque thing. Three days

after his arrival in Bombay his resignation was in the Viceroy's hands. With it was payment for the passage of his successor—the losing of which money left him almost penniless.

The Official Mind declared Gordon's resignation was an insult to the Viceroy, to every proper saheb, to the Empire at large. The news was broadcast over the world.

That damned eccentric!

That damned, sentimental troublemaker!

That damned Scots Don Quixote!

And England laughed—though, in a distant part of the world, the news was gladly received. China was contemplating war against the predatory Russian. Li Hung Chang, informed of Gordon's action in Bombay, telegraphed him to come to Pekin. Gordon asked the War Office for six months' leave. The request was refused, and he threw up his commission without regard to pension, writing:

"If you say I cannot retire by commutation of pension, I resign my commission and make you a present of its value, about six thousand pounds."

The press, both yellow and pink, attacked him; and, for once, he hit back. Accused of being an adventurer, going to China, his old hunting ground, to extract whatever personal benefit he could out of an armed conflict between China and Russia, he declared:

"I protest as being regarded as one who wishes for war in any country. With only a small degree of admiration for military exploits, I esteem it a far greater honor to promote peace than to gain any paltry honors in a wretched war. My object in going to China is to persuade the Chinese *not* to go to war with Russia."

He did just that. Arriving at Tientsin in July,

1880, he saw Li Hung Chang who agreed with him.
Then he proceeded to Pekin where he attended a War
Council meeting under Prince Chun.   They were all
for trouble.   They were tired of Russia's threats and
insults.   Gordon harangued them.

"The thought of your going to war is sheer idiocy."

"It is what?"

"Idiocy!"

The interpreter could not or would not translate the
word.   Gordon obtained a dictionary and pointed it
out.   Finally he persuaded them.   They decided to
maintain peace, and he added:

"In case you are invaded, I shall show you what to
do."

Returning to Tientsin he busied himself for a couple
of weeks drawing up a full defense scheme against a
possible Russian attack.   He handed it to Li Hung
Chang and started on his way home.   En route he
was met by a telegram.   His resignation was not accepted and his leave canceled.   His only notice of
this typical War Office pettiness was a terse wire in
reply:

> "You might have trusted me.
> "GORDON."

Though they would not accept his resignation his
employers could find nothing for him to do.   His outspoken honesty had been too much of a thorn in Downing Street's fleshy posterior.   Thus, despite the fact
that it was a busy time for army officers, he was relegated to the waiting list until he grew bored with
inaction.   He turned his attention and his administrative genius to the Irish question and found the same
old story, a mingling of cruelty and stupidity.   His
solution was the purchase of the estates from the land-
lords and releases to the farmers on fair terms.   But

the Irish problem was too active a thing, too fertile
a spot for politicians, to permit of so easy a settlement.
Besides, who was this army officer who dared to turn
against his own class? To hell with him! Ought he
be court-martialed and shot!

England did not appreciate him. England did not
like him. But there were others who did.

Just as China had sent for him in her time of need,
as the Khedive had regarded him as his right arm in
the Soudan, so the King of the Belgians realized his
rare worth and offered to send him to the Congo. He
did not accept. For the time being he must stick to
his last, even if there was no work to be done on it.
But after a year of loafing he became desperate and
cabled to the government of the Cape of Good Hope,
suggesting his services in the settlement of the threatening trouble with the Basutos. The Cape Town gentry did not even bother to answer him; so he looked
elsewhere—and found.

A fellow engineer officer had received a regular appointment to Mauritius. Mauritius! Fever-ridden
hole! Did not suit his taste at all. He offered to
exchange. Gordon heard of the appointment and the
attitude of the appointee. He was willing to go to
Mauritius instead of the other. The War Office approved, and he was off to waste the best part of a
year supervising the repair of barracks and the clean-
ing out of drains.

"Chinese" Gordon, "Soudanese" Gordon employed
as a contractor and a master-plumber! A glorious,
fantastic, unconsciously Gargantuan jest on the part
of the War Office! A jest so intensely of Britain—
of that Britain which, according to Gordon, has not
been made by her statesmen, but by her gentlemen-
adventurers!

By this time the gentry at the Cape had found time to open their mail and to read Gordon's communication. The Basuto affair had not been as easy as anticipated. Would Gordon care to fix it up? He did. In 1882 he sailed for Cape Town and, as soon as possible, went up country to work on the commission appointed to settle the trouble. Here he learned a lesson from young Cecil Rhodes about the psychology of African natives and, after that precocious youth had left to busy himself with the Bechuanaland annexation, turned to see how the Basutos might be given at least a fair deal. It was difficult. But he made up his mind to succeed.

Three Basuto chiefs were brought to heel. Acting to the limit of his powers, Gordon granted them all he could. A stern disciplinarian, he believed in the honor of his fellow-men, whatever their creed or color, and worked on the assumption that freedom once given was always appreciated. The fourth chief, Masufa Mohsesh, would not attend the conference. He was a tough old warrior and reputed to be as treacherous as a snake. Gordon, though warned that such action was the wildest folly, went to the man's kraal. They were getting on famously and were discussing terms when news arrived that, tired of the delay, the Cape gentlemen, calmly forgetting Gordon's danger, had despatched an expeditionary force to clean out the district. Why Masufa did not murder Gordon on the spot has never been explained. Perhaps he recognized the high, fearless honor in this peculiar Scot and respected him.

But Gordon was furious. He hurried back to Cape Town and tendered his resignation. He could not act for people who could so easily break their faith—and his. Again the tragic comedy of the *"wangs"*—played this time in South Africa.

On reaching England he once more received advances from the King of the Belgians.

"For the moment I have no mission to offer you, but I wish much to have you at my disposal, and to take you from this moment as my counsellor. You can name your own terms. You know the consideration I have for your great qualities."

A fair enough offer from this Leopold who, so lyingly, has been represented as a wholesale assassin of helpless blacks. But Gordon just then had a little money, and he wanted to fulfill an old desire. The keynote of his life was ever his endeavor to find the truest ring at the heart of a question. Against the Taipings, at grips with the poverty of the lower Thames, in the matters of slavery in the Soudan and the Basuto affair, he invariably jumped decades of official dawdling to discover the right nail and endeavor to hit it. Travel had taught him much. His mind had become broadened. He had been in intimate contact with the adherents of various alien religions. And, throughout, he had remained a God-fearing, God-loving man in the personal sense. Creeds, cults, and religious fads found no supporter in him. But the Man of Nazareth was to him a living principle, not a dead emblem and dogma. He believed in the Christ of the Gospel, not in the Christ of the Church—indeed, for years, he had been unable to bring himself to enter a church. Now he wanted to see the Christ, to walk with Him and talk with Him . . . and so he went to His native land, to Palestine, where, the Bible in his pocket, he was able to go for long rides and, with the actual scenes before him, rebuild on the spot the drama of nineteen hundred years before.

"A mystic and a mathematician" some one had called him, adding that Gordon would never be satisfied with any particular deity until he was able to take every problem to him for solution and, at the same time, express his exact size in terms of feet and inches. Perhaps so. At all events, he spent a year as a sapper-archæologist-devotee reconstructing Solomon's Temple, placing the Cross in its correct position, and following the disciples in their adventurous, amazing three years. The idea of making faith and science kiss never occurred to him. Here was the field of battle upon which one great faith had justified itself. His own he had proved time and time again. What more was to be done about it? Nothing—unless some narrow, limited, sniveling brotherhood endeavored, as many did, to paint the caste mark of its stilted creed upon his forehead . . . then, at such an attempt, he would express his views—rather forcefully.

Towards the end of 1883 he left Palestine. The King of the Belgians still wanted him. He would resign for good and all from the army and offer his services where they were appreciated and wanted. In the notes kept during the last days before leaving for Brussels the following are heavily underlined:
"Now that the hour is come my fear is fled."
"Use well the interval."
"Prepare to meet thy God."
It was in this mood that he went to Leopold, finding, at the Belgian capital, a notification from the War Office that his idea of serving with a foreign power would not be sanctioned. His superiors added their regret that they themselves were unable to find anything for him to do. He took the bull by the horns and penned his final retirement, petitioning: "to retire from Her Majesty's service without any claim for pension."

But, in the meantime, things had been happening in Egypt; trouble was approaching at a gallop.

Tewfik, the new Khedive, had not been long in his palace before the vultures, Jews and Greeks, Levantines and British and French, descended in earnest, demanding their one hundred per cent. England—not without a thought of the Suez Canal and India—had decided to help the composite, cosmopolitan Shylock. The bombardment of Alexandria had been followed by Tel-el-Kebir. Egypt, though only temporarily occupied, according to official hypocrisy, had been in reality annexed for good. The Egyptian army, to give it something else to do and think about, had been marched south, under Hicks Pasha, to occupy the Soudan. Then, down there, had arisen the hermit of Abba Island, Mahomet Achmed, that genius-impostor-leader-villain-spiritual-fanatic who called himself the Mahdi, the Messiah. During November, 1883, he had annihilated the army under Hicks Pasha and threatened the garrisons placed by the British along the upper Nile.

With the usual question of "prestige" buzzing in their bonnets, the powers-behind-the-army—dubbed "Statesmen" for some unknown reason—were scratching their poor, bewildered heads.

What a pickle! What a mess!

And, at such a moment, they were called upon to accept the resignation of a certain person by the name of Gordon.

Gordon!

Who was he?

Some bounder of a sapper officer with damned peculiar ideas.

Well—he was not going to serve with the Belgians. Let him retain whatever rank he had, with the unemployed pay of that same rank. He was told so and took no notice. He made his final plans for proceeding to the Congo. Then some impudent, misguided outsider heard of it and wrote to the War Office, telling precisely who Gordon was and what he had achieved.

What?

Fellow had been in Khartum . . . knew the Soudan
. . . had been employed for several, years by the
Khedive . . . ?

Interesting!

Eh? Perhaps the man of the hour . . . ?

Well—perhaps. . . .

There were conferences, discussions. Rheumatic old
generals and smooth under-secretaries talked, talked.
The result was that, at noon on the 17th January,
Gordon received a telegram from Lord Wolseley to
report at once in London.

The next day he was there; had a prolonged conversation with Wolseley; and, in the afternoon was taken
to see several members of the Cabinet. Before introducing him to the sanctum Wolseley informed him
that the government had decided to evacuate the Soudan and not to guarantee future administration there.
Would he undertake the job? He would indeed.

Later on he described what happened:

"They said, 'Did Wolseley tell you our orders?' I said, 'Yes.'
I said, 'You will not guarantee future government of Soudan
and you wish me to go up and evacuate now.' They said, 'Yes,'
and it was over and I left at 8 P.M. for Calais."

So, at last, they had found employment for Gordon.
Yet no one knew why. The announcement was made
through the usual channels in due course and met with
numerous protests.

A brother engineer officer of the new appointee was
asked by somebody quite proper and quite "county":

"Why have the government sent a Chinaman to the
Soudan? What can they mean by sending a native of
that country to such a place?"

Such was his fame.

With his instructions *carte blanche* was understood. Evacuate the garrisons. That was the core of the orders, and there was little else besides. Remembering old experiences, he decided to proceed by the Red Sea, crossing the desert from Suakim to Berber. But, the moment he was off, other plans were made behind his back. Orders caught him en route sending him via Cairo and up the Nile Valley. This was just what he did not want. Cairo was no place to commence the work to which he had been assigned. He protested, but complied, and received from Tewfik his former rank as governor-general of the Soudan. It was thought that this dignity would lighten his task. It did the opposite.

His ideas of the operations before him crystallized as he journeyed to Khartum. His employers, generous in their promises, generous, too, in breaking them, had given him to understand that he was to have a free hand. The task was terribly difficult. He knew the land, and the men sitting at the other end of the wires did not. The first point he insisted on was in the matter of communications. He was supposed to rid the Soudan of all traces of Khedival government. Office holders, petty governors, garrisons were to be sent down stream where they belonged. Thus communications must be kept open between Cairo and Khartum, at least. He made fair suggestions, remarkably economical. The dangerous link in the chain was at its far end, from Khartum through Berber to Abu Hammed. He wanted seven hundred and fifty men to be distributed over this stretch and went forward expecting that it would be done.

It was not.

On the 1st February, 1884, he reached Korosko, setting off from there across the desert to Abu Hammed the next day. He realized the enormity of the enterprise. The ground to be evacuated included the former Equatorial Province. The road in back would have to be kept open. He decided to start from Khartum, evacuate that district, pass up the river, sending garrisons and their hangers-on home as he went. As soon as his rear seemed in peril, he would advance farther and faster and proclaim the southernmost provinces as part of the Congo under the protection of the King of the Belgians. Then the communications behind, toward Egypt, could be abandoned and the Soudan itself revert to its original owners.

Colonel Stewart, who was with him, approved, and the recommendation was sent back. The British government vetoed it immediately, without offering an alternative suggestion. Instead, soldiers, who should have held the lines of communication, were moved to the Nile to build defenses against a possible Mahdist invasion of Lower Egypt . . . it was as though the men who were running the show had already given up hope of Gordon's success, had already condemned him to death, were already climbing into the last ditches, yelling:

"*Sauve qui peut!*"

In the meantime Gordon, reaching Abu Hammed on the evening of the 8th February, was surprised to find conditions there fairly normal. Conferences with local administrators showed him that he could afford to do his work by stages. It would be necessary to maintain the higher office holders whilst the evacuation was going on. But again the "Statesmen" objected. He must clean out the area at once, lock, stock and barrel.

From Berber, on the 11th, he despatched a further suggestion. If the mess which would follow the complete removal of the machinery of government was to be in any way protected from the insurgents, it would be better for him to go in person to the Mahdi and come to some sort of understanding. It was typical of him—the man who had bearded the *"wangs,"* the slavers, the Abyssinians, and the Basutos in their native dens.

The government objected.

"Evacuate!"

It was all they could think about.

He shrugged his shoulders and went to Khartum where the reception accorded him by the inhabitants warmed his heart. Black liked him. So did Yellow and Brown—if not White. Moslems liked this believing Christian. So did Buddhists and heathens—but not other Christians. Here, in Khartum, the poor people knew nothing of Downing Street and Whitehall. But they knew Gordon. They hailed him as their savior.

With his former suggestions turned down, he forwarded a new one. If the government was to be suspended and the area left open to the Mahdi's attacks, there was one man who might replace the Egyptian officials and act as a buffer until the territory was cleared. This was Zubair, the king of the slavers whom he had fought so long and whose eldest son had been shot by Gessi. Once more his recommendation was not approved. Once more the big-wigs back home knew more than the man on the spot. Gordon was to carry out orders—carry out orders—carry out orders!

Help from outside?

Ridiculous!

Carry out orders—and be damned to it!

He did it, to the best of his ability—which was the best of the best man's ability. In Khartum he declared that he had come to "hold the balance level." The government being over, lists of outstanding taxes were publicly burned, the prisons opened and the miserable inmates—mostly debtors—released. Instruments of torture were broken up before the eyes of the townspeople.

He declared:

"I will not fight with any weapons but justice."

Then he set about evacuating the helpless from Khartum. Available boats were filled and sent downstream. The sight of these going and of the numbers that must follow made him again realize the importance of an open river; and he sent word to Cairo:

"Send two hundred men to Berber."

Sir Evelyn Baring forwarded the message to London, attaching a tag which said:

"I did not consider it desirable to comply with the request."

Not that the authorities remained inactive. On the contrary, they were quite active—active with a stupidity worthy of Gentleman Burgoyne. Gordon having asked for his rear to be secured and having had that rear, by orders, changed from Suakim to the Nile, a force was landed at the former place . . . and threw the fat on the fire.

The Khartum situation at that time was dangerous, but not precisely pressing. On the 29th the British, advancing from Suakim, fought the Arabs at El Teb and defeated them with heavy casualties. They moved on, massacring more Arabs at Tamai. Promptly the whole country rose in arms. Tribesmen gathered from near and far. Operations were launched against the Nile valley. The Turkish occupation—said the sons of Shem—was bad enough. But the British—bless them not the Lord Allah!—were infidels. North, south, east, west, was the guttural cry:

"Kill—kill—for the faith!"

During the first week in March news reached Khartum that a movement was on foot to cut communications with Lower Egypt south of Berber. On the 11th of the month the telegraph line was found to have been severed. The same evening Arab cameleers were seen within sight of the town. The noose had been thrown and was being tightened—the noose fashioned simply by the British government's refusal to pay attention to the recommendations of the man it had sent out with a supposedly free hand to do a certain task.

So there was to be a siege. This was Gordon's professional line, the building of defenses and laying out a system of forts. All around the desert riders were loping up, closing in; and he set the Khartum garrison to digging, foraging, building wire entanglements, placing ground mines.

The operations began ominously. A successful attack against the encroaching hordes was, in the twinkling of an eye, changed to defeat, when the leaders of the troops deliberately turned an advantage over to the enemy who was about to run away. The cry of "Treason!"—so fatal to a defended town—went up. There followed a hurried trial, and two Pashas were shot. It was the only way to meet the situation. Yet, though it stiffened discipline, it raised a certain intangible barrier between the foreign commander and his troops.

For obvious reasons, little is known of the happenings in Khartum between March and September. The Arabs tried no general assault, but preferred sitting on their lines, making occasional local attacks which they never pressed home, while Gordon could do little but hope for the relief that had been promised him.

September brought the rise of the river—the proper time to do any clearing out necessary. Gordon supervised this himself. On the paddle-steamer *Abbas* he placed everything of importance for shipment to Dongola: his journals of the siege, official papers, letters from friends and enemies—and his European companions as well as fifty soldiers. Thus Colonel Stewart went, Power, the French consul M. Herbin, and members of the Greek colony. Gordon was thus left alone, in his great palace, to wait for the relief force which Stewart was to see expedited.

The siege continued. During the evenings he wrote in his journals a résumé of each day's work and his thoughts. Of the work—petty successes, trying reverses, and ever the steady tightening of the lines about Khartum—little can be said.

But—his thoughts. For instance:

"*September 13th.* I speak for myself when I say I have been in dire anxiety, not for my own skin, but because I hate to be beaten, and I hate to see my schemes fail; but that I have had to undergo a tithe of what any nurse has to undergo, who is attached to a querulous invalid, is absurd."

That was three days after a step had been taken by his government on behalf of him. On September 10th a shipment of boat sections left England for Cairo, designed for a probable expedition to the rescue of Khartum. Government members considered it a waste of money. News of British troops approaching Dongola reached Gordon. But he was remarkably accurate in his estimate of the real situation:

"*September 17th.* I have the strongest suspicion that these tales of troops at Dongola and Merowe are all gas-works, and that if you wanted to find Her Majesty's forces you would have to go to Shepheard's Hotel at Cairo."

Two days later, he wrote:

"The sole and only object of my mission was to get out the garrisons and refugees without loss of life. . . . Baring deigned to say he would support me! Of course, that was an enormous assistance, to have his approbation. My asking for Zubair to come up was the last drop in the cup, and henceforth I am a complete pariah. . . . As for all that may be said of our holding out, &c., it is all twaddle, for we had no option: as to why I did not escape with Stewart, it is simply because the people would not have been such fools as to let me go . . . even if they had been willing for me to go, I would not have gone and left them to their misery. . . . Any one reading the telegram 5th May, Suakim, 29th April, Massowah—Egerton saying, 'Her Majesty's Government does not entertain your proposal to supply Turkish or other troops in order to undertake military operations in Soudan, and consequently if you stay in Khartum you should state your reasons,' might imagine that one was luxuriating up here. . . ."

On the following day some notes came through from downstream dated 22nd August. One was from the inspector of Soudan Telegraphs giving the latest news, and the other from Major Horatio Herbert Kitchener (afterwards Lord Kitchener of Khartum) asking if he could be of any help. Kitchener was then at Dongola, and the letter had been addressed to Stewart. On the 23d arrived a further communication from Kitchener to Gordon himself. In it he made inquiries as to "exactly when you will be in difficulties as to provisions and ammunition." With the Mahdi's men closing in steadily, Gordon regarded this as "light-hearted jocularity." This particular jocularity was given full play when, the codes having gone downstream with the *Abbas,* a whole flood of cipher messages came through from Dongola.

The daily entries in his journals continued. The lack of information troubled him. He wrote on September 24th:

"Either these officers outside do not care to spend a sou on spies to give me information or else they think it is a matter of supreme indifference to me whether I know what is going on or not; and I must say when my messengers do come back they bring scarcely any information of import. There is a lot of 'I hope you are well', etc.; men like Kitchener and Chermside might be expected to have more brains than that."

One of his amusements was letting prisoners and deserters from the desert see themselves for the first time in a mirror:

"An escaped soldier came in from the Arabs—no news. He was so dreadfully itchy I could not keep my patience or keep him in the room. He saw himself in the mirror, and asked who it was; said he did not know! and really he did not seem to know."

Which was the first time and started a game:

"Great female squawking under the window of the serail, approaching to yells. . . . The black slut was delighted to see herself in the mirrors and grinned and smirked at her reflections. . . ."

Primitive fun—which delighted him. But soon the strain began to tell as, alone, he wandered about, supervising the work of clerks whom he could not trust and inspecting lines of leaders whose loyalty he questioned:

"*September 25th.* You can scarcely imagine the state one gets in when one is constantly hearing explosions; what with guns, mines and musketry, one's nerves get strained and nothing can drop without one thinking it is an explosion. . . . Man is essentially a treacherous animal; and although the Psalmist said *in his haste* 'all men are liars,' I think he might have said the same *at his leisure.*"

He sent his boats on expeditions up and down the river against the Arab lines. A very mild offensive—but the only one he could keep up. There was the feeding of 40,000 people under his care to add to his troubles. His underlings did everything they could to turn this business to profit, and he could only check up on their depredations on the public stock by careful supervision. But he knew that the populace was bled whenever his back was turned, and he commented:

"There is nothing like a civil war to show what skunks men are."

On the 30th September his second journal went down to Berber. He was then dallying with the idea of having himself replaced by the Turkish Minister of War, Abdel Kader. The War Office—with more than usual stupidity—had been accusing him of insubordination in not leaving Khartum with Stewart and Power, the British consul. His comment was chilly:

"October 5th. I should consider Her Majesty's Government completely exonerated from all responsibility with respect to myself if they sent me the order 'Shift for yourself; we do not mean to extricate the garrisons.' I should then make my arrangements, and (telling the people how I am situated with no hope of relief for them) should make a bolt to the Equator in six weeks' time. There could be no dishonor in that . . . for my presence here would only exasperate the Arabs instead of being any good to the people here."

Late October saw a startling development. On the 21st the Mahdi came to Khartum and, with his picked warriors, closed his lines tighter; and, on the next day, sent a communication to Gordon giving details of the fate of the *Abbas.* Colonel Stewart and all his companions had been massacred, all the papers taken, and, to back up his statement, the Mahdi enclosed a complete list of documents found.

At the same time a note came through from Kitchener at Debbeh, inquiring as to the people aboard the *Abbas,* expressing fear that they had been killed, and announcing that the relief column under Wolseley was at Wady Halfa and would probably start from there in November.   In this letter were two enclosures which touched Gordon, though they made him smile at the wondrous ways of bureaucracy.

The first enclosure read:

"Berlin, 10th April, 1884.

"General,

"Notwithstanding they abandoned you, and they did not at all follow your instructions, I hope you will be victorious, and your name engraved in the history of the world.

"I am, dear General,

"Your most obedient servant,

"TH. ROTH."

And the second enclosure:

"Berlin, 4th May, 1884.

"Dear Sir,

"I had the honor to write you on the 10th April.   Meanwhile I permitted me to do the following:

"On the 22nd April I wired to Earl Granville: For Heaven's sake, help Gordon, Khartum.

"And confirmed this despatch with the following letter:

" 'Berlin, 22nd April, 1884.

" 'My Lord,

" 'I have the honor to confirm my telegram of this afternoon: For Heaven's sake, help Gordon, Khartum.

" 'Your lordship may be kind enough to excuse such a telegram.

" 'As I am admirer of Gordon, and as he had the kindness to do his best to become liberated my brother Gottfried Roth, who is said prisoner of the Mahdi, and to whom your lordship congratulated when he captured at Sint a band of slaveholders with several hundred slaves some years ago, I considered it a duty to do something too for Gordon.   And so the idea to wire to your lordship, who perhaps may be able in consequence of your powerful position to let have Gordon what he wants.

" 'I have the honor, &c.'

"I had the pleasure to receive the following letter from the Secretary of State, Sir J. Pauncefort:

" 'Sir,
" 'I am directed by Earl Granville to acknowledge the receipt of your telegram and letter of the 22nd inst., urging that assistance may be given to General Gordon at Khartum.
" 'I am, Sir,
" 'Your most obedient humble servant,
" 'J. PAUNCEFORTE.' "

To which Gordon's comment in his journal was:

"Roth did not get much change out of his lordship!"

While Roth and Pauncefort exchanged this strange correspondence, Gordon was revolving the question of surrender, because of the cowardly behavior of the few foreigners left in Khartum. He even considered what effect his embracing the Moslem faith, or pretending to do so, would have. He scorned the idea; but, logically, worked it out; remembering how a number of Greeks, captured by the Mahdi, had accepted the Moslem faith and married a number of nuns, also captured by the Mahdi; arriving at the conclusion that his embracing the creed of Islam would be a mistake, an expensive blow to Britain; that it would be far cheaper, far easier, far better to die quickly, as a Christian.

As the weeks went by, he grew impatient, drawing maps in his journals to show how the expedition should be moved on Khartum, taking particular exception to Kitchener.

Still the ring closed slowly, mercilessly. On November 12th he described one of many encounters:

"Last night three slaves came in from Omdurman. At 11 P.M. they reported Arabs meant to attack to-day at dawn. It was reported to me, but the telegraph clerk did not choose to

tell me till 7 A.M. to-day. . . . This is our first encounter with
the Mahdi's personal troops. One tumbles at 3 A.M. into a
troubled sleep; a drum beats—tup! tup! tup! It comes into a
dream, but after a few moments one becomes more awake, and
it is revealed to the brain that *one is in Khartum*. The next
query is, where is this tup, tupping going on? A hope arises it
will die away. No, it goes on, and increases in intensity. The
thought strikes one, 'Have they enough ammunition?' (The
excuse of bad soldiers.) One exerts oneself. At last, it is no
use, up one must get, and go on the roof of the palace; then
telegrams, orders, swearing and cursing goes on till about
9 A.M. Men may say what they like about glorious war, but
to me it is a horrid nuisance (if it is permitted to say anything
is a nuisance which comes to us). I saw that poor little beast,
the *Husseinyeh* (a Thames launch) fall back, stern foremost,
under a terrific fire of breach loaders. I saw a shell strike the
water at her bows; I saw her stop and puff off steam, and I
gave my glass to my boy, sickened unto death. . . . My boy
said, '*Husseinyeh* is sick' . . . then telegraph said, 'She is
aground.' . . ."

On the next day the Arabs extended their lines and
surrounded the city completely. There was not fifteen
days' food supply. Between eighteen and nineteen
hundred of the defenders had been killed. On the 14th
November he sent another steamer downstream with
his last journal, some letters, and a note to Wolseley:
"As it seems impossible that we shall meet again in
this world, I would ask you to see that my family does
not lose by my death."
He owed money to the Cairo government, the King
of the Belgians and the Foreign Office—four thousand
five hundred and six pounds all told. And he added:

"However, as it seems all this is at an end, I do not think it
too much for Her Majesty's Government to pay Cairo what
I owe it, £2,100; and also the King of the Belgians, £570;
and to take any pay due me against the sum I owe the Foreign
Office."

With some final instructions and comment he closed his journal:

"If I was in command of the 200 men of the Expeditionary Force, which are all that are necessary for the movement, I should stop just below Halfeyah, and attack the Arabs at that place before I came on here to Khartum. I should then communicate with the north fort, and act according to circumstances. Now MARK THIS, if the Expeditionary Force, and I ask for no more than 200 men, does not come in ten days, *the town may fall;* and I have done my best for the honor of our country. Good-by,

"C. G. GORDON.

"You send me no information, though you have lots of money.
"C. G. G."

On the 14th December the head of the Expeditionary Force reached Korti, remaining there for sixteen days while its tail closed up, then moving across the desert towards Metemma, battling with the Arabs at the wells of Abu Klea, reaching the Nile again at Gubat. On the 21st January, when the advance guard got into touch with some steamers which had been waiting in midstream for one hundred and twelve days, connection was made with the besieged town. On the 24th General Sir Charles Wilson, commanding, embarked on one of these steamers and, accompanied by a second boat containing a small detachment of soldiers, proceeded on the hundred-mile trip to Khartum.

It was reached on the 28th. As Sir Charles sailed round the bend he noticed that no flag flew from the palace roof. The boats were fired on by men stationed in the windows of the houses. Thousands of Arabs, standing along the banks of the Nile, waved the flags of the Mahdi and howled in derision; jeered at the British who had come too late; might, with greater justice, have jeered especially at the one Briton who, loving Little England and hating Big England, had sentenced Gordon to death: Gladstone who, with his smooth, oily, hypocritical casuistry, had refused to admit the danger that threatened the Scot whom his own Ministry had sent out to the Soudan and who, with the telegram giving the facts of Gordon's imminent doom actually in his pocket, had assured the House of Commons that the man was absolutely safe and that it was unnecessary to hurry.

At all events, the drama was over.

Two days earlier, on the morning of the 26th, as Wilson's boats were working through the twelve miles of the Sixth Cataract, the Arabs made their final assault. They advanced shortly before daybreak; pushed their way through the starving, weakened defenders; and, the town in their possession, made for the palace.

Gordon could not give up without a fight. He led his small headquarters' guard towards the reserve ammunition supply, established in the Church of the Austrian Mission.

The houses about this building had been razed for safety's sake, and as the handful of men, "Chinese" Gordon some ten yards in the lead, entered the open space they were confronted by a body of Arabs coming in from the other side.

There was a long pause. Then Gordon called for fire. But, before his men could obey the command, the enemy had loosed a volley. Their shooting was not very good. Only one man was hit. His name was Gordon.

So he died; and the Mahdists cut off his head and sent it through the desert in token of triumph.

There was a smile on the lips of the head.

Perhaps it thought of Gordon's letter in which he expressed his hope that he might be rescued and saved, lest the howling dervishes of certain Methodist and

Baptist sects call him a martyr and "make a tin Jesus out of me" . . . perhaps he thought of his last letter to his sister when, knowing that death was near, he summed up his own character:

"I am quite happy, thank God, and, like Lawrence, I have *tried* to do my duty."

THE END